THE ULTIMATE
HOW IT WORKS
ENCYCLOPEDIA

THE ULTIMATE HOW IT WORKS ENCYCLOPEDIA

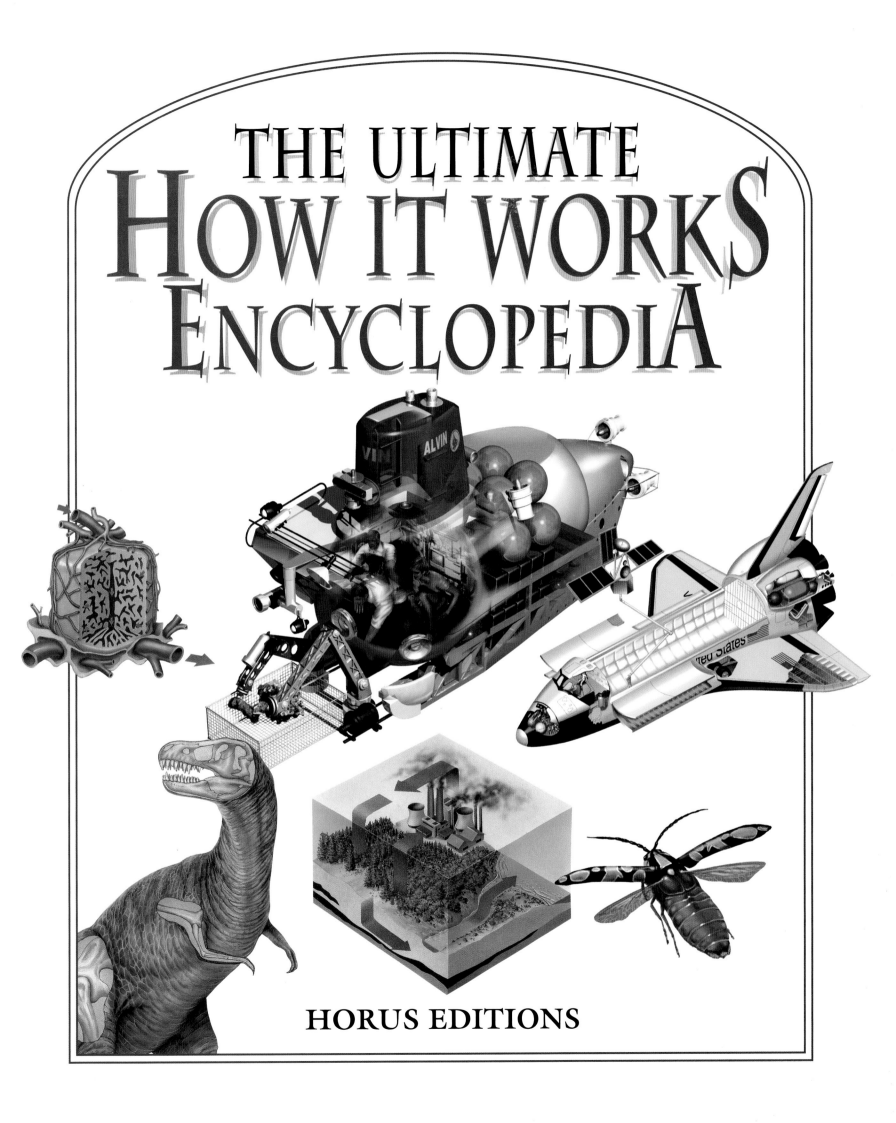

HORUS EDITIONS

Copyright © 2002 Horus Editions Limited

**This edition first published 2002
by Books Are Fun Ltd.,
123, North Main Street,
Fairfield, IA 52556, U.S.A.**

Series editor Liz Miles
Design by Paul Richards, Steve Weston and Richard Rowan
Cover design by Richard Rowan
Illustrations by Jeff Bowles, Jim Channell, David Hardy,
Gary Hincks, Stuart Lafford, Ruth Lindsay, Shane Marsh,
Denys Ovenden, Sebastian Quigley, Mike Saunders,
Steve Seymour, Steve Weston, Gerald Witcomb, David Wright

Text by Michael Allaby, Dr Kate Barnes, Stuart Clark,
Stephen Hall, Gerald Legg, Rober Muir Wood

ISBN 1-58209-396-2

Printed in Singapore

THE ULTIMATE HOW IT WORKS ENCYCLOPEDIA

CONTENTS

THE
WORLD OF
ANIMAL LIFE

Text by Gerald Legg
Illustrated by Steve Weston

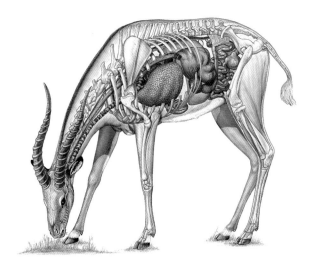

THE WORLD OF
ANIMAL LIFE
CONTENTS

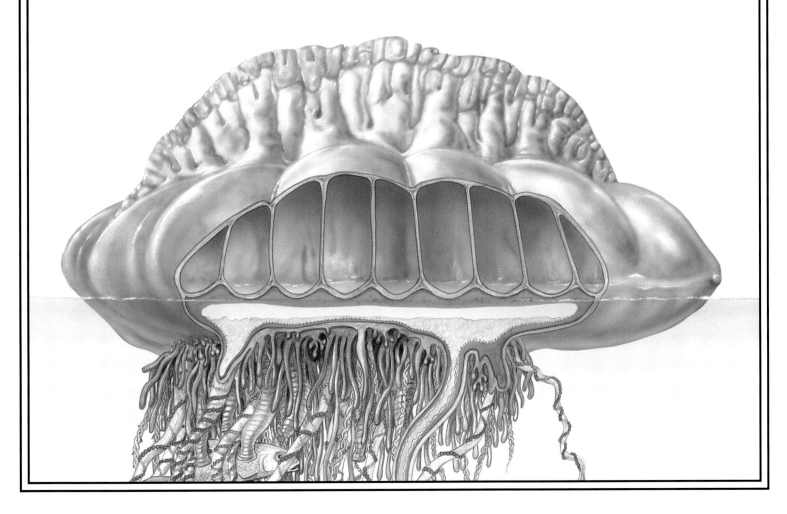

Bony Fish

THIS COLOURFUL fish, called an Anthias, is a tropical fish that lives amongst coral. It is one of the 20,000 different kinds of fish that have a bony skeleton.

To move through water, fish have a special shape. Most have a long body, pointed at the front and narrowing at the tail. It is smooth, without any untidy bits sticking out. However, not all fish are streamlined like this. Some fish that live amongst coral, seaweed, or on the sea bed move differently, so they need a different body shape.

Some fish hunt, while others scavenge, eating up dead material that is floating around. To feed, many fish approach their meal and quickly open their mouth when they are close to it. This movement of the bones around the mouth and gills opens up the throat. Water rushes in, bringing the food with it.

EEL

FLYING FISH

SEAHORSE

ANGEL FISH

Fins
Fish use their fins in all kinds of ways. Eels have a long dorsal fin that ripples, gently propelling them along the sea bottom. Flying fish have big wing-like fins on their chest (pectoral fins). Angel fish use their fins to dart in and out of their coral hideouts. Seahorses have a fin on their back (the dorsal fin) that enables them to hover and move delicately through seaweed.

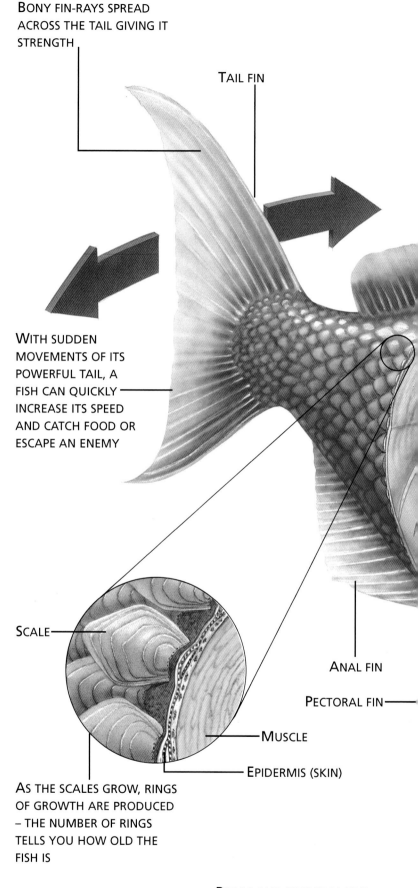

BONY FIN-RAYS SPREAD ACROSS THE TAIL GIVING IT STRENGTH

TAIL FIN

WITH SUDDEN MOVEMENTS OF ITS POWERFUL TAIL, A FISH CAN QUICKLY INCREASE ITS SPEED AND CATCH FOOD OR ESCAPE AN ENEMY

SCALE

ANAL FIN

PECTORAL FIN

MUSCLE

EPIDERMIS (SKIN)

AS THE SCALES GROW, RINGS OF GROWTH ARE PRODUCED – THE NUMBER OF RINGS TELLS YOU HOW OLD THE FISH IS

PELVIC AND PECTORAL FINS STEER THE FISH, MOVE IT UP AND DOWN IN THE WATER, AND ALSO ACT AS BRAKES

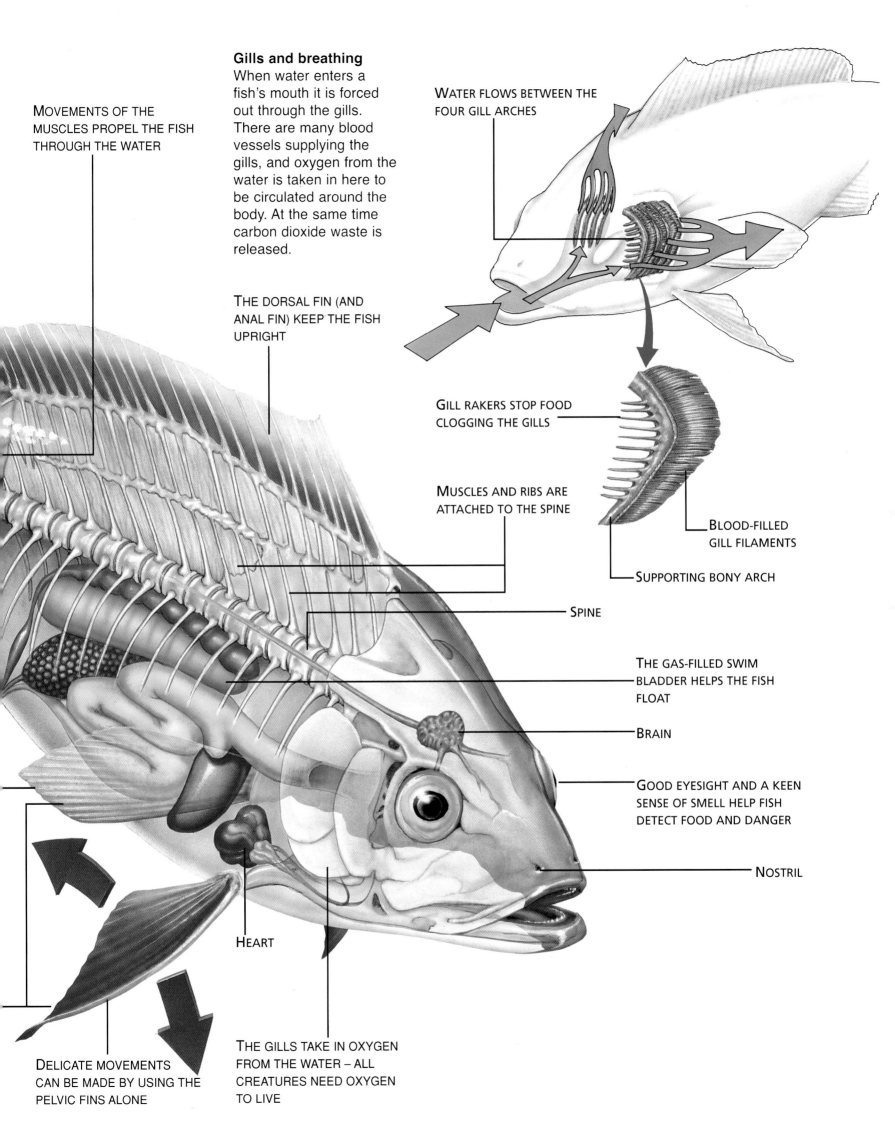

MOVEMENTS OF THE MUSCLES PROPEL THE FISH THROUGH THE WATER

Gills and breathing
When water enters a fish's mouth it is forced out through the gills. There are many blood vessels supplying the gills, and oxygen from the water is taken in here to be circulated around the body. At the same time carbon dioxide waste is released.

WATER FLOWS BETWEEN THE FOUR GILL ARCHES

THE DORSAL FIN (AND ANAL FIN) KEEP THE FISH UPRIGHT

GILL RAKERS STOP FOOD CLOGGING THE GILLS

MUSCLES AND RIBS ARE ATTACHED TO THE SPINE

BLOOD-FILLED GILL FILAMENTS

SUPPORTING BONY ARCH

SPINE

THE GAS-FILLED SWIM BLADDER HELPS THE FISH FLOAT

BRAIN

GOOD EYESIGHT AND A KEEN SENSE OF SMELL HELP FISH DETECT FOOD AND DANGER

NOSTRIL

HEART

DELICATE MOVEMENTS CAN BE MADE BY USING THE PELVIC FINS ALONE

THE GILLS TAKE IN OXYGEN FROM THE WATER – ALL CREATURES NEED OXYGEN TO LIVE

Bird Flight

THE OSPREY is a bird of prey. It flies over rivers, lakes, and seas hunting for fish. On spotting a fish it can make a dramatic dive, feet-first, into the water. After grabbing its prey, the hawk-like bird will soar up into the sky.

Like all birds, to push its body upwards, the osprey must beat its wings downwards against the air. The wings of a bird have a special curved shape (aerofoil) which produces lift and keeps the bird in the air as it flies. The wing-shape also means birds can glide or soar on rising currents of air. Birds hardly need to beat their wings if they can 'ride' on a wind that is flowing upwards over a hill. A bird steers itself by changing the tilt of its wings, or by twisting its tail like a rudder.

THE 'WRIST' BONES ARE FLEXIBLE SO THE WINGS CAN BE TILTED, ALLOWING THE BIRD TO TWIST AND TURN IN FLIGHT

THE PRIMARY FEATHERS ARE THE MAIN FLIGHT FEATHERS

THE SECONDARY FEATHERS GIVE THE WING A LARGE SURFACE AREA

BROAD TAIL FEATHERS ACT LIKE A RUDDER FOR STEERING THE BIRD

THE SHARP, CLAWED TOES ARE CALLED TALONS

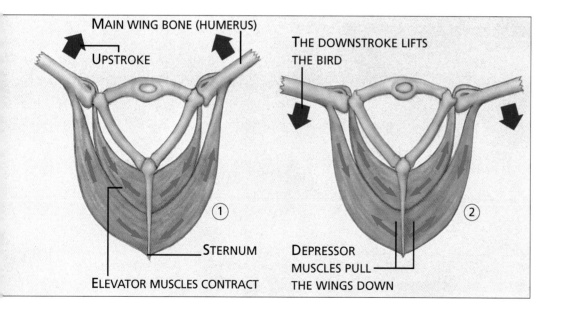

MAIN WING BONE (HUMERUS)

UPSTROKE

THE DOWNSTROKE LIFTS THE BIRD

① ②

STERNUM

ELEVATOR MUSCLES CONTRACT

DEPRESSOR MUSCLES PULL THE WINGS DOWN

A bird's wingbeat
To fly through the air, or hover, a bird must beat its wings. A pair of large breast muscles make each wing move. For an upward stroke (1) the depressor muscles relax (lengthen) and the elevator muscles contract (shorten). Like a pulley, this lifts the wing bones. For a downward stroke (2), to lift the bird, the bigger, stronger depressor muscles must contract to pull the wing bones down.

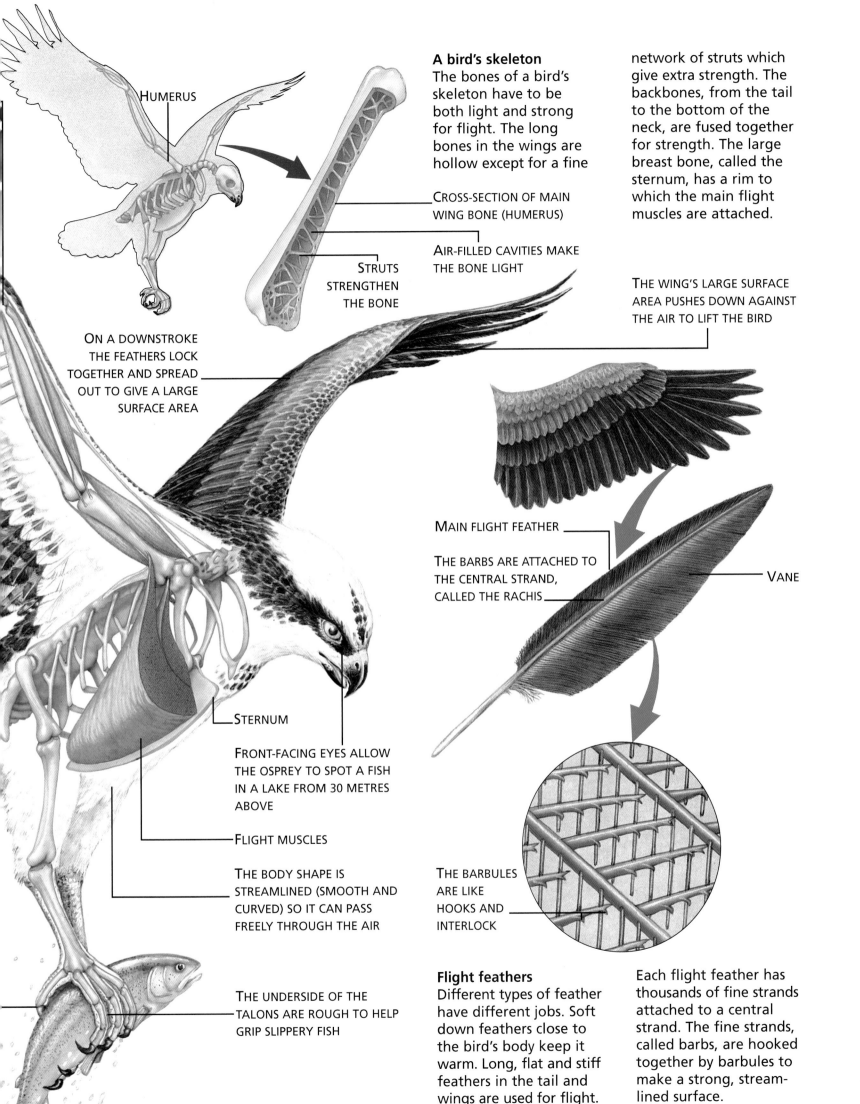

HUMERUS

A bird's skeleton
The bones of a bird's skeleton have to be both light and strong for flight. The long bones in the wings are hollow except for a fine network of struts which give extra strength. The backbones, from the tail to the bottom of the neck, are fused together for strength. The large breast bone, called the sternum, has a rim to which the main flight muscles are attached.

CROSS-SECTION OF MAIN WING BONE (HUMERUS)

STRUTS STRENGTHEN THE BONE

AIR-FILLED CAVITIES MAKE THE BONE LIGHT

ON A DOWNSTROKE THE FEATHERS LOCK TOGETHER AND SPREAD OUT TO GIVE A LARGE SURFACE AREA

THE WING'S LARGE SURFACE AREA PUSHES DOWN AGAINST THE AIR TO LIFT THE BIRD

MAIN FLIGHT FEATHER

THE BARBS ARE ATTACHED TO THE CENTRAL STRAND, CALLED THE RACHIS

VANE

STERNUM

FRONT-FACING EYES ALLOW THE OSPREY TO SPOT A FISH IN A LAKE FROM 30 METRES ABOVE

FLIGHT MUSCLES

THE BODY SHAPE IS STREAMLINED (SMOOTH AND CURVED) SO IT CAN PASS FREELY THROUGH THE AIR

THE BARBULES ARE LIKE HOOKS AND INTERLOCK

THE UNDERSIDE OF THE TALONS ARE ROUGH TO HELP GRIP SLIPPERY FISH

Flight feathers
Different types of feather have different jobs. Soft down feathers close to the bird's body keep it warm. Long, flat and stiff feathers in the tail and wings are used for flight.

Each flight feather has thousands of fine strands attached to a central strand. The fine strands, called barbs, are hooked together by barbules to make a strong, stream-lined surface.

13

Seeing with Sound

LAND ANIMALS that are active during daylight use their eyes to see. But how do creatures that move around in the dark see? Marine animals that live in the dark ocean depths and nocturnal land animals that move around at night have a special way of 'seeing'. They use a system called echolocation which allows them to build up a 'sound picture' of everything around them. Most bats use echolocation. The bats make a series of short, sharp sounds. The sounds bounce off objects in their path. Then the bats pick up the echoes (returning sounds) and can tell if an object is moving, how far away it is, and what it is made of.

LONG, THIN FINGER BONES SUPPORT THE WING

A MEMBRANE OF ELASTIC SKIN STRETCHES BETWEEN THE FINGER AND ARM BONES TO FORM THE WING

THE RIBS PROTECT THE LUNGS, HEART, LIVER, AND STOMACH

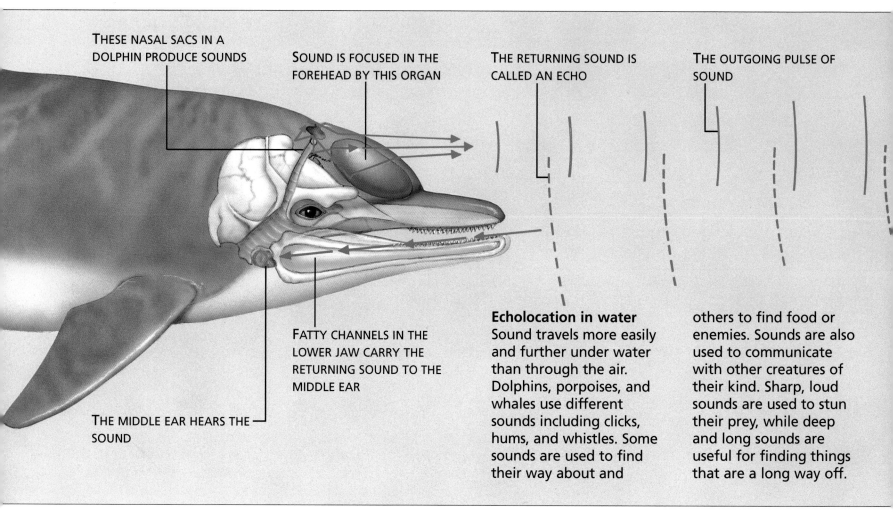

THESE NASAL SACS IN A DOLPHIN PRODUCE SOUNDS

SOUND IS FOCUSED IN THE FOREHEAD BY THIS ORGAN

THE RETURNING SOUND IS CALLED AN ECHO

THE OUTGOING PULSE OF SOUND

FATTY CHANNELS IN THE LOWER JAW CARRY THE RETURNING SOUND TO THE MIDDLE EAR

THE MIDDLE EAR HEARS THE SOUND

Echolocation in water
Sound travels more easily and further under water than through the air. Dolphins, porpoises, and whales use different sounds including clicks, hums, and whistles. Some sounds are used to find their way about and others to find food or enemies. Sounds are also used to communicate with other creatures of their kind. Sharp, loud sounds are used to stun their prey, while deep and long sounds are useful for finding things that are a long way off.

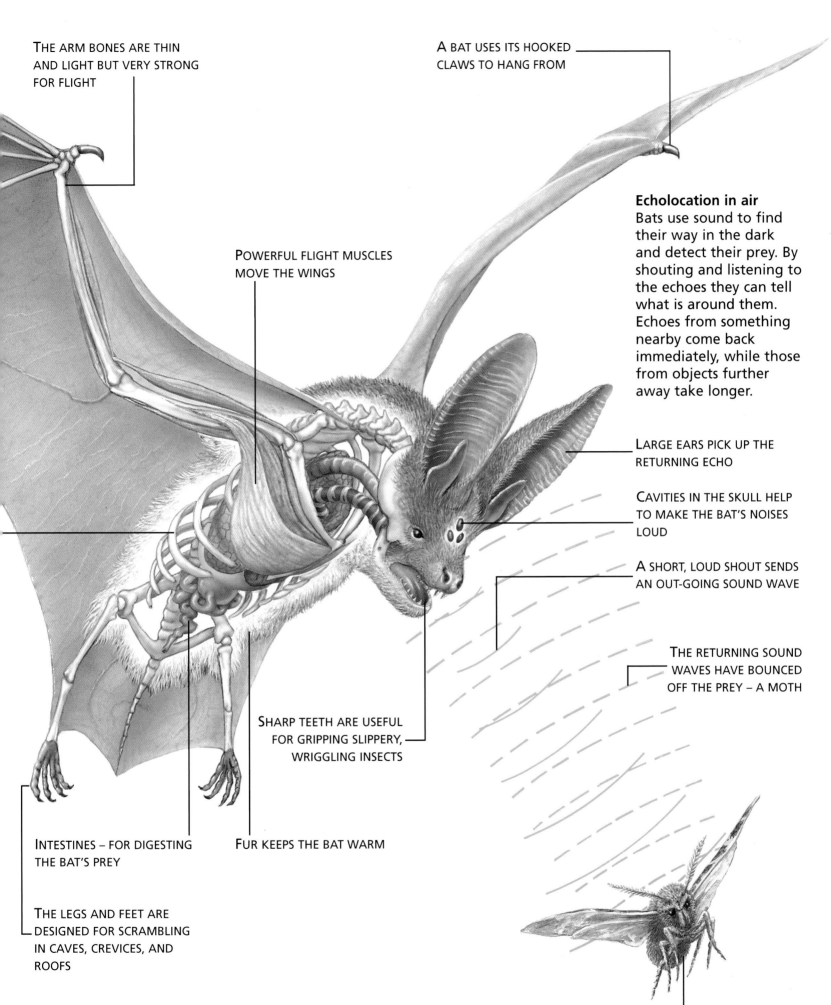

THE ARM BONES ARE THIN AND LIGHT BUT VERY STRONG FOR FLIGHT

A BAT USES ITS HOOKED CLAWS TO HANG FROM

POWERFUL FLIGHT MUSCLES MOVE THE WINGS

Echolocation in air
Bats use sound to find their way in the dark and detect their prey. By shouting and listening to the echoes they can tell what is around them. Echoes from something nearby come back immediately, while those from objects further away take longer.

LARGE EARS PICK UP THE RETURNING ECHO

CAVITIES IN THE SKULL HELP TO MAKE THE BAT'S NOISES LOUD

A SHORT, LOUD SHOUT SENDS AN OUT-GOING SOUND WAVE

THE RETURNING SOUND WAVES HAVE BOUNCED OFF THE PREY – A MOTH

SHARP TEETH ARE USEFUL FOR GRIPPING SLIPPERY, WRIGGLING INSECTS

INTESTINES – FOR DIGESTING THE BAT'S PREY

FUR KEEPS THE BAT WARM

THE LEGS AND FEET ARE DESIGNED FOR SCRAMBLING IN CAVES, CREVICES, AND ROOFS

SOME MOTHS SQUEAK TO CONFUSE A BAT'S ATTACK

A Spider's Web

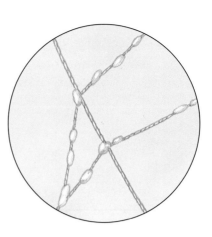

PREDATOR IS an animal that hunts and kills other animals to feed itself. The garden spider is a predator that spins a web to catch its prey. During late summer the large webs of adult spiders can be found amongst low plants and bushes. Sitting upside-down in the centre of the web the spider waits for insects to blunder into its web. It then rushes across, seizing and killing its victim.

If frightened by a bird, which might eat it, the spider will run to safety. It may hide under a leaf or drop to the ground on a silken safety line, the thread that trails from its body so that it never loses contact with its web. Spiders also use their silk to wrap and protect their eggs.

Sticky beads
The spider uses a special silk for trapping insects. At first this silk is coated in a sticky layer. As the silk is fixed to the web's thread, the spider uses its back legs to twang the thread like a guitar string. This breaks the coat into a series of sticky beads.

SPIDERS HAVE FOUR PAIRS OF SEVEN-JOINTED LEGS

THE SUCKING STOMACH DRAWS FOOD INTO THE INTESTINE AND MOUTH HAIRS TRAP ANY SOLID PARTICLES

VENOM (POISON) FROM THIS SAC IS INJECTED INTO THE SPIDER'S PREY TO SUBDUE AND KILL IT

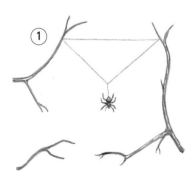

AS IT DANGLES ON THE LINE THE SPIDER SPINS A Y-FORK (1)

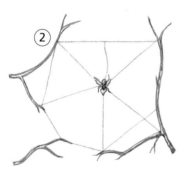

IT ADDS MORE SPOKES TO THE WHEEL TO MAKE A STRONG WEB (2)

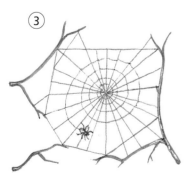

A SUPPORTING SPIRAL IS LAID DOWN BEFORE THE FINAL STICKY SPIRAL (3)

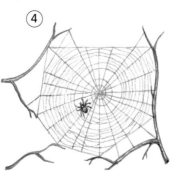

THE WEB IS COMPLETE AND READY FOR CATCHING INSECTS (4)

Web spinning
To begin its web the spider either floats its silk across a gap so the silk catches on the other side or it walks around trailing the silk behind it. The silken rope is then pulled tight and fixed. Climbing across this line, the spider lays down a stronger one. A loose loop is spun and a Y-shaped fork is created. More spokes are added to help the spider walk across the web and wind its thread round in a spiral. The spider uses its long legs to keep the web an even shape as it spins.

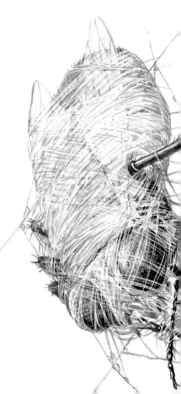

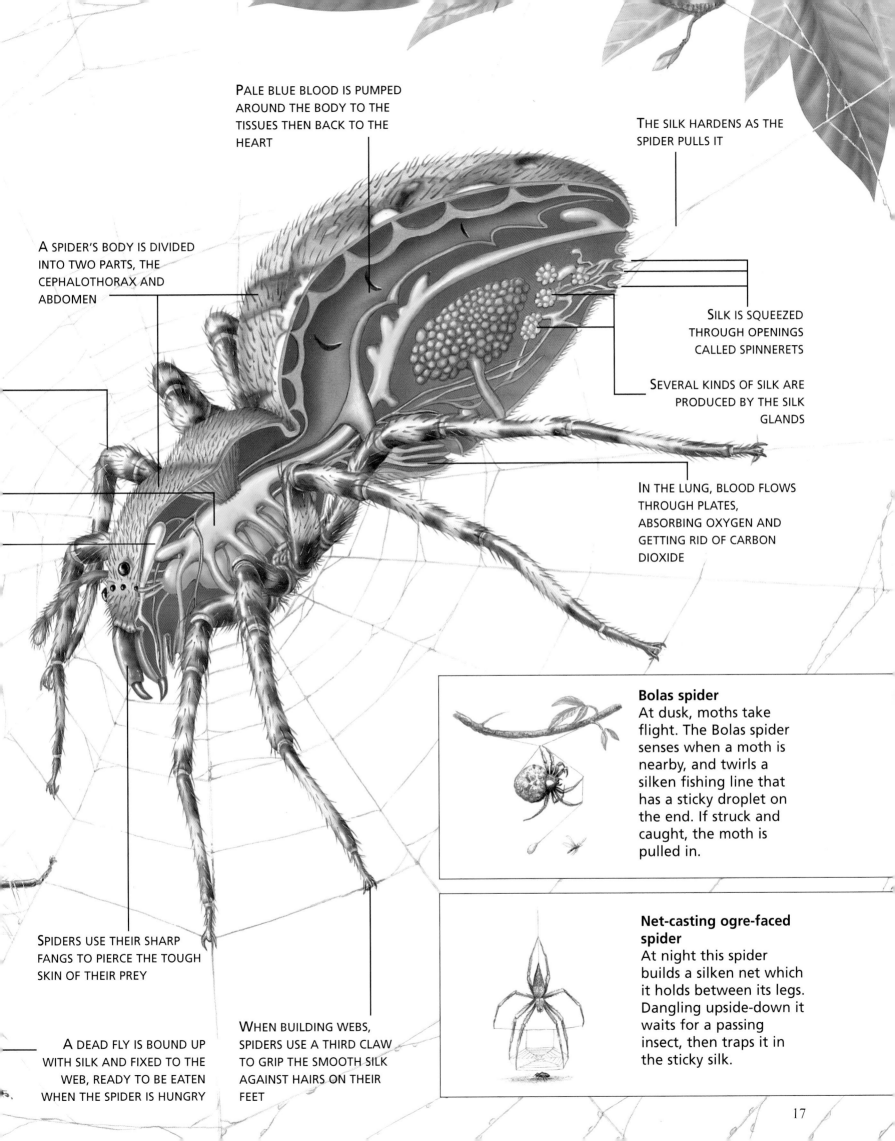

PALE BLUE BLOOD IS PUMPED AROUND THE BODY TO THE TISSUES THEN BACK TO THE HEART

THE SILK HARDENS AS THE SPIDER PULLS IT

A SPIDER'S BODY IS DIVIDED INTO TWO PARTS, THE CEPHALOTHORAX AND ABDOMEN

SILK IS SQUEEZED THROUGH OPENINGS CALLED SPINNERETS

SEVERAL KINDS OF SILK ARE PRODUCED BY THE SILK GLANDS

IN THE LUNG, BLOOD FLOWS THROUGH PLATES, ABSORBING OXYGEN AND GETTING RID OF CARBON DIOXIDE

SPIDERS USE THEIR SHARP FANGS TO PIERCE THE TOUGH SKIN OF THEIR PREY

A DEAD FLY IS BOUND UP WITH SILK AND FIXED TO THE WEB, READY TO BE EATEN WHEN THE SPIDER IS HUNGRY

WHEN BUILDING WEBS, SPIDERS USE A THIRD CLAW TO GRIP THE SMOOTH SILK AGAINST HAIRS ON THEIR FEET

Bolas spider
At dusk, moths take flight. The Bolas spider senses when a moth is nearby, and twirls a silken fishing line that has a sticky droplet on the end. If struck and caught, the moth is pulled in.

Net-casting ogre-faced spider
At night this spider builds a silken net which it holds between its legs. Dangling upside-down it waits for a passing insect, then traps it in the sticky silk.

17

Grazing Animals

IMPALA ARE large grazing antelope found in the savanna woodlands and grasslands of Africa. They live in herds of ten to several hundred individuals. Each herd is led by one of the older males. Younger males act as guards. If they are frightened by another animal, such as a lion, they make a sneezing sound to warn the others, and then the herd bounds away.

An impala can get a good hold on plants and grass by wrapping its long tongue around them. Their sharp incisors (front teeth) bite off blades of grass and plant shoots to eat. The molars (back teeth) have large flattened tops which are ideal for grinding grass. Grass is difficult to digest (break down) and to get enough food impalas have to eat a lot of grass. They eat quickly and then retire to digest it in safety, chewing it a second time. This system of digestion is called rumination.

A four-part stomach
Swallowed food passes into the rumen (1) where it is broken down into small balls of cud. The cud is returned to the mouth for more chewing. Once swallowed again, the food is digested back in the rumen (1), then the reticulum (2). Next, water is squeezed from the food in the omasum (3) and further digested in the abomasum (4) before passing into the intestines.

THE POINTED ANTLERS ARE FOR DEFENCE AND FIGHTING

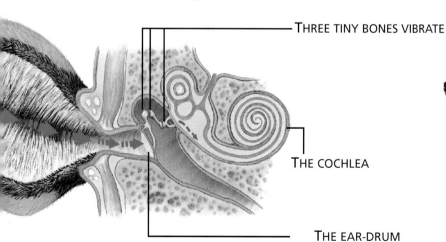

THREE TINY BONES VIBRATE

THE COCHLEA

THE EAR-DRUM

Listening for danger
Impalas' ears listen for danger. Sound travels into the ear and vibrates the ear-drum. This moves three tiny bones, which in turn move a membrane (thin tissue) causing the liquid in the cochlea to move. This triggers tiny hairs which send signals to the brain.

LARGE EYES CAN SEE ALL AROUND

SHARP INCISORS BITE THROUGH TOUGH BLADES OF GRASS

WHEN FOOD IS SWALLOWED IT PASSES DOWN THE OESOPHAGUS

MOLARS GRIND THE FOOD

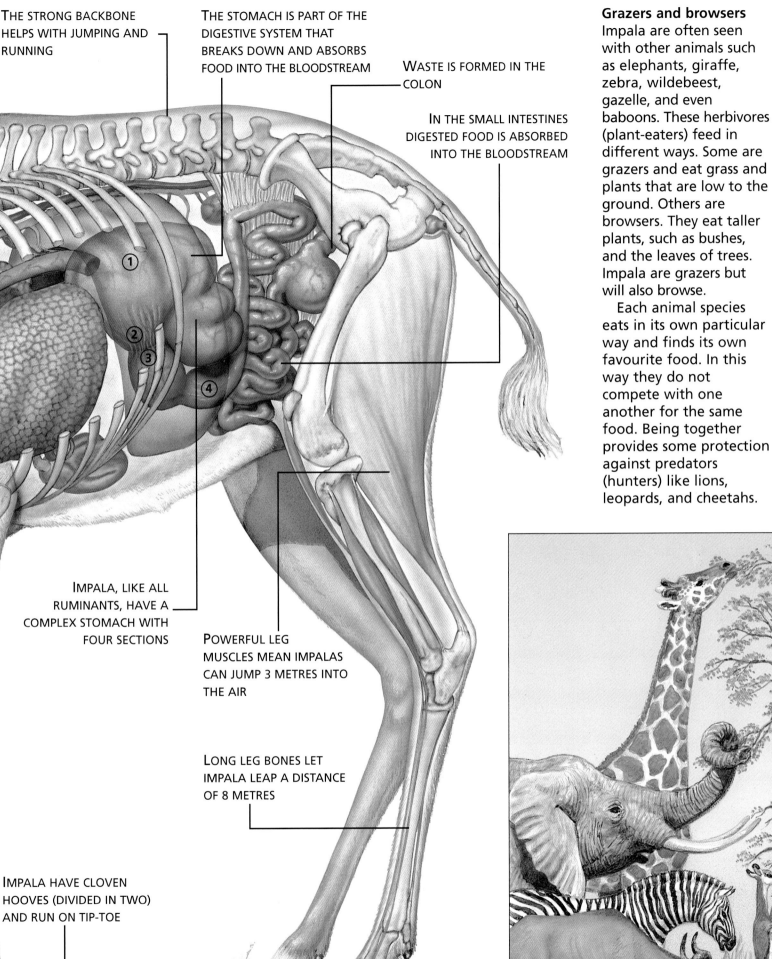

THE STRONG BACKBONE HELPS WITH JUMPING AND RUNNING

THE STOMACH IS PART OF THE DIGESTIVE SYSTEM THAT BREAKS DOWN AND ABSORBS FOOD INTO THE BLOODSTREAM

WASTE IS FORMED IN THE COLON

IN THE SMALL INTESTINES DIGESTED FOOD IS ABSORBED INTO THE BLOODSTREAM

IMPALA, LIKE ALL RUMINANTS, HAVE A COMPLEX STOMACH WITH FOUR SECTIONS

POWERFUL LEG MUSCLES MEAN IMPALAS CAN JUMP 3 METRES INTO THE AIR

LONG LEG BONES LET IMPALA LEAP A DISTANCE OF 8 METRES

IMPALA HAVE CLOVEN HOOVES (DIVIDED IN TWO) AND RUN ON TIP-TOE

Grazers and browsers
Impala are often seen with other animals such as elephants, giraffe, zebra, wildebeest, gazelle, and even baboons. These herbivores (plant-eaters) feed in different ways. Some are grazers and eat grass and plants that are low to the ground. Others are browsers. They eat taller plants, such as bushes, and the leaves of trees. Impala are grazers but will also browse.

Each animal species eats in its own particular way and finds its own favourite food. In this way they do not compete with one another for the same food. Being together provides some protection against predators (hunters) like lions, leopards, and cheetahs.

Hunters

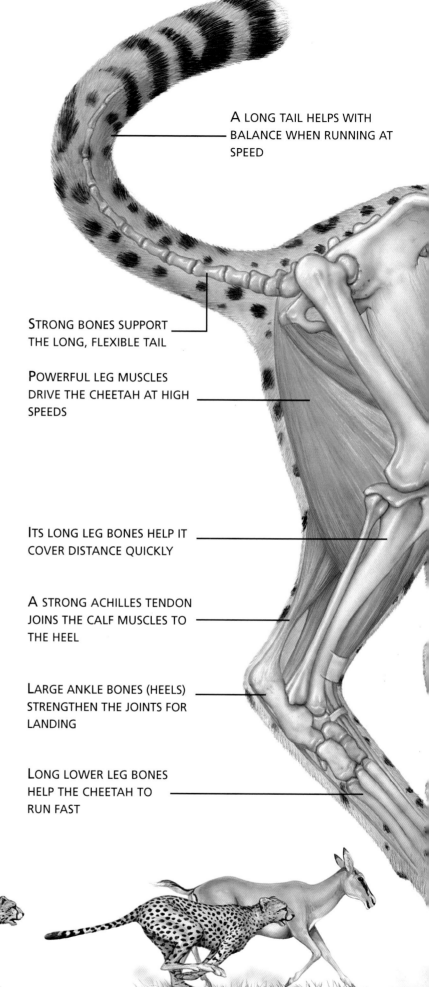

HUNTING ANIMALS have special features and skills for catching their prey. The big cats, including the lion, tiger, leopard, jaguar, and cheetah (*right*), hunt the largest animals. They have to be clever, fast, and strong to catch them. Their jaws are short and strong, and they have a powerful skull and large sharp teeth so that they can quickly tear their prey apart. They use their long canine teeth to stab their victims and chisel-like incisors to nip through tough skin. They also have razor-sharp chewing teeth which slice quickly through flesh.

Of all the cats the cheetah is the best known for its hunting ability. It can reach 90 kilometres per hour, making it the fastest animal on four legs. Its slim body is designed for speed.

A LONG TAIL HELPS WITH BALANCE WHEN RUNNING AT SPEED

STRONG BONES SUPPORT THE LONG, FLEXIBLE TAIL

POWERFUL LEG MUSCLES DRIVE THE CHEETAH AT HIGH SPEEDS

ITS LONG LEG BONES HELP IT COVER DISTANCE QUICKLY

A STRONG ACHILLES TENDON JOINS THE CALF MUSCLES TO THE HEEL

LARGE ANKLE BONES (HEELS) STRENGTHEN THE JOINTS FOR LANDING

LONG LOWER LEG BONES HELP THE CHEETAH TO RUN FAST

Hunting

Cheetahs have special features which help them hunt. Their eyes are designed to detect moving prey against the horizon. Hiding in the grass, the cheetah selects its victims. Young gazelle are chased when they are as much as 500 metres away; adult gazelle, who are more alert, are chased when they are up to 50 metres away. A cheetah cannot run at high speed for long as its body would overheat and it would die. To help it cool off, the cheetah has wide nostrils to draw in cooling air. Once it has caught up with its prey the cheetah needs to kill it quickly, as lions and hyenas could easily steal its hard-earned meal. When it bites the neck of small prey, it uses special sensors in its teeth and jaw muscles to find the right spot.

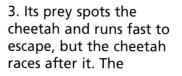

The chase
1. The cheetah stalks its victim before beginning its high-speed chase.

2. Ears back and eyes fixed on its prey, the cheetah bounds forward and begins to build up speed.

3. Its prey spots the cheetah and runs fast to escape, but the cheetah races after it. The cheetah matches the prey's speed and movements before trying to knock it over.

Gripping claws

Most cats use their claws for climbing, running, fighting, and killing. The cheetah uses its claws to grip the ground as it runs. They are its main weapon for catching prey and they help to maim the animal before the kill.

THE STRONG SPINE CAN LENGTHEN AND SHORTEN AS THE CHEETAH RUNS

LARGE LUNGS HOLD ENOUGH AIR FOR RUNNING AND COOLING OFF

ITS LONG, CURVED CLAWS GRIP THE GROUND AS THE CHEETAH RUNS AND HELP IT TO MAIM ITS PREY

RIDGES ON THE SOLES ACT LIKE THE TREAD ON A TYRE

UNLIKE THE CLAWS ON MOST CATS, CHEETAHS' CLAWS CAN ONLY BE PARTLY RETRACTED

STRONG MUSCLES FOR RUNNING ARE ATTACHED TO ITS SHOULDERS AND FORE-LIMBS

A CHEETAH'S EARS ARE SMALL TO KEEP ITS HEAD STREAMLINED, BUT ITS HEARING IS ACUTE

ITS EYES CAN JUDGE DISTANCES ACCURATELY

THE SENSITIVE NOSE CAN DETECT THE SMELL OF PREY OR DANGEROUS ANIMALS, SUCH AS LIONS AND HYENAS

THE CHEETAH HAS POWERFUL JAWS FOR CATCHING AND EATING PREY

THE LONG FORE LIMBS LENGTHEN ITS STRIDE

STRONG WRIST BONES SUPPORT ITS PAWS AS IT RUNS

4. Running alongside its prey, the cheetah rakes its side with its claws and trips it up.

5. Once the prey has fallen, it is seized by the throat and suffocated. This can take several minutes. The cheetah has to be careful not to get injured as its victim struggles.

Snakes

THIS SNAKE is called a green bamboo tree viper. It comes from southeast Asia and can grow up to one metre in length. It lives in trees which it can easily climb using a strong tail and rough scales to grasp the twigs and leaves. The viper feeds on small mammals, birds, lizards, and frogs. When baby vipers are born about a dozen appear at a time. Before they are born baby vipers hatch out of their eggs while the eggs are still inside their mother's body.

Because snakes do not have arms or legs to help them catch their food, many have venom (poison) instead. The venom can kill the live animal so that it is ready to eat. Some snakes do not use venom. Instead they feed on prey that is too slow or too small to escape. They either grab and eat it quickly, or coil their bodies around it and suffocate it.

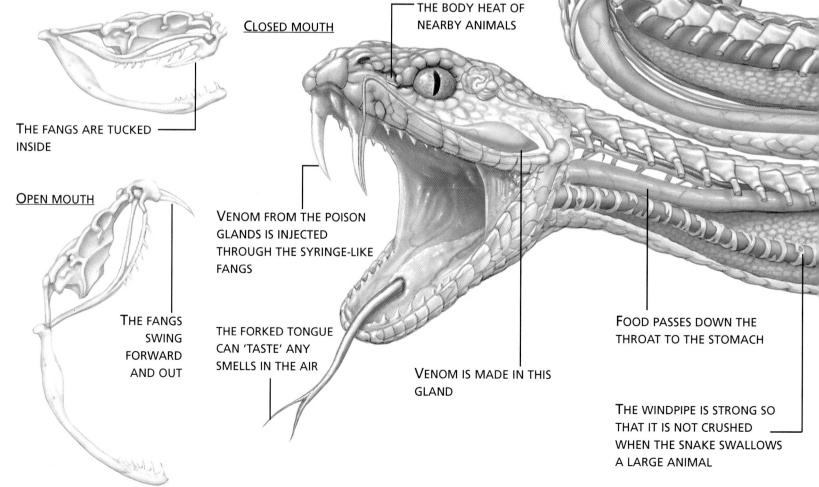

Shedding its skin
As the skin wears and the body grows, snakes must shed their skin. A new skin forms beneath the old. The old skin splits at the head and the snake scrapes it back, peeling it off like a sock.

THE BACKBONE IS VERY FLEXIBLE

DIGESTION OF FOOD STARTS IN THE STOMACH

THIS ORGAN PICKS UP THE BODY HEAT OF NEARBY ANIMALS

<u>CLOSED MOUTH</u>

THE FANGS ARE TUCKED INSIDE

<u>OPEN MOUTH</u>

THE FANGS SWING FORWARD AND OUT

VENOM FROM THE POISON GLANDS IS INJECTED THROUGH THE SYRINGE-LIKE FANGS

THE FORKED TONGUE CAN 'TASTE' ANY SMELLS IN THE AIR

VENOM IS MADE IN THIS GLAND

FOOD PASSES DOWN THE THROAT TO THE STOMACH

THE WINDPIPE IS STRONG SO THAT IT IS NOT CRUSHED WHEN THE SNAKE SWALLOWS A LARGE ANIMAL

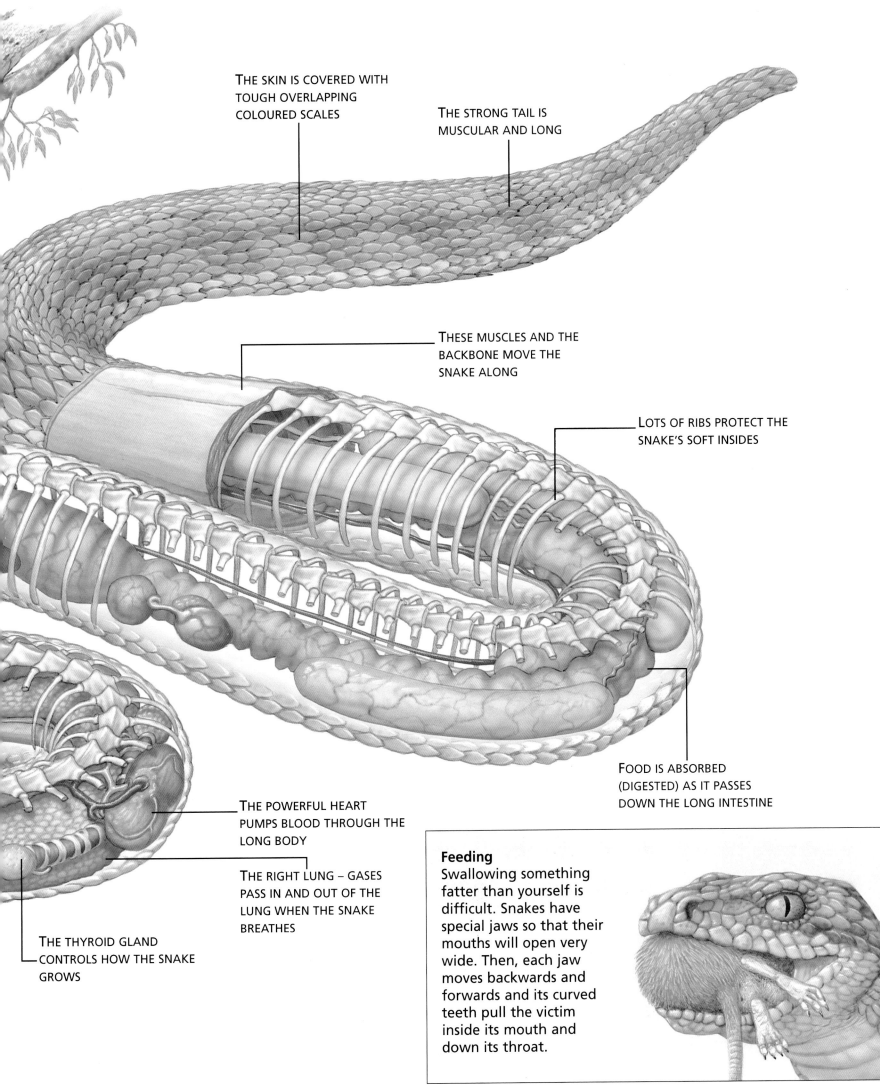

THE SKIN IS COVERED WITH TOUGH OVERLAPPING COLOURED SCALES

THE STRONG TAIL IS MUSCULAR AND LONG

THESE MUSCLES AND THE BACKBONE MOVE THE SNAKE ALONG

LOTS OF RIBS PROTECT THE SNAKE'S SOFT INSIDES

FOOD IS ABSORBED (DIGESTED) AS IT PASSES DOWN THE LONG INTESTINE

THE POWERFUL HEART PUMPS BLOOD THROUGH THE LONG BODY

THE RIGHT LUNG – GASES PASS IN AND OUT OF THE LUNG WHEN THE SNAKE BREATHES

THE THYROID GLAND CONTROLS HOW THE SNAKE GROWS

Feeding
Swallowing something fatter than yourself is difficult. Snakes have special jaws so that their mouths will open very wide. Then, each jaw moves backwards and forwards and its curved teeth pull the victim inside its mouth and down its throat.

Sea Mammals

WHALES, SEALS, and sealions are all marine (sea-dwelling) mammals. Being mammals they are warm-blooded, breathe air, and give birth to live young who are suckled on milk produced by their mother. Seals and sealions do not live in the sea all the time. They come ashore to rest and rear their young. Whales spend all their life in the sea and never go on land except accidentally, if they become stranded.

Whales are perfectly designed for their ocean life. They are smooth, streamlined and have a powerful tail, making them excellent swimmers. They often dive to depths where there is no light, but they know where they are by using sound. This system of 'seeing' is called echolocation (*see pages 14–15*).

Blowhole
A whale's nostrils are on top of its head. They close up when the whale travels downwards. As it surfaces, waste air in the lungs expands and is forced out of the blowhole.

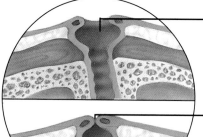

AS THE WHALE SURFACES, AIR IN THE LUNGS EXPANDS AND IS FORCED OUT

THE BLOWHOLE IS CLOSED AS THE WHALE SWIMS UNDERWATER

CROSS-SECTIONS OF A WHALE'S BLOWHOLE

A HUMPBACK WHALE CAN WEIGH UP TO 80 TONNES

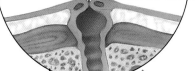

HORNY KNOBS OF SKIN ARE HOME TO WORMS AND OTHER CREATURES

THE BALEEN ARE ATTACHED TO THE UPPER JAW

Baleen
Hard brush-like plates, called baleen, hang down inside the whale's mouth. Each of the hundreds of plates are covered in fine bristles. As its mouth opens, water floods in, sometimes carrying with it the whale's favourite food of tiny shrimp-like creatures called krill. When its mouth closes, the water is forced out through the bristles, trapping the krill.

THE TONGUE SQUEEZES WATER FROM THE MOUTH, SCRAPES THE KRILL FROM THE BALEEN, AND PUSHES IT DOWN THE THROAT

THE JAWS OPEN VERY WIDE WHEN IT FEEDS

PLEATS (FOLDS IN THE SKIN) UNFOLD AS THE MOUTH FILLS WITH WATER

A THICK LAYER OF FATTY TISSUE CALLED BLUBBER LIES UNDER THE SKIN. IT KEEPS THE WHALE WARM AND AFLOAT

THE DORSAL FIN STOPS THE WHALE FROM ROLLING OVER

WHALES HAVE A POWERFUL MUSCULAR TAIL

THE BROAD TAIL MOVES UP AND DOWN, PUSHING THE WHALE THROUGH THE WATER

WHEN THE WHALE IS DEEP UNDERWATER, AIR FROM ITS SMALL LUNGS GOES INTO ITS NOSE AND THROAT

POWERFUL MUSCLES FOR SWIMMING

Types of whale
There are two types of whale: toothed and baleen. Toothed whales use their teeth to catch prey. Some eat fish while others catch squid, seals, and penguins. Baleen whales do not have teeth. Instead they filter food from the sea.

Whales have been hunted for their meat and oil. Some are now rare and almost extinct.

FOOD IS STORED IN THE GIANT FRONT STOMACH AND THEN DIGESTED IN A REAR STOMACH

DIGESTION CONTINUES IN THE INTESTINES

RIGHT WHALE (BALEEN)

A WHALE'S POWERFUL HEART HAS TO PUMP NEARLY A THOUSAND TIMES MORE BLOOD AROUND ITS BODY THAN A HUMAN HEART

SPERM WHALE (TOOTHED)

RIBS PROTECT THE ORGANS

NARWHAL (TOOTHED)

KILLER WHALE (TOOTHED)

PADDLE-LIKE FRONT LEGS ARE USED FOR STEERING AND KEEPING ITS BODY STEADY

THE LOWER BONES IN THE FLIPPER ARE SIMILAR TO THE BONES IN A HUMAN HAND

DOLPHIN (TOOTHED)

Self-defence

ANIMALS HAVE to defend themselves against attack. They do this in different ways. Some use violence and they may be big and fierce, armed with sharp teeth, poison, or strong claws. Gentle animals like antelope can also be violent, using their antlers to fight off an enemy. A few creatures use special defences. Porcupines have spines, camels spit, and bees sting. Disguise can also be used for self-protection. Some animals use colour and the shape of their body to disguise themselves. This defence is called camouflage. They are coloured to match their surroundings, making them invisible to predators. Some look like leaves, others like stones. Their colouring can also act as a warning, signalling that they are poisonous or dangerous.

Insect camouflage
Insects are often camouflaged to match their surroundings. They hide away amongst the leaves and stems of plants where they live. As they eat they move slowly to avoid drawing attention to themselves.

THE LANTERN BUG MATCHES THE COLOUR OF THE LEAVES

A prickly ball
Hedgehogs are bold and move about noisily at night, hunting for worms, insects, snails, and even small snakes. They can do this because they are protected from most predators by stiff spines on their back and sides. The spines are in fact hollow, sharp hairs. If frightened a hedgehog rolls up into a tight prickly ball as its muscles contract (shorten).

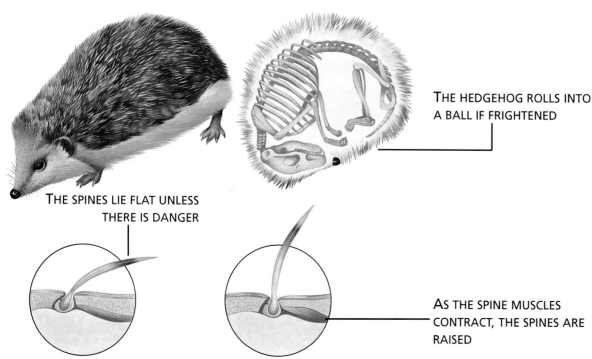

THE HEDGEHOG ROLLS INTO A BALL IF FRIGHTENED

THE SPINES LIE FLAT UNLESS THERE IS DANGER

AS THE SPINE MUSCLES CONTRACT, THE SPINES ARE RAISED

WHEN THE BODY IS DEFLATED, THE SPINES LIE FLAT

Colourful chameleons

Chameleons are gentle, slow moving lizards that can change colour to match their surroundings. They also change colour depending on their mood. When a chameleon becomes angry a brown substance in its skin, called melanin, is pushed to the surface. This darkens its colour. Other colours are produced by special red, yellow, blue, and white cells in its skin. When a chameleon is calm its skin changes to green. Green is produced when its yellow skin cells enlarge over its blue cells. The chameleon's colour change is rapid and controlled by the brain and chemicals in the blood.

A CHAMELEON'S EYES STICK OUT AND GIVE ALL-ROUND VISION

A MUSCULAR TONGUE DARTS OUT OF ITS MOUTH TO CATCH AN INSECT, A STICKY TIP WILL CATCH THE FLY

THE SKIN IS MADE UP OF MILLIONS OF CELLS

FINGERS AND TOES GIVE A FIRM GRIP

COLOURED SKIN CELLS EXPAND AND SHRINK TO MAKE DIFFERENT COLOURS

Porcupine fish

Porcupine fish are not designed to swim fast. Instead, they are designed to survive well. They have an armour of spines to protect them. If necessary they can inflate their bodies by swallowing water or air, and swell like a balloon. Once inflated they float, often upside down. As a floating ball of spines it is almost impossible for a predator to bite them, let alone swallow them!

THE NORMALLY SMALL PORCUPINE FISH GROWS INTO A THREATENING BALL OF SPINES

THE PORCUPINE FISH'S WIDTH INCREASES FROM 6 TO 20 CENTIMETRES

WHEN THE BODY IS INFLATED, THE SPINES STICK OUT

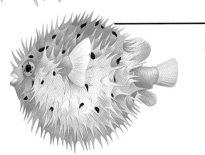

Tortoise shell

Tortoises and their cousins, turtles and terrapins, live inside a tough, protective shell. When they are in danger they can hide their legs, head, and tail inside the shell. The shell is made of bony plates that fit together like a jigsaw puzzle. A tough horny layer covers and protects the whole shell. The tortoise's body is fixed to the shell along its backbone, and at its hips and shoulders.

THE TORTOISE'S LEGS, TAIL, AND HEAD ARE TUCKED INSIDE THE SHELL

27

Inside Shells

SOME ANIMALS live inside a shell. They belong to the mollusc family, which includes snails, clams, and mussels. Octopus and squid are also molluscs but they do not have a shell. Molluscs live in water – in the sea, and in rivers, lakes, and ponds – and on land. Their body is made up of four parts. There is a head, with eyes, tentacles, and a mouth. There is also a muscular foot. Above the foot is a lump which holds the internal organs. Finally, there is a sheet of tissue, called the mantle, which grows over the lump and produces the shell. Some molluscs have more than one shell. These are made of a tough chalky substance. Between the body tissues and the mantle is a space which holds the gills (for breathing) and openings from the intestine, reproductive organs, and kidneys.

Snail

Snails glide along on a large foot. This does not simply help the snail to get from place to place; it is also joined with the head and contains many of its organs, including its brain, eyes, tentacles, and mouth. This is why snails are called gastropods, which means 'head-foot'. Their long coiled intestine is tucked away inside their shell, together with the kidney and reproductive organs. Snails mostly eat plant material but some eat other snails, drilling holes into them to get at them.

Spiral shell

Over 75,000 different kinds of snails are known. Each snail lives in its own type of coloured shell. The shell has an opening called the aperture and is usually twisted into a spiral. Each spiral twist is called a whorl. Shells are coloured for camouflage or to warn off predators because they are poisonous. The largest, the trumpet conch, can reach over 450 cm while the smallest, the pupa, is less than 4 mm long.

SHELL WITH HORNY OUTER LAYER CONTAINING COLOURING. LOWER LAYERS OF CRYSTALS MAKE THE SHELL HARD

THE KIDNEY REMOVES WASTE

THE REPRODUCTIVE ORGANS

WHORLS ABOVE BODY WHORL FORM THE SPIRE

RIBS AND GROOVES PATTERN THE SHELL

BODY WHORL CONTAINING MOST OF THE SNAIL

THE SNAIL PRODUCES SLIME TO SLITHER ON

TENDONS STRENGTHEN THE FOOT

BODY AND FOOT EXTEND THROUGH THE APERTURE

THE FOOT HAS MUSCULAR RIPPLES TO HELP THE SNAIL GLIDE ALONG

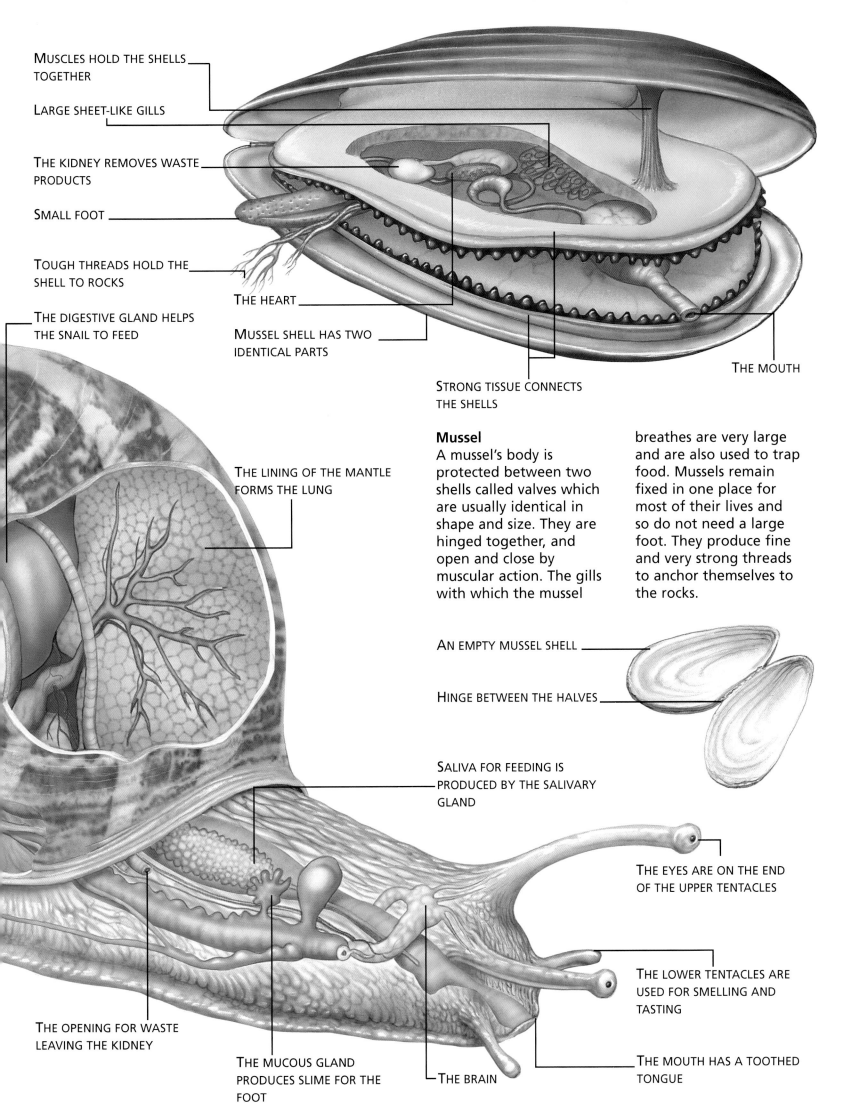

MUSCLES HOLD THE SHELLS TOGETHER

LARGE SHEET-LIKE GILLS

THE KIDNEY REMOVES WASTE PRODUCTS

SMALL FOOT

TOUGH THREADS HOLD THE SHELL TO ROCKS

THE DIGESTIVE GLAND HELPS THE SNAIL TO FEED

THE HEART

MUSSEL SHELL HAS TWO IDENTICAL PARTS

STRONG TISSUE CONNECTS THE SHELLS

THE MOUTH

THE LINING OF THE MANTLE FORMS THE LUNG

Mussel

A mussel's body is protected between two shells called valves which are usually identical in shape and size. They are hinged together, and open and close by muscular action. The gills with which the mussel breathes are very large and are also used to trap food. Mussels remain fixed in one place for most of their lives and so do not need a large foot. They produce fine and very strong threads to anchor themselves to the rocks.

AN EMPTY MUSSEL SHELL

HINGE BETWEEN THE HALVES

SALIVA FOR FEEDING IS PRODUCED BY THE SALIVARY GLAND

THE EYES ARE ON THE END OF THE UPPER TENTACLES

THE LOWER TENTACLES ARE USED FOR SMELLING AND TASTING

THE OPENING FOR WASTE LEAVING THE KIDNEY

THE MUCOUS GLAND PRODUCES SLIME FOR THE FOOT

THE BRAIN

THE MOUTH HAS A TOOTHED TONGUE

Spineless Life

MANY ANIMALS do not have a backbone. They are called invertebrates and include corals, worms, insects, and snails. Their muscles are supported by firm tissue, bags of gas or liquid, or a hard outer skeleton. Animals with no hard skeleton make a soft, easy meal, so some hide away in tubes or burrows; others are able to defend themselves with spines and stings.

The Portuguese man-of-war is a soft-bodied invertebrate. It is unusual in that it is made up of various small animals called polyps. Each polyp performs a different function: feeding, digesting, stinging, reproducing, and keeping afloat. It is blown along on the warm seas, kept afloat by a bladder full of gas, which acts as a sail. Its tentacles hang down several metres, catching fish to eat.

A WEB OF NERVE CELLS CARRIES INFORMATION TO THE DIFFERENT ANIMALS IN THE COLONY

POLYPS HAVE DIFFERENT FUNCTIONS, INCLUDING FEEDING, DIGESTION, AND REPRODUCTION

THE FEEDING POLYPS' TENTACLES CONTRACT (SHORTEN), PULLING PREY UP TO BE DIGESTED

Deadly weapons

The tentacles on a man-of-war carry special cells called cnidocysts that contain deadly weapons. When touched, triggers fire poison-filled threads. The threads shoot out and spear the victim, injecting it with poison. Once fired the cells are replaced by new ones.

A BARB (LIKE A FISH-HOOK) IS RELEASED WITH THE POISON-FILLED THREAD

DOZENS OF TENTACLES, HANGING DOWN 10 METRES, ARE USED TO SNARE PASSING PREY

EACH POISONOUS CELL HAS A TRIGGER

CELLS THAT HAVE BEEN FIRED ARE REPLACED

THE PREY IS STUNNED BY THE POISONOUS STING, SNARED BY THE THREADS, AND PULLED UP BY THE TENTACLES

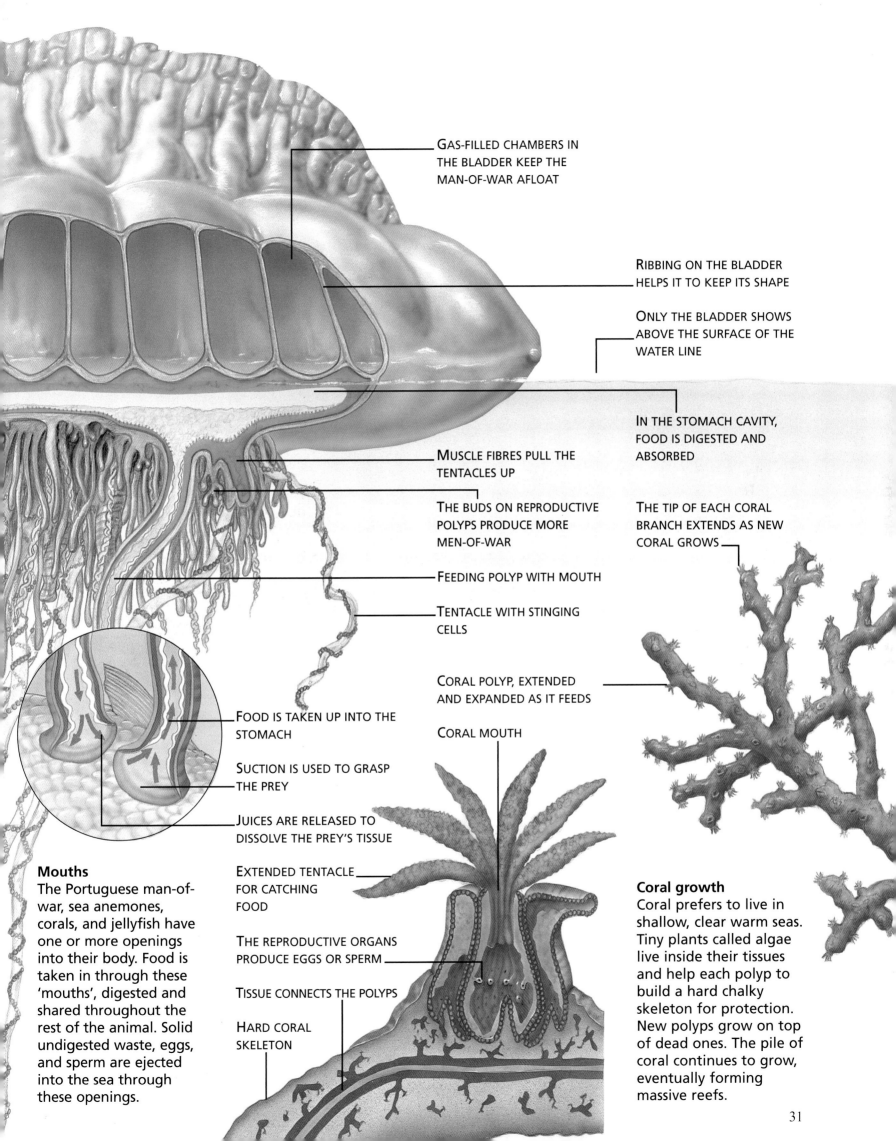

GAS-FILLED CHAMBERS IN THE BLADDER KEEP THE MAN-OF-WAR AFLOAT

RIBBING ON THE BLADDER HELPS IT TO KEEP ITS SHAPE

ONLY THE BLADDER SHOWS ABOVE THE SURFACE OF THE WATER LINE

IN THE STOMACH CAVITY, FOOD IS DIGESTED AND ABSORBED

MUSCLE FIBRES PULL THE TENTACLES UP

THE BUDS ON REPRODUCTIVE POLYPS PRODUCE MORE MEN-OF-WAR

THE TIP OF EACH CORAL BRANCH EXTENDS AS NEW CORAL GROWS

FEEDING POLYP WITH MOUTH

TENTACLE WITH STINGING CELLS

CORAL POLYP, EXTENDED AND EXPANDED AS IT FEEDS

CORAL MOUTH

FOOD IS TAKEN UP INTO THE STOMACH

SUCTION IS USED TO GRASP THE PREY

JUICES ARE RELEASED TO DISSOLVE THE PREY'S TISSUE

EXTENDED TENTACLE FOR CATCHING FOOD

THE REPRODUCTIVE ORGANS PRODUCE EGGS OR SPERM

TISSUE CONNECTS THE POLYPS

HARD CORAL SKELETON

Mouths
The Portuguese man-of-war, sea anemones, corals, and jellyfish have one or more openings into their body. Food is taken in through these 'mouths', digested and shared throughout the rest of the animal. Solid undigested waste, eggs, and sperm are ejected into the sea through these openings.

Coral growth
Coral prefers to live in shallow, clear warm seas. Tiny plants called algae live inside their tissues and help each polyp to build a hard chalky skeleton for protection. New polyps grow on top of dead ones. The pile of coral continues to grow, eventually forming massive reefs.

31

Insect Life

THERE ARE more insects and different types of insects than any other animal. Insects make use of almost every type of environment, from the dark, damp forest floor to the dry heat of the desert. Their bodies are covered in a tough but light armour called cuticle. Cuticle can be soft and flexible or very hard. For example, the jaw of a cockroach can cut through a lead pipe! Cuticle is also waterproof. The cuticle is one of the main reasons that insects are so successful.

The insect's body is divided into three parts: head, thorax, and abdomen. The head carries the eyes, antennae (feelers), and mouth parts, and it also houses the brain. The thorax supports the wings and three pairs of legs, and is the powerhouse for the insect's movement. The abdomen holds the intestines and other internal organs.

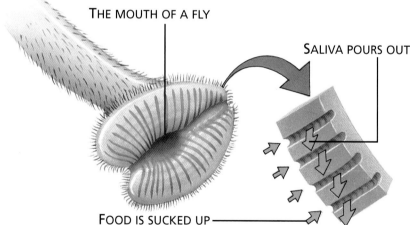

THE MOUTH OF A FLY

SALIVA POURS OUT

FOOD IS SUCKED UP

Tools for eating
Insects have three sets of 'jaws', or mouth parts. The designs of these parts can vary enormously between different species. Some chew, others bite or cut, stab, pierce, rasp, pinch, drill, inject, or lick.

Flies eat almost any liquid or semi-liquid food, from rotting filth to nectar. Saliva is poured down from the fly's salivary glands and spread onto the food. The saliva mixes with the food and is used to soften it if it is very hard. The fly then uses delicate tubes to suck the meal up into its stomach.

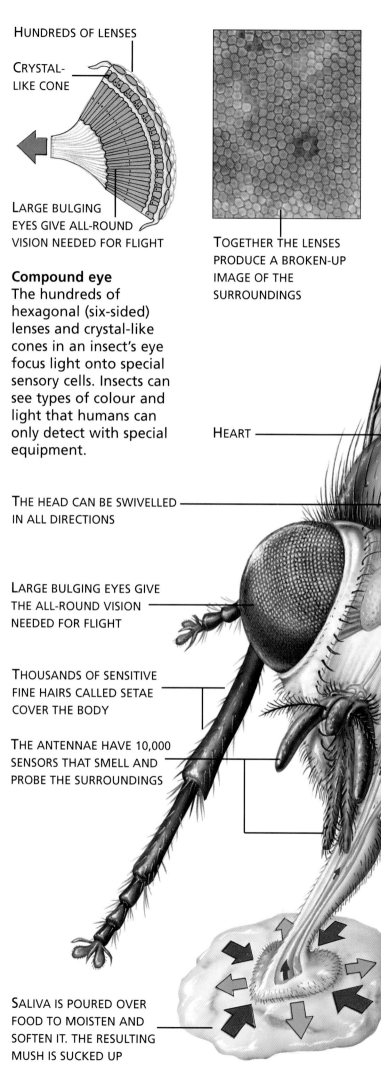

HUNDREDS OF LENSES

CRYSTAL-LIKE CONE

LARGE BULGING EYES GIVE ALL-ROUND VISION NEEDED FOR FLIGHT

TOGETHER THE LENSES PRODUCE A BROKEN-UP IMAGE OF THE SURROUNDINGS

Compound eye
The hundreds of hexagonal (six-sided) lenses and crystal-like cones in an insect's eye focus light onto special sensory cells. Insects can see types of colour and light that humans can only detect with special equipment.

THE HEAD CAN BE SWIVELLED IN ALL DIRECTIONS

HEART

LARGE BULGING EYES GIVE THE ALL-ROUND VISION NEEDED FOR FLIGHT

THOUSANDS OF SENSITIVE FINE HAIRS CALLED SETAE COVER THE BODY

THE ANTENNAE HAVE 10,000 SENSORS THAT SMELL AND PROBE THE SURROUNDINGS

SALIVA IS POURED OVER FOOD TO MOISTEN AND SOFTEN IT. THE RESULTING MUSH IS SUCKED UP

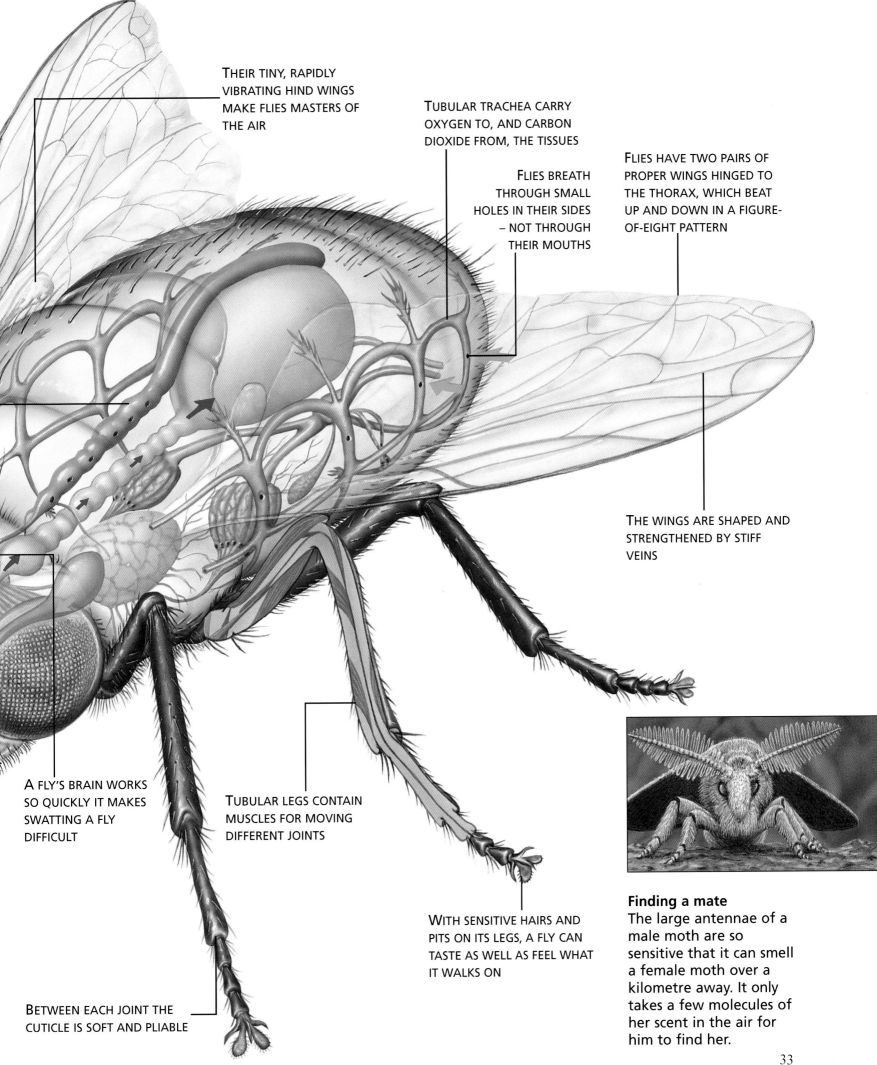

THEIR TINY, RAPIDLY VIBRATING HIND WINGS MAKE FLIES MASTERS OF THE AIR

TUBULAR TRACHEA CARRY OXYGEN TO, AND CARBON DIOXIDE FROM, THE TISSUES

FLIES BREATH THROUGH SMALL HOLES IN THEIR SIDES – NOT THROUGH THEIR MOUTHS

FLIES HAVE TWO PAIRS OF PROPER WINGS HINGED TO THE THORAX, WHICH BEAT UP AND DOWN IN A FIGURE-OF-EIGHT PATTERN

THE WINGS ARE SHAPED AND STRENGTHENED BY STIFF VEINS

A FLY'S BRAIN WORKS SO QUICKLY IT MAKES SWATTING A FLY DIFFICULT

TUBULAR LEGS CONTAIN MUSCLES FOR MOVING DIFFERENT JOINTS

WITH SENSITIVE HAIRS AND PITS ON ITS LEGS, A FLY CAN TASTE AS WELL AS FEEL WHAT IT WALKS ON

BETWEEN EACH JOINT THE CUTICLE IS SOFT AND PLIABLE

Finding a mate
The large antennae of a male moth are so sensitive that it can smell a female moth over a kilometre away. It only takes a few molecules of her scent in the air for him to find her.

33

Changing Shape

MONARCH BUTTERFLIES live in North America. Like all butterflies, they begin life as caterpillars. While they are caterpillars, monarchs eat the leaves of milkweed plants for energy and growth. Other animals find these plants poisonous and leave them alone, but these caterpillars are not affected by the poison. In fact, they make use of it for their own defence. They store it, making themselves taste nasty so predators (hunters) leave them alone, even after they have become butterflies.

After metamorphosis (the process of changing shape), the caterpillars become butterflies. Like all butterflies, the monarch butterfly sips nectar from flowers. Nectar provides the energy needed to fly. They fly to new places so they can find plants to lay their eggs on. They also use flight to escape from enemies or find a mate.

HORNS FRIGHTEN PREDATORS

THE LONG INTESTINE DIGESTS LEAVES

SUCKER-LIKE CLASPERS GRIP PLANTS

2) Metamorphosis
A caterpillar just eats and grows. Because it has stretchy skin it can grow bigger for a while, but eventually its skin becomes too tight. Then it has to moult (shed its skin) for a new, larger one. It does this four times. Just before the

A BABY CATERPILLAR CLIMBING FROM ITS EGG

THE CATERPILLAR SOON GROWS

THE ANTENNAE HELP TO FIND FOOD AND A MATE

THE BRAIN

ITS COMPOUND EYES ARE LIKE A FLY'S (*SEE PAGE 32*)

ITS LONG COILED TONGUE EXTRACTS NECTAR

THE UPPER BODY (THORAX) HOLDS THE MUSCLES WHICH WORK THE WINGS

1) From egg to caterpillar
The female monarch butterfly lays her eggs in groups on the surface of a leaf. Some other butterflies lay them singly. The eggs are tiny but very tough. They protect the growing baby caterpillars inside from rain, sun, and parasites (insects that live on other insects). To escape from the eggs the baby caterpillars bite their way out using their tiny jaws. After hatching, the caterpillars eat the rest of the egg shells before moving away to feed on leaves.

THE CATERPILLAR EVENTUALLY TURNS INTO A CHRYSALIS – IT THEN DEVELOPS INTO AN ADULT BUTTERFLY

last moult it fixes itself to a twig, using special silk that it makes, and turns into a pupa, or chrysalis. Within the chrysalis the insect changes form, ready to be born again – but this time as a butterfly. These changes are called metamorphosis.

THE ADULT BUTTERFLY EMERGES FROM THE CHRYSALIS

LARGE WINGS BEAT UP AND DOWN ALLOWING THE BUTTERFLY TO FLY THROUGH THE AIR

TINY SCALES COVER THE WINGS

BRIGHTLY COLOURED WINGS LET BUTTERFLIES TALK TO EACH OTHER AND WARN PREDATORS TO KEEP AWAY

3) Emergence
Sixteen weeks ago the caterpillar hatched. Now it has completely changed. The chrysalis splits and the adult butterfly emerges. At first it looks strange because its wings have been screwed up tight inside the chrysalis. Having crawled from the chrysalis the butterfly rests and uses air to inflate its wings. The wings become dry, ready for the butterfly to use.

Migration
In the autumn, monarch butterflies travel southward for over 3,200 kilometres, from Canada and northern USA to Florida, Mexico, and California. Here, crowds of them gather on pine trees. In spring they fly north, laying eggs along the way. Then they die.

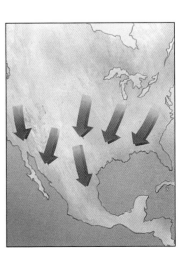

INTESTINE FOR DIGESTING NECTAR

THE ABDOMEN CONTAINS THE BODY'S MAIN ORGANS

A Frog's Life

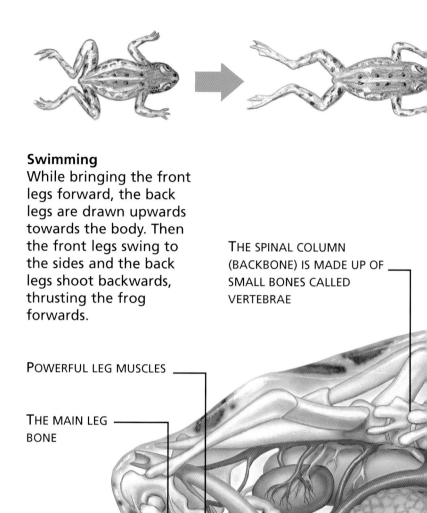

L IKE ALL FROGS, the Colombian horned frog is cold-blooded and has a moist skin. Horned frogs like this one live in tropical American forests, hiding amongst the moss and dead leaves of the forest floor. They are very aggressive and will even try to eat animals that are bigger than they are.

Frogs have a large head, bulging eyes, and a wide mouth. The front legs are shorter than the back legs, which usually have an extra long heel for jumping. Frogs can swim, and they depend on water to keep themselves moist and to raise their young. They can breathe both in and out of water. When underwater they breathe through their skin.

Swimming
While bringing the front legs forward, the back legs are drawn upwards towards the body. Then the front legs swing to the sides and the back legs shoot backwards, thrusting the frog forwards.

THE SPINAL COLUMN (BACKBONE) IS MADE UP OF SMALL BONES CALLED VERTEBRAE

POWERFUL LEG MUSCLES

THE MAIN LEG BONE

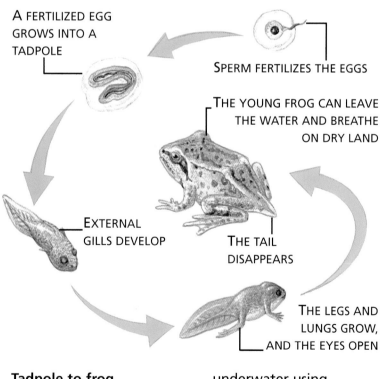

A FERTILIZED EGG GROWS INTO A TADPOLE

SPERM FERTILIZES THE EGGS

THE YOUNG FROG CAN LEAVE THE WATER AND BREATHE ON DRY LAND

EXTERNAL GILLS DEVELOP

THE TAIL DISAPPEARS

THE LEGS AND LUNGS GROW, AND THE EYES OPEN

ANKLE BONES

THE BROAD WEBBED BACK FEET MAKE SWIMMING EASIER

THE STOMACH

Tadpole to frog
A female frog lays her eggs in water. The mass of eggs is called spawn. The spawn is fertilized by sperm from the male frog. The fertilized eggs then grow into balls of cells which develop into tadpoles. At first, tadpoles are blind and breathe underwater using external gills. But gradually they change into frogs – a process called metamorphosis. Their eyes open, their legs grow, and their lungs develop. When their lungs have grown they can leave the water and use the lungs to breathe.

ON LAND AIR IS BREATHED IN AND OUT OF THE LUNGS

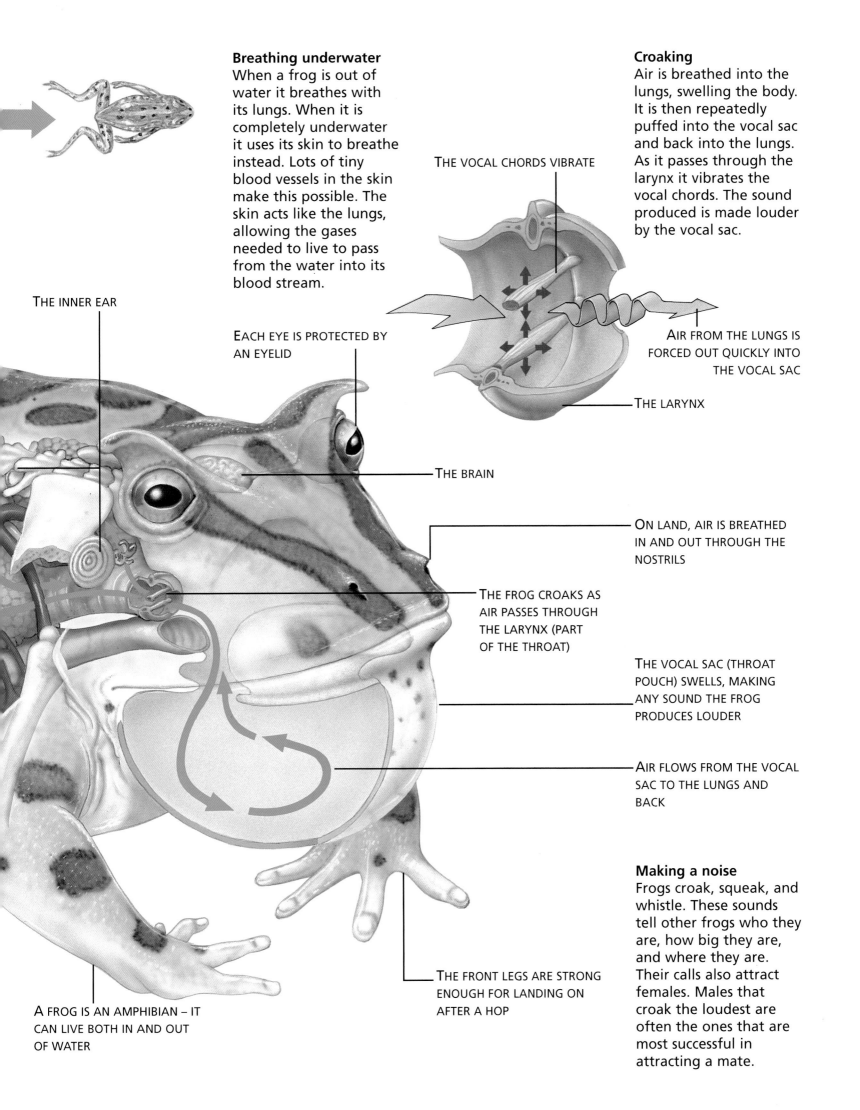

Breathing underwater
When a frog is out of water it breathes with its lungs. When it is completely underwater it uses its skin to breathe instead. Lots of tiny blood vessels in the skin make this possible. The skin acts like the lungs, allowing the gases needed to live to pass from the water into its blood stream.

Croaking
Air is breathed into the lungs, swelling the body. It is then repeatedly puffed into the vocal sac and back into the lungs. As it passes through the larynx it vibrates the vocal chords. The sound produced is made louder by the vocal sac.

THE VOCAL CHORDS VIBRATE

AIR FROM THE LUNGS IS FORCED OUT QUICKLY INTO THE VOCAL SAC

THE LARYNX

THE INNER EAR

EACH EYE IS PROTECTED BY AN EYELID

THE BRAIN

ON LAND, AIR IS BREATHED IN AND OUT THROUGH THE NOSTRILS

THE FROG CROAKS AS AIR PASSES THROUGH THE LARYNX (PART OF THE THROAT)

THE VOCAL SAC (THROAT POUCH) SWELLS, MAKING ANY SOUND THE FROG PRODUCES LOUDER

AIR FLOWS FROM THE VOCAL SAC TO THE LUNGS AND BACK

Making a noise
Frogs croak, squeak, and whistle. These sounds tell other frogs who they are, how big they are, and where they are. Their calls also attract females. Males that croak the loudest are often the ones that are most successful in attracting a mate.

THE FRONT LEGS ARE STRONG ENOUGH FOR LANDING ON AFTER A HOP

A FROG IS AN AMPHIBIAN – IT CAN LIVE BOTH IN AND OUT OF WATER

Baby Mammals

MAMMALS ARE warm-blooded animals which feed their young with milk. Most mammals are covered in hair, which helps to keep them warm. Their milk comes from special milk glands called mammary glands. Even mammals that lay eggs, like the spiny anteater and duck-billed platypus, produce milk for their young. All other mammals give birth to live babies, which develop inside the mother's uterus. They are attached to the uterus by a tube called the umbilical cord. Through the cord they get food and oxygen, which helps them grow. Small mammals develop faster than large ones: a mouse takes about 2 weeks to develop while an elephant takes 22 months. Humans develop for 9 months. When the mammal is ready to give birth, chemicals in her body cause her uterus to push the baby out.

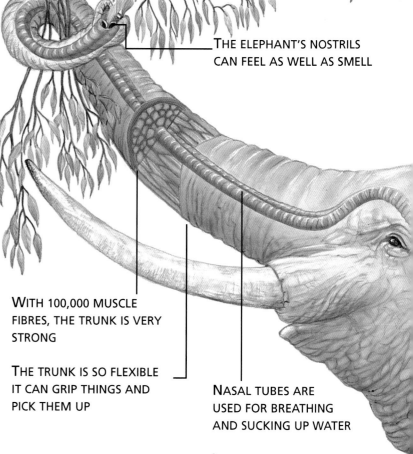

THE ELEPHANT'S NOSTRILS CAN FEEL AS WELL AS SMELL

WITH 100,000 MUSCLE FIBRES, THE TRUNK IS VERY STRONG

THE TRUNK IS SO FLEXIBLE IT CAN GRIP THINGS AND PICK THEM UP

NASAL TUBES ARE USED FOR BREATHING AND SUCKING UP WATER

LARGE EARS ALLOW EXCESS HEAT TO ESCAPE

Marsupials

Marsupials are mammals that give birth to babies which are not fully developed. The baby continues to develop in a pouch on the mother's tummy. In the pouch the baby can crawl to one of the mother's nipples to suck milk.

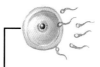

FERTILIZATION: A MALE SPERM-CELL JOINS AN EGG

A BALL OF CELLS FORMS AT THREE DAYS

A TWO-MONTH OLD FOETUS (ACTUAL SIZE); ITS EYES ARE NOT YET FULLY DEVELOPED

Fertilization and development

Every mammal starts out as a tiny egg produced by the mother. To become a baby mammal the egg has to be joined by a sperm-cell from the father. This process is called fertilization. The fertilized cell divides into a ball of cells, which becomes fixed to the wall of the female's uterus. The ball of cells then develops into what we call a foetus, as its head, body, and legs begin to grow.

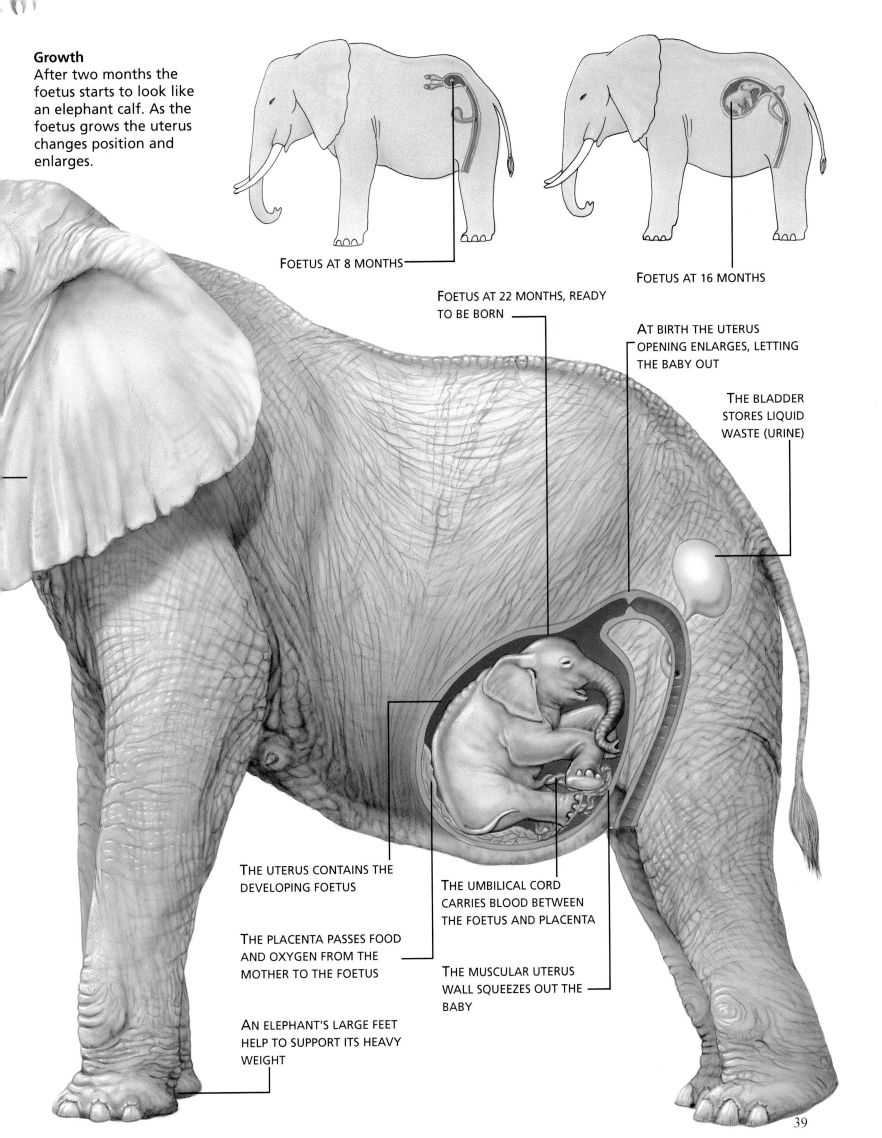

Growth
After two months the foetus starts to look like an elephant calf. As the foetus grows the uterus changes position and enlarges.

FOETUS AT 8 MONTHS

FOETUS AT 16 MONTHS

FOETUS AT 22 MONTHS, READY TO BE BORN

AT BIRTH THE UTERUS OPENING ENLARGES, LETTING THE BABY OUT

THE BLADDER STORES LIQUID WASTE (URINE)

THE UTERUS CONTAINS THE DEVELOPING FOETUS

THE UMBILICAL CORD CARRIES BLOOD BETWEEN THE FOETUS AND PLACENTA

THE PLACENTA PASSES FOOD AND OXYGEN FROM THE MOTHER TO THE FOETUS

THE MUSCULAR UTERUS WALL SQUEEZES OUT THE BABY

AN ELEPHANT'S LARGE FEET HELP TO SUPPORT ITS HEAVY WEIGHT

Hatching Eggs

PHEASANTS, LIKE ALL birds, lay eggs. Pheasants lay 8 to 15 eggs at a time. Eggs are strong rounded structures which hold and protect the chick as it develops. The shell is made of chalky crystals, which makes it strong, and it is lined with a tough membrane. This protects the chick from drying up and allows oxygen to pass in and carbon dioxide waste to travel out. Within the shell the chick rests in a soft jelly-like fluid. It receives food from the yellow bag of yolk. On the outside, egg shells are lightly coloured and are often flecked with brown so that they are not easily seen within the nest. Nests help the hen to protect her eggs and make it possible for her to sit on them, keeping them warm.

Pheasant nests
It is important to hide the nest and eggs from foxes and stoats. To do this a simple hollow is scraped in the ground under a hedge or a layer of plants. It is sometimes lined with a little surrounding plant material. The plain olive-brown or grey coloured eggs can hardly be seen.

Embryo development
After the female and male bird have mated, the tiny fertilized egg cell divides into more and more cells to form a patch of cells, the embryo. As the embryo develops the cells continue to divide, eventually organizing themselves into tissues and organs. Some of the cells move and form folds which later develop into different structures. But not all of the cells become part of the chick. Some become blood vessels that take food from the yolk to the developing chick, others form a bag to hold waste as the chick grows.

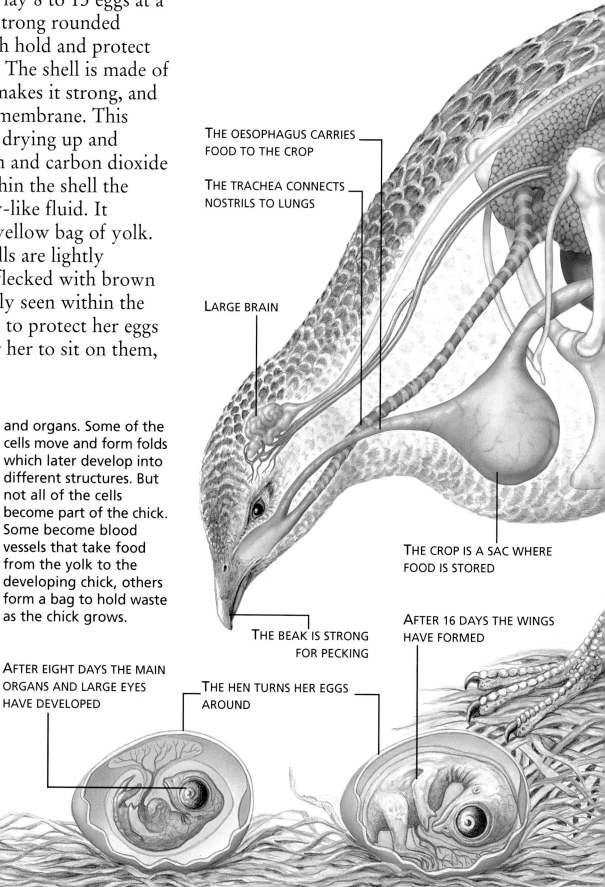

THE OESOPHAGUS CARRIES FOOD TO THE CROP

THE TRACHEA CONNECTS NOSTRILS TO LUNGS

LARGE BRAIN

THE CROP IS A SAC WHERE FOOD IS STORED

THE BEAK IS STRONG FOR PECKING

THE HEN TURNS HER EGGS AROUND

AFTER 16 DAYS THE WINGS HAVE FORMED

TWO DAYS AFTER THE EGG IS LAID, THE HEART IS PUMPING BLOOD TO THE YOLK-SAC

AFTER EIGHT DAYS THE MAIN ORGANS AND LARGE EYES HAVE DEVELOPED

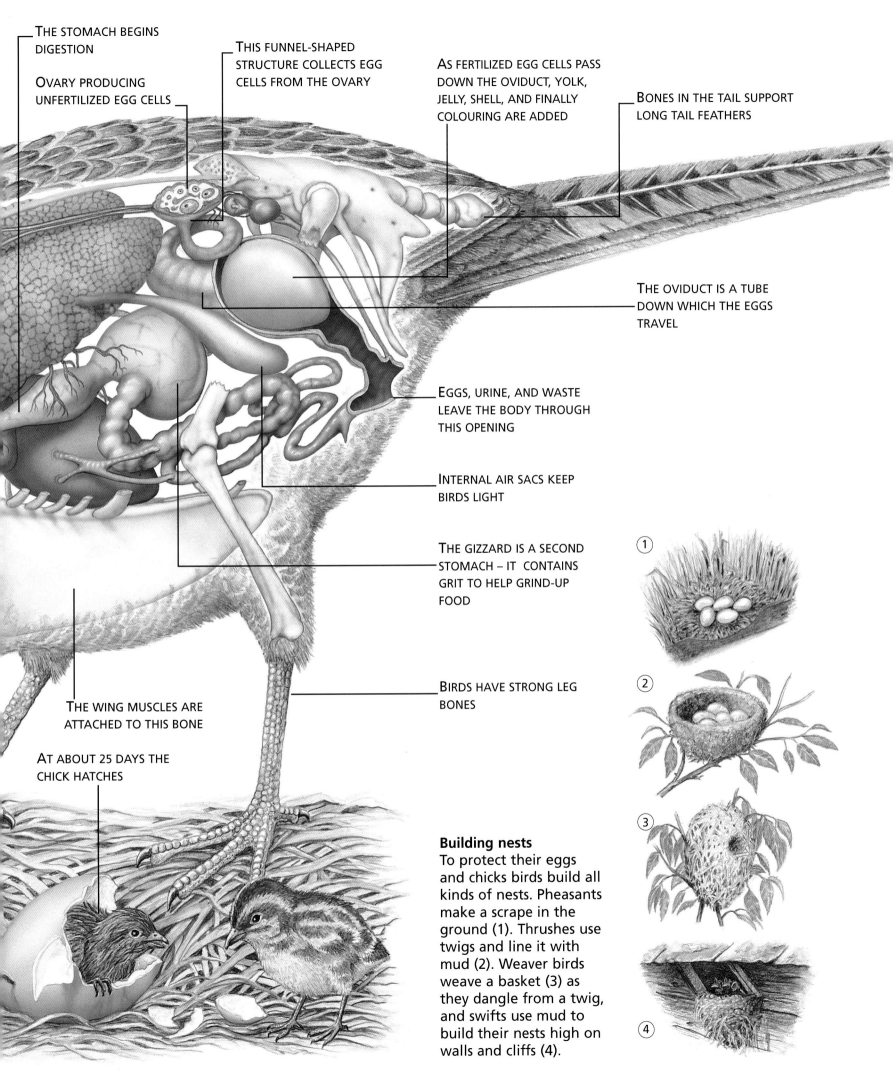

THE STOMACH BEGINS DIGESTION

OVARY PRODUCING UNFERTILIZED EGG CELLS

THIS FUNNEL-SHAPED STRUCTURE COLLECTS EGG CELLS FROM THE OVARY

AS FERTILIZED EGG CELLS PASS DOWN THE OVIDUCT, YOLK, JELLY, SHELL, AND FINALLY COLOURING ARE ADDED

BONES IN THE TAIL SUPPORT LONG TAIL FEATHERS

THE OVIDUCT IS A TUBE DOWN WHICH THE EGGS TRAVEL

EGGS, URINE, AND WASTE LEAVE THE BODY THROUGH THIS OPENING

INTERNAL AIR SACS KEEP BIRDS LIGHT

THE GIZZARD IS A SECOND STOMACH – IT CONTAINS GRIT TO HELP GRIND-UP FOOD

BIRDS HAVE STRONG LEG BONES

THE WING MUSCLES ARE ATTACHED TO THIS BONE

AT ABOUT 25 DAYS THE CHICK HATCHES

Building nests
To protect their eggs and chicks birds build all kinds of nests. Pheasants make a scrape in the ground (1). Thrushes use twigs and line it with mud (2). Weaver birds weave a basket (3) as they dangle from a twig, and swifts use mud to build their nests high on walls and cliffs (4).

① ② ③ ④

41

Desert Animals

CAMELS LIVE in deserts. Their bodies are specially designed to survive the desert's hot days and cold nights. They can also cope with the wind-blown sand and long periods without water. For nearly 4,000 years, since they were first domesticated (tamed) in Arabia, they have helped people live and travel in the desert. Camels can run at 16 kph – some are bred specially for racing. They can even swim. When walking, camels move at about 4 kph and can travel nearly 50 kilometres each day. But they do not like going up hills. Camels are able to carry loads of up to 1,000 kilograms. This makes them ideal pack animals, which is why they are sometimes called 'ships of the desert'.

The camel's hump
Some camels have one hump, others have two. The one-humped dromedary originally lived in Arabia. The two-humped bactrian camel is found in Mongolia and Turkestan. A camel's hump is filled with fat. Well-fed camels have firm, upright humps. Once in the desert, away from a supply of food, they use the fat as a source of energy and water. When most of the fat has been used up the hump shrivels and flops over.

THE FAT-FILLED HUMP

SOFT WOOLLY HAIR STOPS THEM COOLING DOWN TOO QUICKLY IN THE COLD NIGHT

THE SKIN HAS HARDLY ANY SWEAT GLANDS TO AVOID TOO MUCH WATER LOSS

A LONG NECK ENABLES THE CAMEL TO DRINK WITHOUT KNEELING DOWN

SMALL HAIRY EARS KEEP OUT SAND

LONG EYELASHES AND BIG EYELIDS PROTECT THEIR EYES FROM THE SUN AND FLYING SAND

THEIR NOSTRILS CAN CLOSE TO KEEP OUT THE SAND

SALIVARY GLANDS HELP DIGEST FOOD

WITH STRONG TEETH AND LIPS, CAMELS CAN EAT TOUGH PLANTS – SALTY PLANTS HELP THEM RETAIN WATER

TOUGH PADS OF SKIN PROTECT THE KNEES AND CHEST WHEN THE CAMEL RESTS ITS WEIGHT

CAMELS HAVE A THREE-CHAMBERED STOMACH AND STRONG INTESTINES THAT CAN DIGEST TOUGH PLANTS, FLESH, SKIN, BONES, AND EVEN TEETH!

TAIL LOOPED OVER THE BODY WITH THE STING READY

STRONG CLAWS TO CATCH ITS PREY

LIKE SPIDERS, SCORPIONS HAVE EIGHT LEGS

Desert scorpion

The yellow colour of desert scorpions means they are well camouflaged in the sand and rocks. During the day desert scorpions hide under stones to avoid the heat of the sun and animals that hunt them. They are nocturnal, coming out at night to find insects and other creatures to eat. To kill their prey scorpions inject venom from the sting at the tip of their tail. Most scorpions are harmless to people, but some are very poisonous and could make a person die in great pain.

LONG MUSCULAR LEGS ENABLE THE CAMEL TO RUN FAST

THE CAMEL HAS A STRONG SKELETON, MAKING IT ABLE TO CARRY PEOPLE AND HEAVY LOADS ACROSS THE DESERT

FOOT PAD

Special feet

Two webbed toes with small nails and a broad soft sole keep the camel from sinking into the soft sand. The tough skin and hairs of the feet prevent them from being burnt by the hot sand and rubbed away by hard rocks.

Arctic Animals

IN THE ARCTIC it is bitterly cold for most of the year. During the short summers the sun shines weakly, and the winters are long and dark. The Arctic Ocean is frozen, only melting and breaking-up around the edges during the summer. The vast ice sheets are bleak and there is only barren land. Only tiny plants can grow, huddled close to the ground, out of the icy wind. Few animals can live here. Those that do have developed special features so that they can survive the freezing conditions. They have plenty of fat and thick fur to keep them warm. Many migrate, sleep or hibernate during the long winter. Despite this the ocean is rich in life, providing food for such animals as polar bears and arctic foxes.

A CROSS-SECTION OF THE SKIN

HAIR GROWS THROUGH THE OUTER SKIN LAYER

THE INNER SKIN LAYER CONTAINS HAIR ROOTS AND BLOOD VESSELS

A LAYER OF FAT UP TO 4 CENTIMETRES THICK PROVIDES WARMTH AND FOOD STORAGE

THE POLAR BEAR USES ITS POWERFUL SHOULDERS TO SWIM THE 'CRAWL'

THE EARS ARE SMALL TO PREVENT HEAT LOSS

A SPECIAL MEMBRANE PROTECTS THE EYE FROM BITTERLY COLD WINDS

THE POLAR BEAR'S LARGE PAWS ARE COVERED IN HAIR – THIS PROTECTS IT FROM THE EXTREME COLD AND HELPS IT WALK ON THE SNOW WITHOUT SINKING

Thick-coated insulation
Winter temperatures can drop to –60°C and rise to +20°C in the summer. To cope with this variation the polar bear grows a thick coat in the autumn to keep out the intense cold, and sheds it in the spring.

THE ENTRANCE HOLE IS NORMALLY CLOSED IN WINTER

HARD-PACKED ICE SURROUNDS THE DEN

MOTHER AND BABY REST IN THE DEN

LONG POWERFUL BACK LEGS HELP THE BEAR TO RUN

WHITE FUR ALLOWS THE POLAR BEAR TO HIDE IN THE SNOW AND STALK ITS PREY

WARM AIR IS TRAPPED IN LAYERS OF FUR

Denning
In the autumn, movement of the ice brings polar bears together to the denning areas. Here they fatten up on meat, berries, moss, and lichen. Some of the males are active all year, but most polar bears spend a lot of time during the cold months sleeping in their den.

LONG HAIRS KEEP THE SKIN DRY AND WARM

SHORT HAIRS PROVIDE SPACE TO TRAP AIR

Double layer of fur
The polar bear's double layer of fur protects it against the cold. When it fluffs up its thick coat, body heat is trapped between the two layers. If it gets too hot it can sleek the fur down, allowing heat to escape.

45

Primates

PRIMATES ARE mammals that have a very large brain. The part of the brain that thinks is especially big, making them very intelligent. Monkeys, chimpanzees, lemurs, and humans are all primates. Most primates live in the warmer parts of the world, except humans, who live in most parts.

Primates can be very big, like the gorilla, which weighs over 270 kilograms. Others, like the mouse lemur, are tiny and weigh only 50 grams. Nearly all of them are very good at climbing trees. To help them do this they have special eyes, hands, and feet. Many have a long tail, too. To communicate high in the trees primates use different sounds. Of all the primates humans make the most sounds.

FOUR LONG, GRIPPING FINGERS, ALSO USED FOR GROOMING

FINGERNAILS PROTECT THE DELICATE FINGERTIPS

A FLEXIBLE WRIST MAKES CLIMBING AND USING TOOLS EASY

STRONG ARM MUSCLES ARE USEFUL FOR CLIMBING TREES

THICK BODY HAIR FOR WARMTH

Chimp expressions
Some primates, such as chimpanzees, show their emotions through facial expressions. These include: (1) mouth closed when attacking – 'you've made me cross'; (2) mouth open to show all the teeth – 'I'm scared'; (3) mouth open, with the bottom teeth showing – 'let's play'; (4) lips pushed forward – 'give it to me'.

A CHIMP'S FLEXIBLE
THUMB CAN GRIP BRANCHES

Gripping thumb

All apes, like this
chimpanzee, can bring
their thumb across to
their other fingers. This
helps them to do all
kinds of things. They can
grip branches when
climbing, hold twigs to
hook termites out from
their nests, and groom
each other.

A ROUNDED SKULL PROTECTS
THE BRAIN

CHIMPANZEES ARE
INTELLIGENT: A LARGE BRAIN
HELPS THEM TO LEARN,
REMEMBER, THINK, AND
SOLVE PROBLEMS

Intelligent chimps

Chimpanzees live in
groups called troops,
moving around the
rainforests where they
live. Each chimp has to
know its place in the
troop. The older male,
the boss chimp, can be
recognized by the
colour of his back, which
is silvery-grey instead of
black. We know chimps
are intelligent because
they help each other
and are good at solving
problems. Chimps talk to
each other by pulling
different faces and
making noises. Baby
chimps have lots to
learn. It takes six years
for them to grow up.

LARGE OUTER EARS GATHER
AND LOCATE SOUNDS

THE INNER EAR PICKS UP
SOUND AND HELPS WITH
BALANCE

CHIMPS HAVE 3-DIMENSIONAL
VISION, WHICH MEANS THEY
CAN JUDGE DISTANCES

THE NOSE AND NOSTRILS ARE
GOOD FOR SMELLING FOOD,
FRIENDS, AND ENEMIES

THE STRONG TEETH ARE USED
FOR FIGHTING AND EATING
PLANTS AND MEAT

A SENSITIVE TONGUE
FOR TASTING

Community Life

MILLIONS OF TERMITES live together in communities called colonies. Each termite does a specific job, like gathering food, looking after the young, or guarding the colony against attack. This means that termites are social insects, as each individual works towards the good of the whole colony. In such a large community, good communication is vital. The termites need to respond to problems as soon as they arise. One way termites communicate is by releasing special chemicals that other termites can smell.

Termites are pale and have soft bodies so they need to avoid dry air and sunlight. They hide away inside their nests and burrows, and only come out at night, if at all. Some termites, like the ones shown here, use soil to make very complicated nests. Others produce more simple structures inside rotting wood.

Soldiers

Ants are the main enemy of termites. The soldier termites defend the colony from attack using their special jaws. Some bite while others use their jaws to spray a sticky glue at the attacker. Soldier termites cannot feed themselves; they are fed by the worker termites.

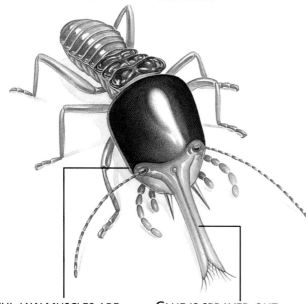

POWERFUL JAW MUSCLES ARE HOUSED IN THE LARGE HEAD

GLUE IS SPRAYED OUT THROUGH THIS TUBE

Air circulation

Millions of termites living together need plenty of fresh air to breathe. They also need to keep the air cool. So termites build their nest in such a way that the air moves through it, keeping the conditions fresh and cool. This circulating air also means that the chemical scents they use for communication will carry from one termite to another.

PIECES OF PLANTS ARE EATEN AND GATHERED BY WORKERS AND TAKEN INTO THE MOUND

FUNGUS IS GROWN ON THE STORED PLANT MATERIAL. THE TERMITES EAT THE FUNGUS AND FEED IT TO THEIR YOUNG

FUNGUS PRODUCTION NEEDS TERMITE DROPPINGS, MOIST AIR, AND A PRECISE TEMPERATURE OF 30–31°C

HOT STALE AIR RISES AND ESCAPES THROUGH THE CHIMNEYS

POROUS CHIMNEY MATERIAL DRAWS IN FRESH AIR AND RELEASES THE STALE AIR

UNDERGROUND CELLARS COOL THE AIR AND GIVE IT MOISTURE

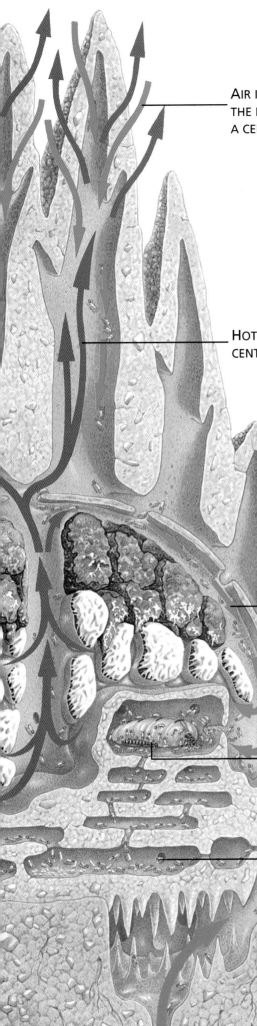

AIR IS DRAWN DOWN INTO THE MOUND AND COOLED IN A CELLAR-LIKE CHAMBER

HOT AIR RISES THROUGH THE CENTRE OF THE MOUND

COLD AIR IS DRAWN DOWN OUTSIDE THE MAIN NEST

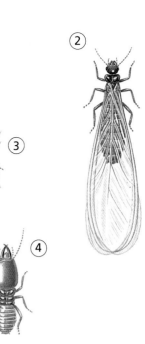

Termite classes
1. Queen. She rules the colony and lays millions of eggs during her life.
2. King. He lives by the queen and fertilizes her eggs.
3. Worker. There are more worker termites than any other kind of termite in the nest. They are always at work: building the nest, gathering food, and tending the young.
4. Soldier. The soldiers defend the colony against attack.

TERMITES AVOID SUNLIGHT WHEN THEY SEARCH FOR FOOD BY USING TUNNELS THAT LEAD TO THE SURFACE

THE QUEEN IN HER CHAMBER, WITH THE KING, HER WORKERS, AND SOLDIERS – EGGS ARE TAKEN AWAY AS SHE LAYS THEM

WORKERS LOOK AFTER THE EGGS IN CHAMBERS WHICH SERVE AS NURSERIES

How the nest is built
A young queen and her king start building their nest by digging a burrow. The queen lays eggs inside a small chamber. The workers that hatch extend the nest, building more chambers and tunnels. As the colony grows the nest gets bigger, forming a huge mound.

POOLS OF WATER BELOW THE CELLARS PROVIDE COOLING MOISTURE

THE
ENVIRONMENT

Michael Allaby

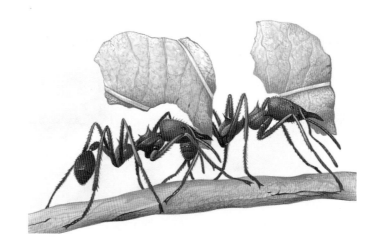

THE ENVIRONMENT
CONTENTS

What is the Environment?

WE CAN think of the whole of planet Earth as the environment. An environment is a place in which living things can find food and shelter. It consists of the surroundings (the rocks, soil, air and water) and the living things themselves. On Earth, life is possible almost everywhere – on dry land, and from the deepest ocean floor to the lower part of the atmosphere. But rather than look at this complete environment it is often easier to look at smaller, more local parts of it.

Two other planets, Mars and Venus, are like our Earth in many ways, but nothing can live on them. One day humans may live on Mars, but to do so they will have to alter the surroundings to make them Earth-like. They will have to create an environment.

Planet Earth
The environment that surrounds us is tiny compared to the depth of the Earth beneath. The Earth is formed in layers. The inner layers are very hot and around 1,000–2,000 kilometres thick. At the centre of the Earth the inner core is made of hot solid metal. This is covered by the outer core, a layer of molten metal. Around the outer core are the inner and outer mantles made of semi-molten rock. The soil and rock on which we live are called the crust – a layer only 5 to 60 kilometres thick. Above, the atmosphere forms a thin outer covering around the Earth.

NEARLY 9 KILOMETRES HIGH, MOUNT EVEREST JUST REACHES THE STRATOSPHERE

THE CRUST IS MADE OF LARGE PLATES THAT MOVE, CAUSING CRACKS, RIDGES AND MOUNTAINS

THE ENVIRONMENT STRETCHES FROM THE BOTTOM OF THE OCEANS TO THE TOP OF THE TROPOSPHERE

THE OUTER MANTLE CONTAINS MOLTEN ROCK THAT SOMETIMES ERUPTS FROM VOLCANOES

THE OUTER CORE IS VERY HOT – THE TEMPERATURE IS OVER 5,000°C

The atmosphere

The Earth's atmosphere can be divided into layers. The weather and most of the Earth's air are in the thinnest layer, called the troposphere (1). Above, in the stratosphere (2) lies the ozone gas that protects us from the Sun's harmful rays. Beyond, are the mesosphere (3) and the thermosphere (4). The exosphere (5) rises to about 700 kilometres, where it merges with the Sun's atmosphere.

THE OZONE LAYER IS ABOUT 25 KILOMETRES ABOVE THE EARTH'S SURFACE – IT PROTECTS US FROM THE SUN'S RAYS

IN THE TROPOSPHERE CLOUDS FORM AND THE EARTH'S WEATHER OCCURS

SPECTACULAR LIGHT DISPLAYS CALLED AURORA SOMETIMES APPEAR IN THE THERMOSPHERE

METEORS BURN UP IN THE MESOSPHERE

PLANTS AND ANIMALS CANNOT LIVE IN THE THIN AIR OF THE STRATOSPHERE

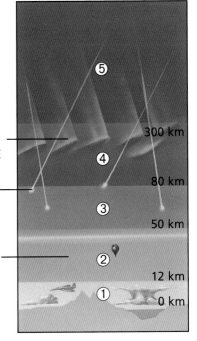

⑤

300 km

④

80 km

③

50 km

②

12 km

①

0 km

Air and Water

AIR AND water change the environment. Along with sunshine they affect climate, the weather and the type of vegetation that grows. At the equator the Sun is almost directly overhead at noon, so places on and near the equator are warmed more strongly than elsewhere. When heated the air moves away from the equator. At the same time cooler air moves towards the equator. This circulation of the air brings us weather. The Earth's winds are a part of this air circulation. Ocean waters, in warm or cold currents, also affect climates because air is warmed or cooled as it passes over them.

Climate

Climate is the range of weather conditions found in a particular area. Generally, the further you go from the equator, the colder the climate becomes. The climate of a region affects the type of vegetation found there. Rain forests (1) grow near the equator where the climate is hot and wet. Deserts (2) are in hot, dry climates. Temperate forests (3) grow in mild climates, while evergreen forests (4) are often found in colder climates. In polar regions (5) there is little vegetation because the climate is dry and very cold.

SOUTH POLE

OVER THE NORTH POLE VERY
COLD, DRY AIR DESCENDS;
THE SEA IN THIS REGION IS
MAINLY FROZEN

THE ARROWS SHOW AIR
CIRCULATION – WINDS ARE A
MAJOR PART OF THIS

Ocean currents

As warm water moves away from the equator, cooler water moves towards it, and the current or flow is swung to one side by the spinning of the Earth. This makes large circular water currents in the oceans. As air passes over the waters it is warmed or cooled by them. The waters also warm or cool the land nearby. On the map warm currents are in red; cold are in blue.

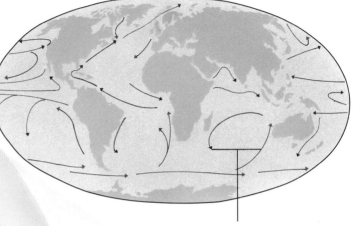

A CIRCULAR OCEAN CURRENT,
CALLED A GYRE

SUNSHINE IS HOTTER
AT THE EQUATOR

AIR THAT HAS RISEN OVER
THE EQUATOR LOSES ITS
MOISTURE, SO WHERE IT
DESCENDS THERE IS A DRY
DESERT CLIMATE

NEAR THE EQUATOR WARM
MOIST AIR RISES AND COOLS;
THE MOISTURE FORMS
CLOUDS AND LOTS OF RAIN
FALLS

THE EQUATOR IS AN
IMAGINARY LINE AROUND
THE EARTH, LYING HALFWAY
BETWEEN THE POLES

Key to vegetation zones

Polar region
Evergreen forest

Temperate forest
Desert
Rain forest

The Ozone Layer

SUNLIGHT, which we see as white, is really a mixture of the colours in a rainbow. The Sun also radiates light which we cannot see, some of it called ultraviolet (UV) light.

If too much UV light reaches the Earth's surface it is harmful and can cause skin cancer. However, a layer of ozone gas in the atmosphere protects us by absorbing some of the UV light. But in some parts of the world, particularly over Antarctica, the ozone layer has become thinner, allowing more UV light to reach the Earth.

THE OZONE LAYER, WHERE OZONE GATHERS, IS 20–25 KILOMETRES ABOVE THE GROUND

AS IT PASSES THROUGH THE OZONE LAYER SOME UV LIGHT IS ABSORBED BY OZONE

A THINNING OF THE OZONE LAYER IS SOMETIMES DESCRIBED AS AN 'OZONE HOLE'

WHERE THE OZONE LAYER IS THIN, MORE UV LIGHT REACHES THE GROUND

TOO MUCH UV LIGHT CAUSES SUNBURN AND SKIN CANCER

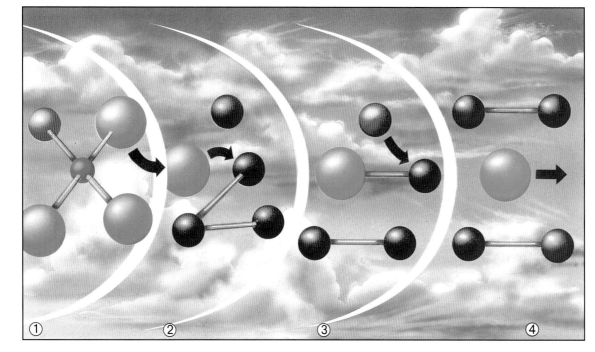

① ② ③ ④

Ozone breakdown
In the ozone layer there are gases which have chlorine atoms in their molecules. These gases include CFCs (chlorofluorocarbons). A CFC molecule with its chlorine atoms is pictured above (1). The chlorine atoms are coloured green.
UV light from the Sun breaks these CFC molecules up, and the chlorine atoms break off and float away. In winter over Antarctica, fierce winds blow around a centre of still air. As winter draws to an end, clouds of ice crystals form in the still air. On the surface of these crystals, the free chlorine atoms join up with ozone molecules (2). This removes an oxygen atom (red) from the ozone molecule, and breaks the molecule up. The spare oxygen atom then leaves the chlorine to join another spare oxygen atom (3). The chlorine is then free to break down another ozone molecule (4). This reduces the amount of ozone in the ozone layer, making an ozone 'hole'. Until recently CFCs have been widely used – in aerosol cans and refrigerators, for example. Now people know that CFCs destroy ozone, their use is being stopped.

ANTARCTICA IS THE
AREA AROUND THE
SOUTH POLE

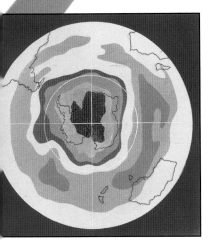

'Ozone hole'

The Antarctica 'ozone hole' was first detected in photographs taken from satellites in space (*left*). Dark blue, purple, pink and red show where the ozone is thin. The size of the hole varies from season to season. When the air warms up in summer, the 'hole' closes up.

WHEN THE AIR WARMS IN
THE SUMMER, THE ICE
CLOUDS DISAPPEAR, MORE
OZONE IS MADE, AND THE
'HOLE' CLOSES UP

COLD WINDS CIRCLE THE
SOUTH POLE

The Greenhouse Effect

THE SUN'S rays pass through the air freely, without warming it. When they reach the surfaces of the ground and sea, the surfaces are warmed. These surfaces then send heat back up into the sky, warming the air. Unlike the incoming Sun's rays, the outgoing heat warms some of the gases in the air. These 'greenhouse' gases are like a blanket holding in heat that would otherwise escape into outer space. This is called the 'greenhouse effect' because, like the glass of a greenhouse, the gases allow energy to pass more easily inwards than outwards. Many industries produce greenhouse gases.

THE AVERAGE TEMPERATURE OF THE EARTH'S SURFACE IS 15°C; WITHOUT THE GREENHOUSE EFFECT IT WOULD BE –23°C

POWER STATIONS BURNING COAL OR NATURAL GAS EMIT GREENHOUSE GASES

THE MOST IMPORTANT GREENHOUSE GAS IS CARBON DIOXIDE

SOME SCIENTISTS BELIEVE THE RELEASE OF GREENHOUSE GASES SHOULD BE REDUCED, OR THE EARTH'S CLIMATE WILL GET HOTTER

CARS, BURNING PETROL, RELEASE CARBON DIOXIDE AS WELL AS NITROUS OXIDE, ANOTHER GREENHOUSE GAS

THE SUN'S INCOMING RAYS PASS FREELY THROUGH THE AIR

GREENHOUSE GASES TRAP SOME OF THE OUTGOING HEAT

THE WARMED SURFACE RADIATES HEAT OUT INTO THE AIR

BURNING FORESTS RELEASE CARBON DIOXIDE, BUT NEW PLANT GROWTH CAN ABSORB IT

WE RELEASE GREENHOUSE GASES MAINLY BY BURNING FUEL IN FACTORIES, POWER STATIONS AND CARS

CATTLE AND SHEEP EMIT METHANE, A GREENHOUSE GAS

FERTILIZERS RELEASE NITROUS OXIDE, A GREENHOUSE GAS

THE OCEANS STORE MORE THAN ONE-THIRD OF THE CARBON DIOXIDE WE EMIT (*SEE PAGES 62–3*)

Gaia, The Living Earth

ALL LIVING organisms alter the chemistry of their environment. When we breathe we remove a little oxygen from the air and add a little carbon dioxide. After digesting food our body rids itself of waste. These two events alone alter the environment.

In 1979 a British scientist, James Lovelock, proposed the Gaia theory. On a 'living' planet, organisms alter their environment, managing or regulating it. In this way, said Lovelock, the Earth regulates itself, making sure there is enough oxygen for animals and carbon dioxide for plants, for example. Shown here is the way in which tiny marine plants and shellfish regulate the Earth's temperature and the amount of carbon dioxide (CO_2) in the air.

Carbon dioxide
Carbon dioxide is a greenhouse gas (*see pages 60–1*). It dissolves in rain and then enters the sea. There, tiny plants and animals use it to make their shells of calcium carbonate. When the organisms die, their shells fall to the seabed. Eventually these are ground down, and form chalk and limestone rocks. Such rocks are very common and often contain fossils of the shells.

This whole process removes carbon dioxide from the air and helps stop the Earth from growing warmer. The average temperature on Earth has always been about 15°C.

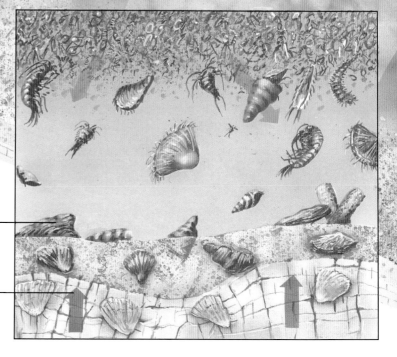

CHALK CLIFFS WERE FORMED OVER MILLIONS OF YEARS BY DEAD MARINE ORGANISMS

CHALK CLIFFS ARE LIKE GIANT STOREHOUSES FOR CO_2 – STORED AS CALCIUM CARBONATE

AS DEAD SHELLFISH AND TINY ORGANISMS DIE AND BREAK UP, SOME CARBON DIOXIDE (CO_2) IS RELEASED

WHEN SEA ORGANISMS DIE THEIR BONES AND SHELLS MAKE A CHALKY SEDIMENT

THE SEDIMENT BECOMES CHALK OR LIMESTONE ROCK, WHICH WILL EVENTUALLY BE THRUST ABOVE THE SURFACE OF THE SEA

CO₂ MOVES FROM THE AIR AND THROUGH RIVERS TO THE SEA

MORE SULPHUR IS RELEASED AS MARINE ORGANISMS GROW – THIS PRODUCES MORE CLOUDS, AND MAKES TEMPERATURES FALL

SEA ORGANISMS USE CO₂ TO MAKE THEIR BONES AND SHELLS

MICROSCOPIC PLANTS (CALLED PHYTOPLANKTON) GIVE THE SEA A CREAMY APPEARANCE BECAUSE OF THEIR CHALKY SHELLS

UNDER A MICROSCOPE THE FOSSILS OF TINY MARINE PLANTS AND SHELLS CAN BE SEEN IN CHALK

TINY MARINE PLANTS WITH CHALKY PLATES (SEEN UNDER A MICROSCOPE WITH OTHER ORGANISMS)

Not too hot, not too cold

In the oceans there are microscopic plant organisms which protect themselves with chalky plates, or shells. To make their shells they use up the greenhouse gas carbon dioxide (CO_2). The tiny plants also release a sulphur gas. This gas helps make most of the clouds we see over oceans. Together these processes help regulate the Earth's temperature.

When skies are clear the Sun's rays warm the Earth and its waters. The ocean's tiny plants then multiply faster and remove more CO_2 from the air. The multiplying plants also release more sulphur, which makes clouds form, cooling the ocean surface (1). As the water temperature cools, the tiny plants begin to die, and as they decompose they release CO_2 back into the air (2). The amount of sulphur is reduced, the skies clear, the ocean warms up, and the cycle begins again.

①

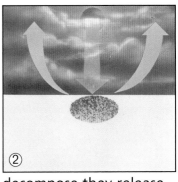

②

Plant Life

SUNLIGHT FALLS ON PLANT LEAVES

CHLOROPHYLL CAPTURES THE SUNLIGHT

PLANTS are among the few living things on Earth that can make their own food. They do this by a process called photosynthesis. Sunlight falling on the plant's leaves is captured by chlorophyll, the substance in the cells that gives the plant its green colour. Energy from the light is used to combine water and carbon dioxide to make food in the form of sugars. This food is then transported to all the other parts of the plant, providing the energy it needs to live and grow. Plants also use energy in taking the minerals they need from the soil to build their cells. The byproduct of photosynthesis is oxygen, which passes out of the plant through its leaves.

IN PHOTOSYNTHESIS OXYGEN IS RELEASED INTO THE ATMOSPHERE

LEAVES ARE GREEN BECAUSE THEY CONTAIN CHLOROPHYLL

WATER TRAVELS UP VESSELS IN THE STEM

WATER AND NUTRIENTS TAKEN UP FROM THE SOIL ENTER THROUGH THE ROOTS

64

CARBON DIOXIDE FROM THE ATMOSPHERE ENTERS THROUGH STOMATA IN THE LEAF

Respiration

All plants, like animals, continuously respire. Respiration is almost the reverse of photosynthesis: oxygen is taken in and carbon dioxide is released. The oxygen is used to break down the sugars the plant has made to produce the energy it needs to live.

During the day photosynthesis occurs faster than respiration so more carbon dioxide is taken in than released. At night photosynthesis stops and carbon dioxide is not taken in; it is only released, through respiration.

CARBON DIOXIDE, OXYGEN AND WATER VAPOUR PASS THROUGH STOMATA

AT NIGHT ONLY CARBON DIOXIDE AND WATER VAPOUR ARE RELEASED

WATER TRAVELS THROUGH THESE TUBES

PHOTOSYNTHESIS TAKES PLACE IN CHLOROPHYLL INSIDE THE CYLINDRICAL CELLS

SUGARS ARE STORED IN THE MESOPHYLL LAYER

THE PALISADE

Inside the leaf

This high-magnification cross-section of a leaf shows the cells, where photosynthesis takes place. Water vapour, oxygen and carbon dioxide enter and leave through tiny holes (called stomata) found mainly on the lower surface. Sunlight is taken in by the cylindrical cells in the palisade layer. The sugars made are then stored in the spongy mesophyll layer beneath, before being transported to other parts of the plant.

Food Webs

GREEN plants make their own food (*see pages 64–5*). They are the first in a line of organisms, along which food-energy is passed. This line is called a 'food chain'. Plants, the 'primary producers', are the first link in the chain. The second link is plant-eating animals, called 'primary consumers'. Animals that eat other animals (meat-eaters) are next. They are called 'secondary consumers'.

In a community of plants and animals there are lots of food chains and many are connected. When each food is linked to the animal eating it, a 'food web' appears like the one shown here.

Food chains
Most food chains begin with green plants. Plant-eaters, such as rabbits, eat the plants. Digesting their food, moving and keeping warm or cool uses up nine-tenths of the energy in the food. So a meat-eater, such as a fox, gets only one-tenth of the food energy eaten by a rabbit. This energy loss can be shown as a pyramid.

ONLY ONE-TENTH OF WHAT A RABBIT EATS IS MADE INTO ITS BODY TISSUE

MEAT-EATERS ARE CALLED CARNIVORES

PLANT-EATERS ARE CALLED HERBIVORES

FOOD WEBS ARE COMPLEX – THIS IS A SIMPLIFIED FOOD WEB OF THE AFRICAN SAVANNAH GRASSLANDS

VULTURES ARE SCAVENGERS, FEEDING ON THE REMAINS LEFT BEHIND BY THE HUNTERS

WITH THEIR STRONG JAWS AND TEETH, HYENAS CAN CRUSH LARGE BONES

THE MARTIAL EAGLE HUNTS MAMMALS AND LARGE BIRDS

A BEE-EATER

THE BANDED MONGOOSE EATS PLANTS AND MEAT – IT IS AN OMNIVORE

COMPOUND STOMACHS ALLOW IMPALAS TO DIGEST GRASS

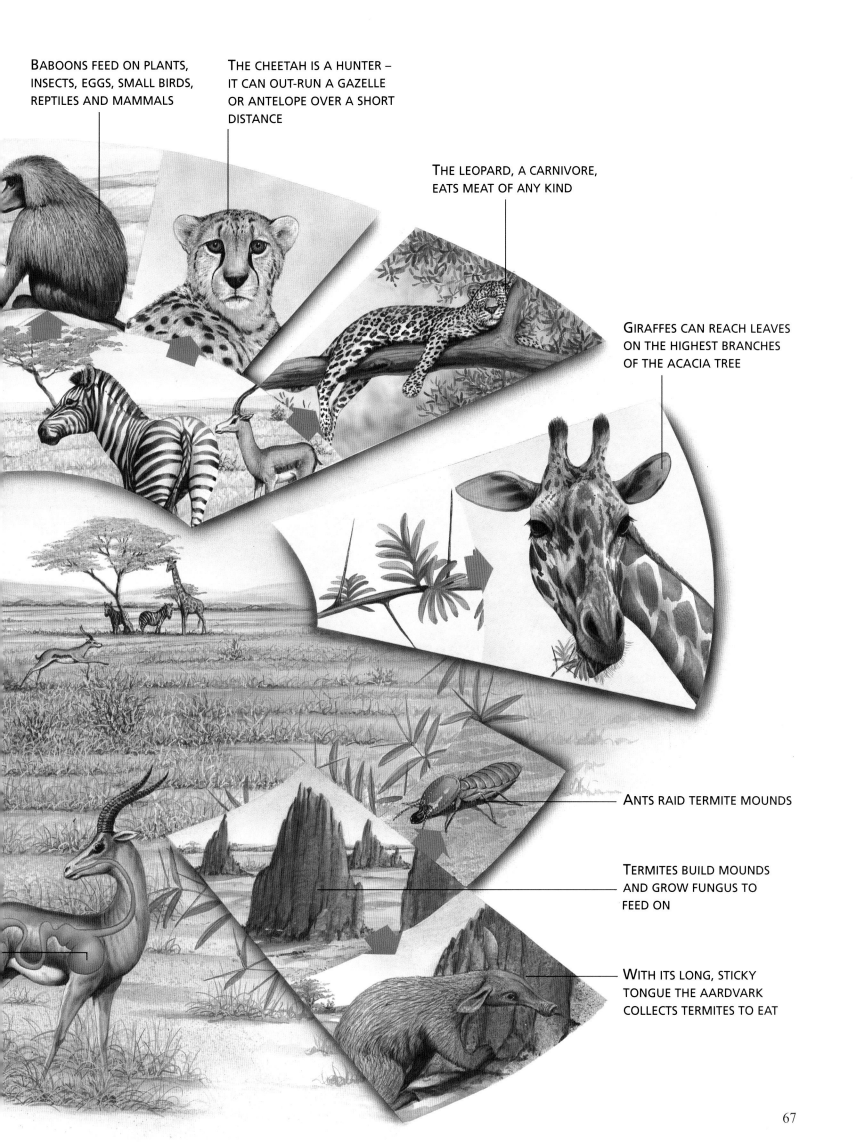

BABOONS FEED ON PLANTS, INSECTS, EGGS, SMALL BIRDS, REPTILES AND MAMMALS

THE CHEETAH IS A HUNTER – IT CAN OUT-RUN A GAZELLE OR ANTELOPE OVER A SHORT DISTANCE

THE LEOPARD, A CARNIVORE, EATS MEAT OF ANY KIND

GIRAFFES CAN REACH LEAVES ON THE HIGHEST BRANCHES OF THE ACACIA TREE

ANTS RAID TERMITE MOUNDS

TERMITES BUILD MOUNDS AND GROW FUNGUS TO FEED ON

WITH ITS LONG, STICKY TONGUE THE AARDVARK COLLECTS TERMITES TO EAT

The Living Oceans

FOOD chains in the oceans, like food chains on the land, begin with photosynthesis in green plants. Most plants in the sea are microscopically small, but there are so many of them they sometimes colour the water. These tiny plants float within 150 metres of the surface, where there is enough sunlight for photosynthesis to occur. Wastes and dead organisms sink slowly from this sunlit zone, providing food for animals living in the twilight zone below. No light reaches deeper than about 180 metres and there is less food available, but some animals survive even at these depths.

LANTERN FISH ARE FAIRLY COMMON IN THE TWILIGHT ZONE

FOOD PARTICLES FALL LIKE RAIN TO ANIMALS ON THE SEA FLOOR

TRIPOD-FISH PROP THEMSELVES ON THEIR FINS TO FEED ON FALLING PARTICLES

Deep-sea vents
At vents in the ocean floor, hot water containing hydrogen sulphide is released. This chemical supports a special food chain of bacteria, worms and fish in depths where there is no sunlight and no photosynthesis.

ANIMALS SUCH AS THESE SEA-CUCUMBERS AND WORMS LIVE IN OCEAN TRENCHES, UP TO 10 KILOMETRES BELOW THE SURFACE

MOST ANIMALS LIVE IN THE SUNLIT ZONE

THESE ARROWS SHOW A SIMPLE OCEAN FOOD CHAIN

PHYTOPLANKTON (MICROSCOPIC PLANTS) USE SUNLIGHT FOR PHOTOSYNTHESIS

ZOOPLANKTON (TINY ANIMALS) FEED ON PHYTOPLANKTON

BELOW THE TWILIGHT ZONE FISH OFTEN HAVE BIG MOUTHS SO THEY CAN CATCH ANY FOOD THAT APPEARS

A GULPER CAN SWALLOW ANIMALS THAT ARE LARGER THAN ITSELF

RAT-TAILED FISH SWIM NEAR THE SEA FLOOR

Food for whales

Krill (*right*) are shrimp-like animals that form vast shoals in Antarctic waters, providing food for many animals. Blue – and other – whales swim through them with their mouths open. When a whale's mouth is full it squeezes the water out through special strainers and swallows the krill.

Migration

GREY WHALES MOVE SOUTH IN WINTER, AWAY FROM THE ICY SEAS IN THE NORTH

AT ALL PLACES other than the equator, the climates of the Earth are seasonal. This means that part of the year is too dry or too cold for plants to grow. But animals must eat, whether plants are growing or not. They must also make sure that their young are born in the right place and at the right time so they will be able to find enough food to feed them. Many animals avoid difficult seasons by migrating. Each year, when their food supply begins to run out, they make journeys, some of them very long.

EACH SPRING AND AUTUMN MONARCH BUTTERFLIES FLY NEARLY 3,000 KILOMETRES

Key to migration routes
- Monarch butterfly
- Grey whale
- Caribou
- Eel
- Swallow
- Wildebeest
- Arctic tern

EELS MIGRATE TO THE SARGASSO SEA

THE LONGEST MIGRATION IS THAT OF THE ARCTIC TERN – TWICE A YEAR IT FLIES FOR FOUR MONTHS NON-STOP

Seasons

The Earth takes a year to orbit the Sun and a day to turn on its own axis. This axis is not at right angles to the Sun's rays, so as the Earth orbits, first one hemisphere and then the other is tilted towards the Sun. This produces the seasons. The hemisphere facing the Sun experiences summer, while the other hemisphere has its winter.

HERE IT IS SUMMER IN THE NORTHERN HEMISPHERE

HERE IT IS SUMMER IN THE SOUTHERN HEMISPHERE

THE EARTH'S AXIS

ARCTIC TERNS FLY 18,000 KILOMETRES TWICE A YEAR BETWEEN THE NORTH AND SOUTH POLES

NORTH AMERICAN CARIBOU SPEND SUMMER IN THE TUNDRA, THEN TRAVEL 800 KILOMETRES TO CONIFER FORESTS

EELS LIVE IN RIVERS IN EUROPE AND AMERICA, BUT MIGRATE TO THE SARGASSO SEA TO BREED

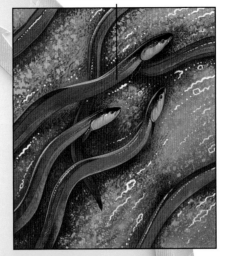

Seasons and the tundra

In winter there is little food in the frozen lands called the tundra (1). Reindeer scratch through the snow, but most animals leave to seek warmer conditions.

Plants grow rapidly during the tundra's brief summer (2). Insects, too, breed and swarm in the ponds and marshes. For a while, food is abundant and many birds and animals arrive to feed.

①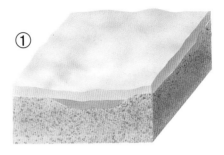

②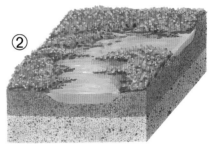

ALL EUROPEAN SWALLOWS MIGRATE TO AFRICA FOR THE WINTER

IN THE SAVANNAH DRY SEASON, WILDEBEEST TRAVEL 320 KILOMETRES FROM THE SERENGETI PLAIN TO LAKE VICTORIA

Niches

WHERE there is anything a living organism can eat or digest, and where there is shelter or enough space, sooner or later these resources will be put to use. The new arrival may be a plant, animal or colony of bacteria. Once settled in its home, the organism has created a 'niche', a place within the larger community of living things.

Find a stone that has been on the ground undisturbed for a long time and you may see lichen or moss growing on it. The plant has found a firm place to fix itself, obtaining the food it needs from the stone, and getting enough water from the moist air or rain. It has found its niche and, in doing so, the plant also provides niches for others, including the tiny animals that feed on it. On a single oak tree (*right*) there may be hundreds of niches.

ON A SINGLE OAK TREE THERE ARE HUNDREDS OF NICHES FOR OTHER PLANTS AND ANIMALS

THE CUCKOO IS A PARASITE – IT USES OTHER BIRDS TO RAISE ITS YOUNG; HERE IT IS THROWING OUT A BLACKBIRD'S EGG TO MAKE ROOM FOR ITS OWN IN THE NEST

THE WOODPECKER'S NEST

A WOODPECKER DRILLS INTO THE BARK TO FIND INSECTS

A MOTH, WITH MARKINGS THAT MAKE IT ALMOST INVISIBLE, RESTS ON A PATCH OF LICHEN

LICHENS, FUNGI AND FERNS USE THE TREE'S BRANCHES AND TRUNK TO SUPPORT THEM

SQUIRRELS EAT ACORNS AND NEST HIGH ABOVE THE GROUND, WHERE THEY ARE SAFE

BANK VOLES FIND FOOD AND SHELTER IN THE GRASS AROUND TREE ROOTS

IN SPRING, CATERPILLARS FEED ON THE TREE'S LEAVES

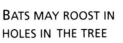

A niche for a beetle
An oak tree shelters and feeds many insects and their young. The grubs of longhorn beetles eat the wood, drilling tunnels as they chew. If there are too many of them the tree can be seriously harmed.

BATS MAY ROOST IN HOLES IN THE TREE

THE TAWNY OWL RESTS IN THE TREE, WATCHING AND LISTENING FOR ITS PREY

MANY SONGBIRDS, LIKE THIS BLACKBIRD, SLEEP AND BUILD NESTS IN BRANCHES

FOOD AND WATER FOR PLANT LIFE COLLECT IN HOLLOWS AND CREVICES IN THE BARK

Urban niche
Foxes eat almost anything and are always ready to try something new. Many of them visit towns and some live there all the time, feeding on scraps thrown out by people. Our parks and gardens shelter them and our dustbins supply food, so foxes have made a niche for themselves near our homes.

SOME TINY WASPS MAKE THE TREE GROW GALLS IN WHICH THEY SHELTER THEIR YOUNG

The Life Cycle of a Lake

AN AREA of land can go through many changes. For example, a lake can become dry land, and the dry land may eventually become woodland. At each stage a different group of plants and animals arrives to live there.

On these pages we can see how a community of living things has occupied a lake and its shores. We can also see the gradual build-up of mud and dead material on the lake bottom. These are signs that the lake will eventually become dry land. On the shoreline new plants are growing that take advantage of the build-up of mud. There are also insects and birds that find shelter in the new growth.

PLANTS GROW IN MUD, WASHED INTO THE LAKE BY RAIN OR CARRIED BY A RIVER

AS MUD COLLECTS, THE LAKE BECOMES SHALLOWER

SOME PLANTS FLOAT ON THE SURFACE, WITHOUT ROOTS

WATER LILIES ARE ROOTED IN THE LAKE BED – THEIR LEAVES FLOAT ON THE SURFACE

DEAD PLANTS SINK TO THE LAKE BOTTOM

LAKES FORM WHERE ROCK STOPS WATER FROM DRAINING DOWNWARDS

THE LAKE IS ALSO HOME TO FISH, LIKE THIS BREAM (*ABOVE*) AND PIKE (*RIGHT*)

SEDGES GROW IN THE WATER-
LOGGED GROUND CLOSE TO
THE EDGES OF THE LAKE

WILLOW AND ALDER DRY THE
SOIL BY TAKING WATER FROM
THE GROUND, SO THESE OAK
AND OTHER TREES CAN GROW

WILLOW TREES GROW BESIDE
THE LAKE, WHERE THE
GROUND IS WET

BIRDS FROM NEARBY TREES
AND SHRUBS HUNT FOR
INSECTS OVER THE WATER

DUCKS AND BIRDS NEST IN
THE REEDS NEAR THE SHORE

REED AND BULRUSHES GROW
IN WATER CLOSE TO THE
SHORE, WITH THEIR ROOTS
SUBMERGED

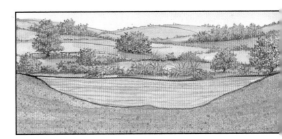

From lake to dry land
At first there is not much
food for plants in the
lake's water, so there are
just a few plants growing
round the edges. As soil
washes in from nearby
land, plants take root in
the lake bed further
from the shore. Mud
and leaves build up, and
more plants take root.
Eventually sediment
fills up the lake, and
instead of a lake we
see dry land.

Ecosystems

AN ECOSYSTEM is a community of plants and animals that live together, drawing on the same food and energy sources from their surroundings. If one community is different from others nearby, it can be studied by itself as an ecosystem.

Tropical rain forests are very rich ecosystems. They grow near the equator, where the climate is hot and wet. They can support many more kinds of plants and animals than are found in cooler climates. Plants grow rapidly and there is no cold or dry season to interrupt them. On this page we see how rain forests provide countless niches and many small ecosystems within the main forest ecosystem.

A CACIQUE BUILDS ITS NEST IN THE CANOPY

TREES CALLED EMERGENTS STAND HIGHER THAN THE OTHER TREES

THE TAMANDUA AND SLOTH LIVE IN THE CANOPY (TREE-TOPS), WHERE THERE IS MORE FOOD, SUCH AS FRUIT AND INSECTS

YOUNG TREES FORM A LOWER CANOPY

EPIPHYTES ARE PLANTS, OFTEN ROOTLESS, THAT GROW ON TREES – THIS IS A BROMELIAD

LIANAS ARE CLIMBERS THAT GROW UP TREES TOWARDS THE LIGHT – THEY HANG LIKE ROPES FROM THE BRANCHES

SAPLINGS AND SHRUBS GROW IN THE SHADY UNDERSTOREY

A JAGUAR HUNTS FOR ITS PREY ON THE DARK FOREST FLOOR

AN ARMY OF ANTS

ABOVE THE GROUND, SPREADING BUTTRESS ROOTS SUPPORT THE HUGE TREES

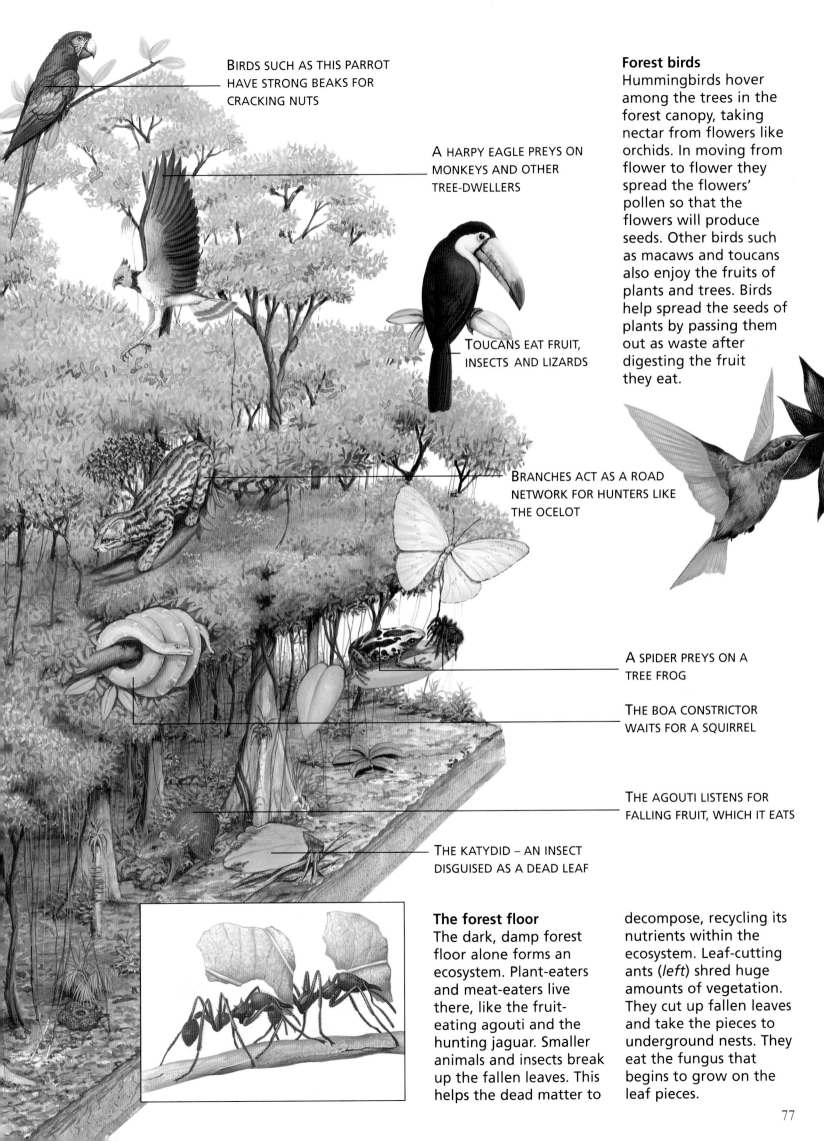

BIRDS SUCH AS THIS PARROT
HAVE STRONG BEAKS FOR
CRACKING NUTS

A HARPY EAGLE PREYS ON
MONKEYS AND OTHER
TREE-DWELLERS

TOUCANS EAT FRUIT,
INSECTS AND LIZARDS

BRANCHES ACT AS A ROAD
NETWORK FOR HUNTERS LIKE
THE OCELOT

A SPIDER PREYS ON A
TREE FROG

THE BOA CONSTRICTOR
WAITS FOR A SQUIRREL

THE AGOUTI LISTENS FOR
FALLING FRUIT, WHICH IT EATS

THE KATYDID – AN INSECT
DISGUISED AS A DEAD LEAF

Forest birds

Hummingbirds hover among the trees in the forest canopy, taking nectar from flowers like orchids. In moving from flower to flower they spread the flowers' pollen so that the flowers will produce seeds. Other birds such as macaws and toucans also enjoy the fruits of plants and trees. Birds help spread the seeds of plants by passing them out as waste after digesting the fruit they eat.

The forest floor

The dark, damp forest floor alone forms an ecosystem. Plant-eaters and meat-eaters live there, like the fruit-eating agouti and the hunting jaguar. Smaller animals and insects break up the fallen leaves. This helps the dead matter to decompose, recycling its nutrients within the ecosystem. Leaf-cutting ants (*left*) shred huge amounts of vegetation. They cut up fallen leaves and take the pieces to underground nests. They eat the fungus that begins to grow on the leaf pieces.

Biomes

WHEN one type of ecosystem covers a vast area it is called a biome. Different climates produce different biomes. There are several biomes in Africa, including tropical rain forest, savannah grassland and desert. A desert biome, such as the Sahara in Africa, forms where there is little rain. Here, temperatures run to extremes, so it can be freezing at night after being extremely hot during the day. Bordering the Sahara desert are savannah grasslands which are also warm and dry, but, unlike the deserts, heavy rains fall here in late spring.

IN THE SAHARA DAY-TIME TEMPERATURES ARE AROUND 40°C

LESS THAN 50 MM OF RAIN A YEAR FALLS IN PARTS OF THE SAHARA

SAND STORMS OCCUR WHEN STRONG WINDS LIFT DUST AND SAND HIGH INTO THE AIR

FENNEC FOX

JERBOA

Biomes map
mixed forest
mountain
grassland
tropical rain forest
semi-desert
desert

THE SAHARA HAS VAST SAND SEAS CALLED ERGS BUT IN PARTS THE LAND IS ROCKY

PLANTS WITH LONG ROOTS FIND WATER DEEP UNDERGROUND

CAMELS CAN SURVIVE WITHOUT WATER FOR MORE THAN TWO WEEKS

DESERT SOIL IS THIN

Desert animals
Animals have adapted to the desert climate. Lizards and jerboa shelter from the heat in burrows. The fennec fox and jerboa (see above) have large ears rich in blood veins, which helps them lose body heat. Ostriches can drink the desert's salty water and do not suffer if their body temperature rises.

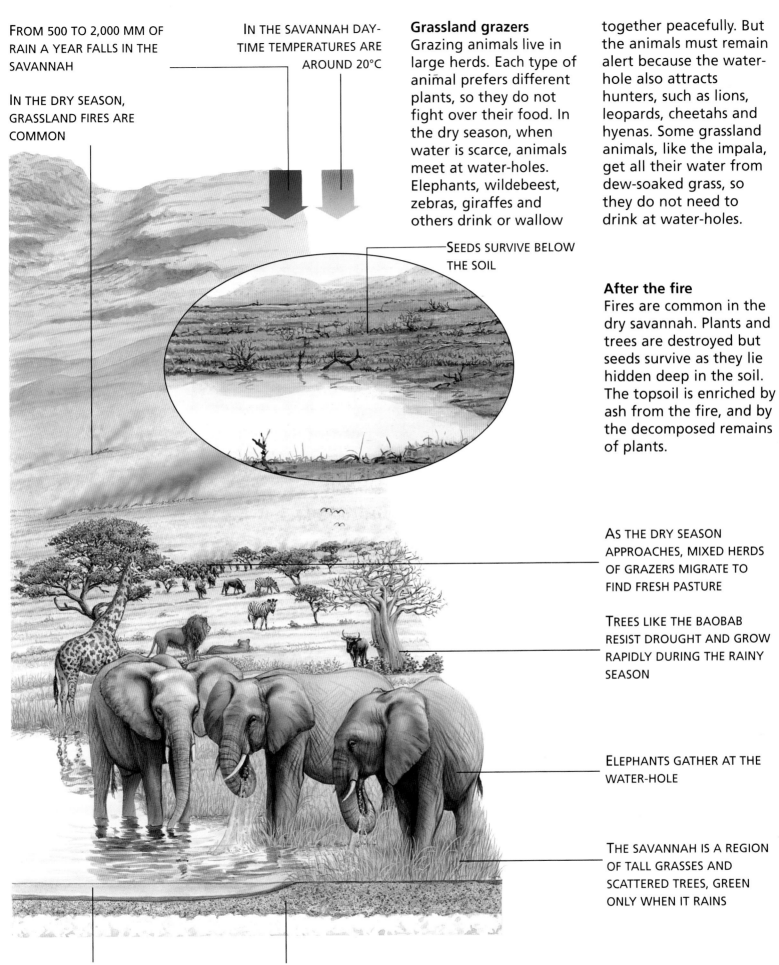

FROM 500 TO 2,000 MM OF RAIN A YEAR FALLS IN THE SAVANNAH

IN THE DRY SEASON, GRASSLAND FIRES ARE COMMON

IN THE SAVANNAH DAY-TIME TEMPERATURES ARE AROUND 20°C

Grassland grazers

Grazing animals live in large herds. Each type of animal prefers different plants, so they do not fight over their food. In the dry season, when water is scarce, animals meet at water-holes. Elephants, wildebeest, zebras, giraffes and others drink or wallow together peacefully. But the animals must remain alert because the water-hole also attracts hunters, such as lions, leopards, cheetahs and hyenas. Some grassland animals, like the impala, get all their water from dew-soaked grass, so they do not need to drink at water-holes.

SEEDS SURVIVE BELOW THE SOIL

After the fire

Fires are common in the dry savannah. Plants and trees are destroyed but seeds survive as they lie hidden deep in the soil. The topsoil is enriched by ash from the fire, and by the decomposed remains of plants.

AS THE DRY SEASON APPROACHES, MIXED HERDS OF GRAZERS MIGRATE TO FIND FRESH PASTURE

TREES LIKE THE BAOBAB RESIST DROUGHT AND GROW RAPIDLY DURING THE RAINY SEASON

ELEPHANTS GATHER AT THE WATER-HOLE

THE SAVANNAH IS A REGION OF TALL GRASSES AND SCATTERED TREES, GREEN ONLY WHEN IT RAINS

WATER-HOLES FORM IN HOLLOWS, WHERE UNDERGROUND WATER SEEPS TO THE SURFACE

SAVANNAH SOIL IS DEEPER THAN DESERT SOIL

Nutrient Cycles

ALL living things, including people, are made of about 20 chemical elements, such as carbon, nitrogen, calcium and sulphur. Plants and animals use these 'nutrients' to build their cells and to provide energy, and must regularly top them up. The nutrients come from the environment – from rocks and from the air. Plants absorb water and mineral nutrients such as sulphur and calcium from the soil. They absorb carbon from the air. Animals take in their nutrients by eating plants or other animals.

All nutrients follow cycles and are returned to the environment, so new living things can live and grow. If nutrients did not move through cycles, soon there would be none left and all life would cease.

The sulphur cycle
The large illustration shows how the nutrient sulphur follows a cycle. Sulphur is taken up from rocks by plants, and passes to animals that eat the plants. Animal wastes and dead animal and plant matter decompose and sulphur is returned to the ground. It is then carried away by groundwater and rivers to the sea. Some sulphur is trapped in mud in estuaries. Here, bacteria release the sulphur in a different form back into the air. Most of the sulphur is taken in by tiny sea plants called plankton. These also release the sulphur in a different form back into the air. Sulphur in the air eventually falls back to the ground in rain.

Volcanoes release extra sulphur from beneath the Earth's crust into the air. They return some of the sulphur that is trapped deep underground to the sulphur cycle.

BACTERIA LIVING IN MUDS AND MARSHES RELEASE A COMPOUND OF SULPHUR (HYDROGEN SULPHIDE)

SULPHUR (IN VARIOUS CHEMICAL FORMS OR COMPOUNDS) DISSOLVES INTO RAIN DROPS

SULPHUR IS RETURNED TO THE LAND IN RAIN

NUTRIENTS IN DEAD PLANTS AND ANIMALS ARE RELEASED BACK INTO THE GROUND THROUGH DECOMPOSITION

SULPHUR IS TAKEN UP BY LIVING PLANTS AND ANIMALS

SULPHUR ORIGINALLY COMES FROM ROCK

ANIMALS AND HUMAN BEINGS NEED SULPHUR TO MAKE PROTEINS (SKIN AND HAIR CONTAIN SULPHUR)

GROUNDWATER AND RIVERS TAKE SULPHUR TO THE SEA

VOLCANOES RELEASE
SULPHUR IN THE FORM
OF SULPHUR DIOXIDE

RAIN CONTAINING SULPHUR
FALLS OVER THE SEA

SEA PLANKTON RELEASE A
SULPHUR COMPOUND CALLED
DIMETHYL SULPHIDE

Decomposition
This is an important
part of any cycle. Tiny
animals, fungi and
bacteria feed on dead
plant and animal
material. This
decomposes it (breaks
it down), returning its
nutrients to the cycle.
The nutrients can then
be used again by living
plants and animals.

CARBON

The carbon cycle
Green plants absorb
carbon dioxide from the
air during photosynthesis.
Living things other than
plants take in carbon by
eating plants or by
eating other animals.
During the decomposition
of dead plant and
animal material, carbon
is released back into the
air as carbon dioxide.
Carbon dioxide also
enters the air during
respiration (when
animals breathe out,
they release carbon
dioxide; plants release it
too). Carbon dioxide also
escapes into the air when
we burn carbon fuels
such as coal, gas and oil.
Tiny marine plants and
shellfish also play a
major part in the carbon
cycle (*see pages 62–3*).

81

Obtaining Nitrogen

A NUTRIENT cycle involves many complicated chemical changes. This is especially true of the nitrogen cycle. Although there is plenty of nitrogen in the air, there is a problem. Plants and animals cannot use nitrogen as a gas; they must have it in the form of food. This means the gas has to be changed into nitrogen compounds, such as nitrates. Bacteria in the soil do this complicated job. They change nitrogen into nitrates, which plants can then use to make proteins (the chemical 'building blocks' from which plant and animal bodies are made). Late in the cycle, animals take in the nitrates when they eat the plants.

THE AIR IS MOSTLY NITROGEN GAS

ENERGY FROM LIGHTNING CHANGES NITROGEN GAS INTO A COMPOUND THAT DISSOLVES IN WATER

NITROGEN COMPOUNDS FALL TO THE SOIL IN RAIN WATER

NITRATES IN WATER ENTER PLANT ROOTS AND FEED THE PLANT

The nitrogen cycle
Nitrates in the soil-water are drawn up through the roots of plants. The plants use the nitrates to make proteins. Animals that eat the plants change the plant proteins into animal proteins.

Animal and plant wastes contain proteins and other nitrogen compounds. So when they decompose, the nitrogen compounds are once more available to plants. Some bacteria, called 'denitrifying' bacteria (*right*), break down nitrogen compounds and release nitrogen gas back into the air.

DENITRIFYING BACTERIA

IN FURNACES AND HOT ENGINES, NITROGEN COMBINES WITH OXYGEN TO FORM NITROGEN OXIDES, WHICH DISSOLVE IN WATER, MAKING ACID RAIN (*SEE PAGE 91*)

FARM FERTILIZERS, MADE IN FACTORIES, PROVIDE EXTRA NITROGEN FOR CROPS

DENITRIFYING BACTERIA IN MARSHLAND MUDS RELEASE NITROGEN GAS BACK INTO THE AIR

NITROGEN FROM FERTILIZERS WASHES INTO RIVERS

BACTERIA RAPIDLY INCREASE IN NUMBER WITHIN EACH NODULE

A NODULE

NITROGEN IS CHANGED INTO NITRATES

BACTERIA

NITRATES ARE MADE BY BACTERIA IN THE ROOT NODULES (CHAMBERS) OF SOME PLANTS

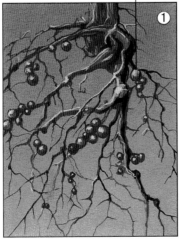

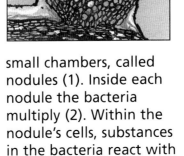

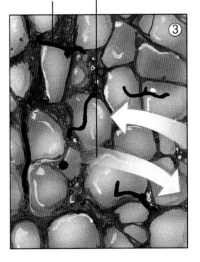

A job for bacteria
When some plants start to grow, bacteria gather around their roots. The bacteria make hairs on the roots expand into small chambers, called nodules (1). Inside each nodule the bacteria multiply (2). Within the nodule's cells, substances in the bacteria react with nitrogen gas to form nitrates (3). The bacteria use sugars from the plant and supply the plant with nitrates to make proteins.

Soil

SOIL is made up of tiny pieces of rock and the decayed remains of dead organisms. The rock fragments have appeared after thousands of years of weathering. Near the surface of the land, the heat of summer makes rocks expand and the cold of winter makes them shrink. This causes the rocks to crack, and rainwater then trickles into the cracks. In winter the water freezes and expands, widening the cracks and causing fragments of rock to break off. Acids in the water weaken the rock so that it breaks apart more easily. Rocks deeper underground are weakened by water that seeps up from below. All these processes, called weathering, help to make soil by breaking up the rock.

MOST SOILS FORM AS DISTINCT LAYERS, LYING ONE ABOVE THE OTHER

WATER MOVES BETWEEN THE PARTICLES OF SOIL

Water in soil
Rainwater moves down from the earth's surface between rock particles until it can go no further. This water under the ground is called groundwater and its upper surface is called the water table. As water dries on the surface of the soil (evaporating into the air) it is replaced by groundwater, drawn upwards through very small spaces. This upward movement of water keeps the soil moist.

MANY TREES HAVE ROOT SYSTEMS AS LARGE AS THE TRUNK AND BRANCHES SEEN ABOVE GROUND

PLANTS GROW WELL IN SOILS THAT CONTAIN PLENTY OF NUTRIENTS (FERTILE SOILS)

ACCORDING TO THE TYPE OF ROCK, SOILS CAN BE SANDY OR CLAYEY

84

SOIL FORMATION MAY
BEGIN WHERE LICHENS
AND MOSSES GROW
ON BARE ROCK

SOIL IN CREVICES PROVIDES
FOOD AND SHELTER FOR
SMALL PLANTS

THE ROOTS OF PLANTS HELP
BREAK UP ROCK INTO SOIL
PARTICLES

THE TOPSOIL IS A LAYER
CONTAINING LOTS OF HUMUS
(DECAYED ANIMAL AND
PLANT MATERIAL)

BENEATH THE TOPSOIL, THE
SUBSOIL CONSISTS OF ROCK
PARTICLES AND SOME HUMUS

BELOW LIES THE ROCK FROM
WHICH THE OVERLYING SOIL
IS MADE

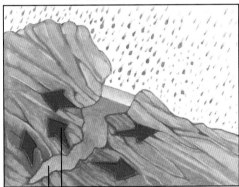

Soil types
Eventually all a soil's
nutrients are drawn
away. This process is like
ageing, and how long it
takes depends on the
climate. Tropical soils (1)
have lost their nutrients
and are infertile, so they
are 'old'. Tundra and
desert soils (2) are

'young' and have barely
started to form because
few plants can survive
the harsh climate, and
plants help to make soil.
Temperate soils (3) are
'middle-aged'. Plants
grow well in a temperate
climate and the soils are
still rich in nutrients.

RAIN FILLS CRACKS IN ROCK

ICE EXPANDS AND WIDENS
THE CRACKS

Break-up of rocks
When water freezes, it
expands and widens
small cracks in rocks. As
the ice melts, the water
drains away leaving
fragments of rock
unsupported. These
fragments break off. So
rocks are broken every
time the temperature
falls below freezing.

Soil Life

THE organisms living in the top few centimetres of soil in a field of grass may weigh more than the cows grazing the pasture. A fertile soil teems with life, from single-celled bacteria to animals the size of moles. Each organism occupies its own niche within the soil ecosystem. Woodlice, for example, eat decaying plant matter and their droppings provide tiny bits of simpler food for smaller organisms.

By living in or on the surface of the soil, organisms actually help to make more soil. They do this by eating and breaking down animal and plant materials.

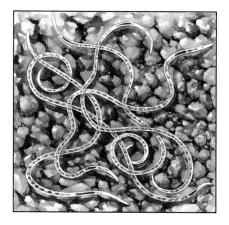

Nematodes
There are a vast number of nematodes (eelworms) in the soil. There may be a million of them living in the first 10 centimetres below a square metre of the surface. They are thread-like and the largest are barely 2 millimetres long (*see above*). They live in the soil water and eat other nematodes or single-celled organisms such as bacteria. Nematodes help control the size of the microscopic soil population.

Mites
There are more mites than any other type of soil animal. Mites are tiny relatives of spiders. Plant-eating mites break leaves into smaller pieces (*see below*). Other mites hunt animals such as nematodes.

FUNGI BREAK DOWN WOOD

A SPIDER HUNTS FOR LICE

EARTHWORMS SURFACE AT NIGHT TO DEPOSIT THEIR CASTS (WASTE MATTER)

WORM TUNNELS GIVE ROOM FOR AIR TO CIRCULATE IN THE SOIL

THE MOLE DIGS LONG TUNNELS, EATING WORMS AND OTHER ANIMALS THAT FALL INTO THEM

A NEMATODE

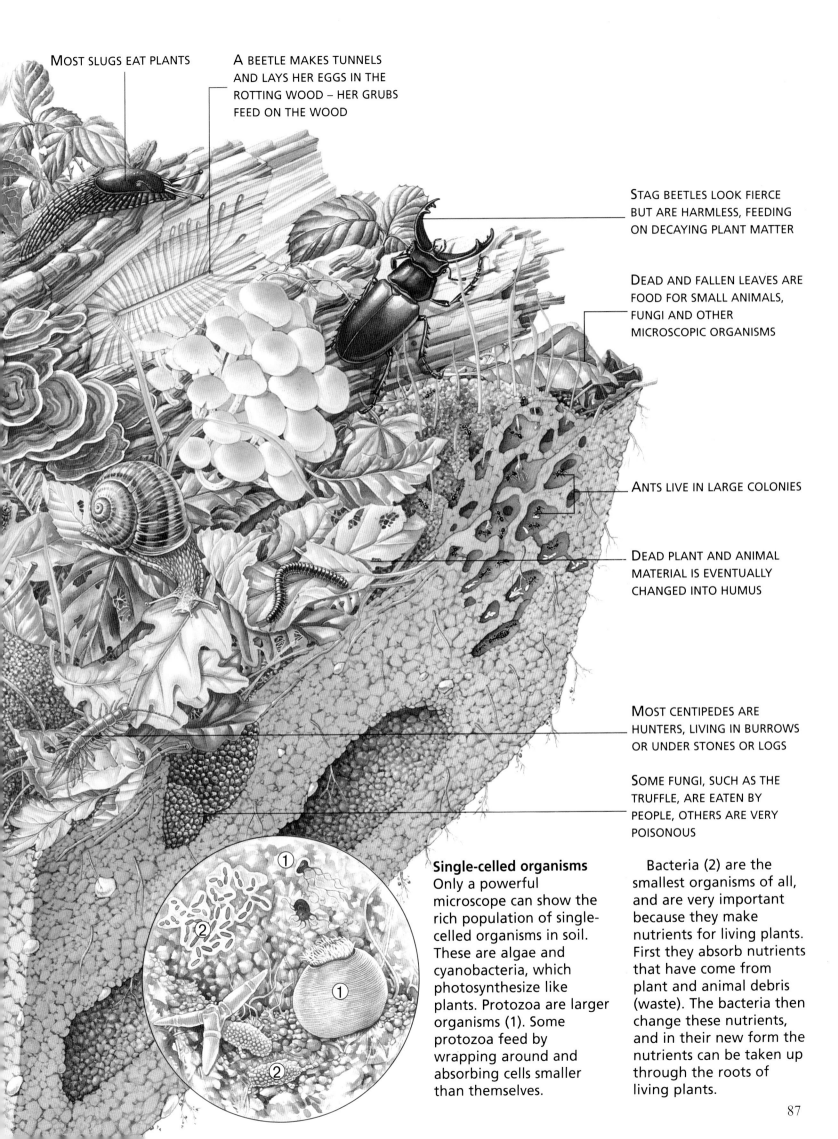

MOST SLUGS EAT PLANTS

A BEETLE MAKES TUNNELS AND LAYS HER EGGS IN THE ROTTING WOOD – HER GRUBS FEED ON THE WOOD

STAG BEETLES LOOK FIERCE BUT ARE HARMLESS, FEEDING ON DECAYING PLANT MATTER

DEAD AND FALLEN LEAVES ARE FOOD FOR SMALL ANIMALS, FUNGI AND OTHER MICROSCOPIC ORGANISMS

ANTS LIVE IN LARGE COLONIES

DEAD PLANT AND ANIMAL MATERIAL IS EVENTUALLY CHANGED INTO HUMUS

MOST CENTIPEDES ARE HUNTERS, LIVING IN BURROWS OR UNDER STONES OR LOGS

SOME FUNGI, SUCH AS THE TRUFFLE, ARE EATEN BY PEOPLE, OTHERS ARE VERY POISONOUS

Single-celled organisms
Only a powerful microscope can show the rich population of single-celled organisms in soil. These are algae and cyanobacteria, which photosynthesize like plants. Protozoa are larger organisms (1). Some protozoa feed by wrapping around and absorbing cells smaller than themselves.

Bacteria (2) are the smallest organisms of all, and are very important because they make nutrients for living plants. First they absorb nutrients that have come from plant and animal debris (waste). The bacteria then change these nutrients, and in their new form the nutrients can be taken up through the roots of living plants.

Rivers

WHEN rainwater falls on bare rock or thin soil, it flows downhill across the surface of the land. If the soil is deep, the rainwater first soaks downwards until it meets rock before it flows downhill. This underground water is called groundwater. In hollows, where rocks are closer to the surface, it runs out as a spring.

On the surface of the land, water flows along channels. A small channel of water is called a stream. The water wears away at the channel, making it deeper. As more water joins the channel from high ground or springs, the tiny stream grows into a river. The river is home to many plants and animals which live in distinct zones: the headwaters, the troutbeck, the minnow reach, the bream zone, and the estuary.

Minnow zone
The river slows as it leaves the hills. Sediment (mud) collects on the stony bottom, and plants take root in it. This is the minnow, or grayling zone. Minnows and graylings feed on small animals such as young fish and insects.

PLANTS SUCH AS THESE TAKE ROOT IN THE RIVER SEDIMENT

ON ALMOST LEVEL GROUND, THE RIVER MEANDERS (ITS PATH TWISTS FROM SIDE TO SIDE)

THE LAND IS NEARLY FLAT HERE – IT IS CALLED THE FLOOD PLAIN

THE RIVER FLOWS OUT TO SEA

Estuary zone
An estuary is where a river widens and meets the sea. The incoming tide brings salty sea water upstream. Where the sea and river waters mix, tiny particles sink to form mudbanks. The sea may deposit sand. Worms and other small animals feed in the mud. They in turn are food for wading birds. The heron hunts for fish in the shallow water (see below).

SEDIMENT BUILDS UP INTO A MUDBANK

THE RIVER BEGINS AS A FAST-FLOWING, SHALLOW HEADSTREAM

IN THE TROUTBECK THERE ARE RAPIDS AND SMALL WATERFALLS – SMALL STONES COVER THE RIVERBED

SALMON MIGRATE UPSTREAM TO BREED IN THE TROUTBECK

Troutbeck

Below the headstream the river flows more slowly. The cold water suits trout, and the zone is called the troutbeck. The current is too fast for sediment (mud) to build up, and stones are dragged along the clear riverbed (*see below*).

IN THE MINNOW ZONE SEDIMENT (MUD) BEGINS TO BUILD UP

THE RIVER FLOW IS DEEP AND SLOW IN THE BREAM ZONE, BETWEEN THE MINNOW ZONE AND THE ESTUARY

THE ESTUARY IS DOWNSTREAM (THE RIVER BEGINS UPSTREAM)

Water cycle

Rivers carry water to the sea and water is then returned to the land as rain. Each day the world's rivers carry a total of about 100 cubic kilometres (km³) of fresh water to the sea. About 875 km³ of water evaporates into the air from the seas, and 160 km³ from the land.

About 775 km³ of water falls as rain over the sea and 260 km³ over land. This is called the water cycle and although the amounts seem large, they are a small part of all the water on Earth. Of the Earth's water, 97 per cent is sea water, and 98 per cent of all fresh water is frozen in the polar ice-caps.

Environmental Damage

WE CANNOT avoid altering our environment and many of the changes we make are beneficial. But a lot of human activities do harm the environment. Clearing rain forests or other natural vegetation to make farmland reduces animal and plant habitats. The plants and animals become confined to smaller and smaller areas, and some species can die out all together. Waste products from our homes and factories can pollute the air, oceans and rivers. Pollution can poison organisms directly, or indirectly by damaging their environment.

Nowhere to live
Golden lion tamarins are tree-dwellers in the tropical forests of South America. When the trees are felled there is nowhere for them to live. There are fewer than 300 left in the wild. Soon the species may die out.

ABOUT 41,000 SQUARE KILOMETRES OF TROPICAL RAIN FOREST ARE CLEARED EACH YEAR (AN AREA BIGGER THAN SWITZERLAND)

TRADITIONAL FARMERS FELL TREES AND BURN THE VEGETATION THEY CANNOT USE

FOREST IS CLEARED TO ALLOW MINING FOR MINERALS

ONCE ROADS ARE BUILT, POOR FARMERS MOVE INTO THE FOREST AND CLEAR THE LAND TO GROW CROPS

THE SOIL IS POOR AND CROPS OFTEN FAIL

IN SOME PLACES CLEARED GROUND BECOMES AS HARD AS CONCRETE

TREES ARE ESSENTIAL TO THE ENVIRONMENT; THEY PROVIDE OXYGEN AND WATER VAPOUR

THE FOREST CANOPY PROTECTS LOWER LAYERS FROM THE FORCE OF RAIN

BARE SOIL IS MORE EASILY WASHED AWAY BY RAIN

Acid rain

Rain is naturally acid, but it becomes more acid when nitrogen oxides (mainly from cars) and sulphur oxides (mainly from power stations) are released into the air as waste gases. A lot of acid in rain and mist can damage plants and animals. Large areas of forest in Europe have been harmed by acid pollution. Plants and fish can be killed by acid rain if it drains into rivers and lakes.

ACID RAIN

WASTE GASES RISE AND CAN BE CARRIED LONG DISTANCES

RAIN WASHES EXPOSED SOIL FROM HILLSIDES

TREES ARE CUT DOWN FOR TIMBER

AFTER TREES ARE REMOVED FROM HILLSIDES, SOIL MOVES DOWNHILL INTO RIVERS

FOREST IS CLEARED TO PROVIDE GRAZING LAND FOR CATTLE

Learning to Live in Harmony

TODAY most large industrial companies take care to cause as little environmental damage as possible. Many are working to restore areas that were damaged in the past.

Mines, such as the china clay mine seen below, can destroy wildlife and produce large waste tips. For every tonne of china clay taken out of the land, there are nine tonnes of waste. But even the large waste tips from a china clay mine can be transformed into green hills. Once the mining has finished, the whole area can be made into a local amenity, such as playing fields or a golf course. The hills may become grazing land for sheep. The illustrations on these pages show how this is done.

GRASS AND OTHER PLANT SEEDS ARE MIXED IN WATER AND SPRAYED ONTO THE TERRACES

ON THE SLOPES THE WASTE IS SHAPED INTO LONG FLAT TERRACES

RESTORATION WORK BEGINS AS SOON AS THE MINING IS FINISHED

AS THE CLAY IS MINED, WASTE IS PILED UP TO FORM UGLY PYRAMIDS

CHINA CLAY HAS MANY USES – THE PAPER IN THIS BOOK CONTAINS IT

TO GET AT THE CLAY A HUGE PIT HAS TO BE DUG

THE CLAY IS WASHED FROM THE ROCK BY HIGH-PRESSURE WATER HOSES

Polluted rivers
In the past, waste from the mine escaped into nearby rivers, colouring them white (1). With modern management the wastes are now held back and the rivers are their natural colour again (2).

THE PYRAMIDS OF WASTE ARE FLATTENED ON TOP

LARGE MACHINES RESHAPE THE LANDSCAPE

Putting vegetation back
Nitrate-producing plants, such as clover (*below*), are included in seed mixtures to put nitrogen back into the soil. Alder trees can be planted to help remove surplus water. While the mining is going on, wastes can be used to build large banks. Trees can be grown on the banks to hide the mine and shield villagers from the dust.

Alaska pipeline
In Alaska, a pipeline was needed to carry oil and gas from the north to the south. Because it crossed the caribou migration route (*see pages 70–1*), it was built on stilts so caribou could pass underneath. Raising the pipe also stopped it from melting the frozen soil. Damage to the frozen soil would affect the area's wildlife.

MINING COMPANIES NOW TRY TO LEAVE THE LAND RESTORED OR SUITABLE FOR NEW USES

WATER-FILLED PITS ARE MADE INTO LAKES FOR RECREATION

A LAKE CAN ATTRACT NEW WILDLIFE, SUCH AS BIRDS

PEOPLE MAY CHOOSE TO HAVE A GOLF COURSE

① ②

THE HUMAN BODY

Text by Kate Barnes

Illustrated by Steve Weston

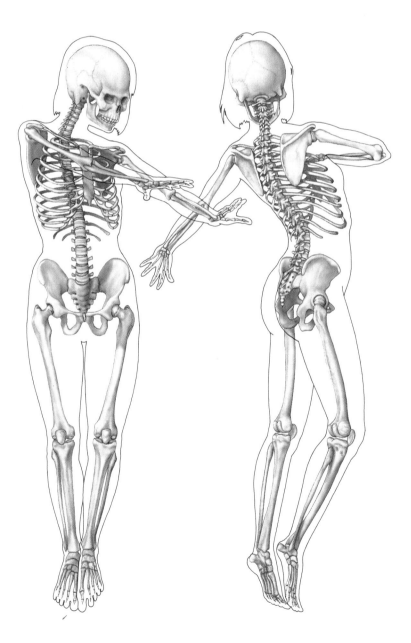

THE HUMAN BODY
CONTENTS

How the Body Works

DO YOU know what lies inside your body and how your body works? The following pages will take you on a voyage of discovery. Along the way you will find out how each system in the body functions and how all the systems work together to make us the complex human beings we are.

In particular, you will see how each part of the body has its own special job to do, how we get the energy to live, and how we defend ourselves from harm. You will also learn about the five senses – vision, hearing, touch, taste, and smell – and how all we think and do is controlled by the brain in communication with our nervous system. This book explains how and why we breathe, how we move, and how we reproduce in order to keep the human race alive.

HANDS ARE COMPLEX BONY STRUCTURES THAT ENABLE US TO CARRY OUT INTRICATE MOVEMENTS

BEHIND THE INTESTINE LIE THE KIDNEYS, WHICH REMOVE WASTE AND PASS IT INTO OUR URINE

OUR SKIN IS A WATERPROOF PROTECTIVE COVERING FOR THE WHOLE BODY

OUR BONY SKELETON PROVIDES A FIRM ATTACHMENT FOR THE BODY'S MUSCLES

WHERE BONES MEET THERE ARE JOINTS, ALLOWING MOVEMENT TO OCCUR

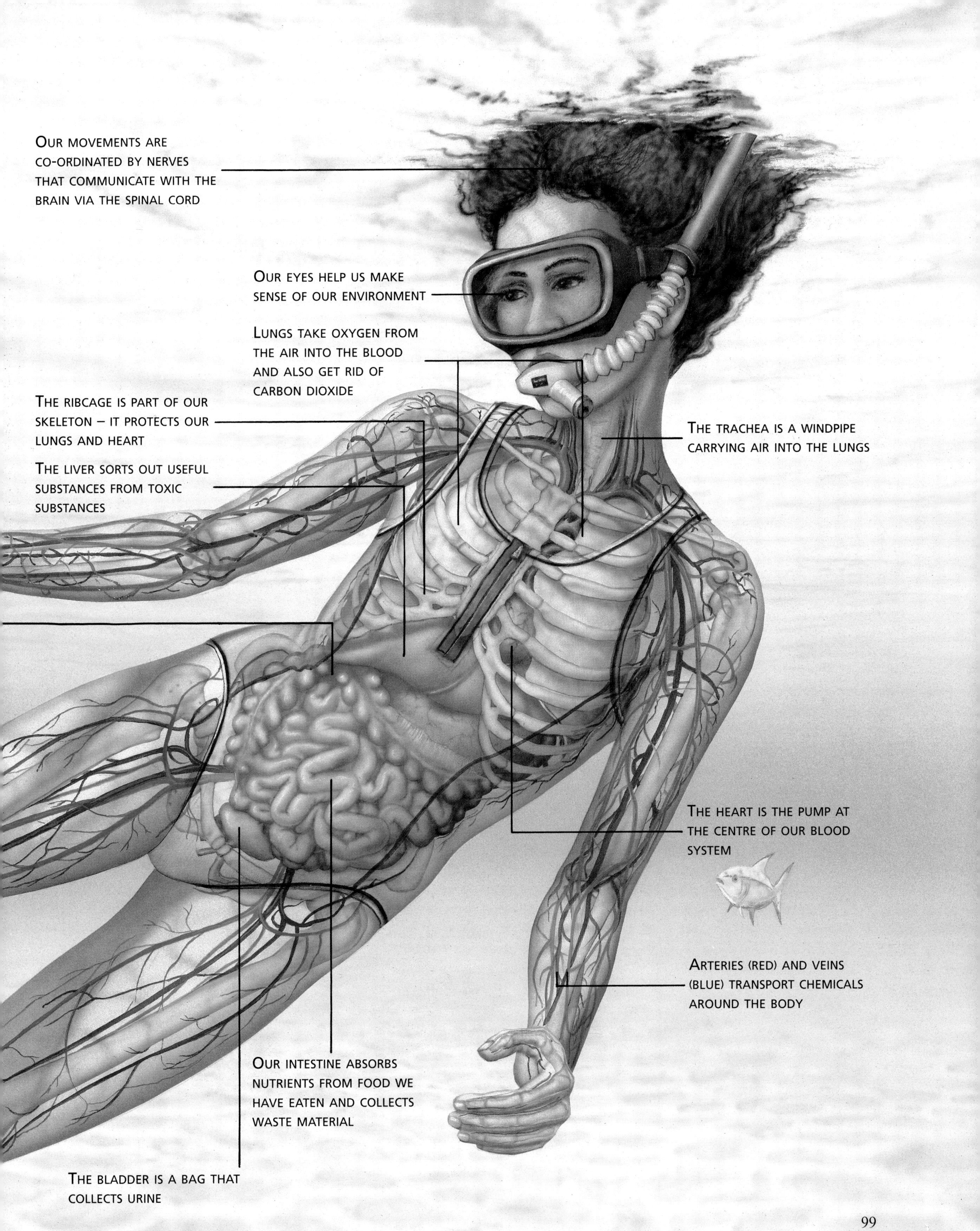

OUR MOVEMENTS ARE
CO-ORDINATED BY NERVES
THAT COMMUNICATE WITH THE
BRAIN VIA THE SPINAL CORD

OUR EYES HELP US MAKE
SENSE OF OUR ENVIRONMENT

LUNGS TAKE OXYGEN FROM
THE AIR INTO THE BLOOD
AND ALSO GET RID OF
CARBON DIOXIDE

THE RIBCAGE IS PART OF OUR
SKELETON – IT PROTECTS OUR
LUNGS AND HEART

THE LIVER SORTS OUT USEFUL
SUBSTANCES FROM TOXIC
SUBSTANCES

THE TRACHEA IS A WINDPIPE
CARRYING AIR INTO THE LUNGS

THE HEART IS THE PUMP AT
THE CENTRE OF OUR BLOOD
SYSTEM

ARTERIES (RED) AND VEINS
(BLUE) TRANSPORT CHEMICALS
AROUND THE BODY

OUR INTESTINE ABSORBS
NUTRIENTS FROM FOOD WE
HAVE EATEN AND COLLECTS
WASTE MATERIAL

THE BLADDER IS A BAG THAT
COLLECTS URINE

99

Cells

IN TOTAL there are about 50 billion cells in your body! Each cell is so small it cannot be seen with the naked eye. However, with the help of a microscope we are able to study cells and discover how they work.

Nearly all cells have a nucleus, which is the control centre of the cell. Ribosomes in cells do as the nucleus tells them. They act like factories, making proteins and other chemicals for our body. To work properly a cell needs energy and this energy comes from the food we eat. Power stations in the cell, called mitochondria, change the energy stored in food into a form of energy that can be used by the cell.

THESE BRANCHING TUBES ARE USED FOR STORAGE AND FOR TRANSPORTING CHEMICALS AROUND THE CELL

THE CELL MEMBRANE ALLOWS FOOD IN THE FORM OF SUGARS TO ENTER, AND ALLOWS WASTE CHEMICALS MADE IN THE CELL TO PASS OUT

THE GOLGI APPARATUS PACKS UP THE PROTEINS MADE BY RIBOSOMES, READY TO BE STORED OR TRANSPORTED

LYSOSOMES HELP BREAK DOWN SUBSTANCES IN THE CELL

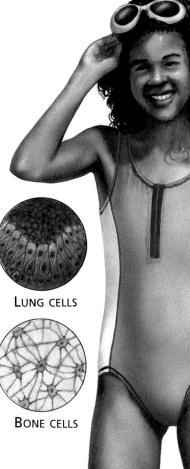

BRAIN CELLS

MUSCLE CELLS

LUNG CELLS

BONE CELLS

BLOOD CELLS

Different cell types

We start life as one cell, which divides into two. These cells also divide, and as more cells grow they form different shapes and sizes. Each of these different types of cell has its own job to do. Similar types of cell will join together to make tissues, which form organs like our brain and lungs (*see left*).

How long a cell lives depends upon the type of cell it is. Skin cells die quickly and are constantly replaced by new cells. Nerve cells should last a human lifetime and cannot be replaced even if they are damaged.

THE CONTROL CENTRE OF THE CELL IS CALLED THE NUCLEUS

CILIA ARE LIKE TINY HAIRS THAT BEAT, PUSHING MUCUS OR FLUID OVER THE CELL SURFACE

INSIDE A CILIA THERE ARE 20 LITTLE TUBES, ARRANGED IN PAIRS, TO MAKE IT STRONG

NUCLEAR MEMBRANE

RIBOSOMES MAKE PROTEINS, AS INSTRUCTED BY THE NUCLEUS

MICROTUBULES ARE HOLLOW TUBES THAT HELP SUPPORT THE CELL SO THAT IT KEEPS ITS SHAPE

MITOCHONDRIA PROVIDE ENERGY FOR THE CELL'S ACTIVITIES

FINGER-SHAPED BUMPS ALLOW MORE CHEMICALS TO BE TAKEN IN THROUGH THE CELL'S WALL

Our body's instructions
Why do some people have dark hair, others light, and why are some people short, while others are tall? The cells in each person's body contain an instruction manual. This acts a little like a program in a computer. The instructions control our body and give us many of our characteristics.

Inside the nucleus of each cell lie tiny threads called chromosomes. Inside the chromosomes are smaller structures called genes. It is in the genes that the instruction manual lies. The instructions are in the form of a chemical called DNA. DNA is shaped like a twisted ladder, known as a double helix.

The Blood System

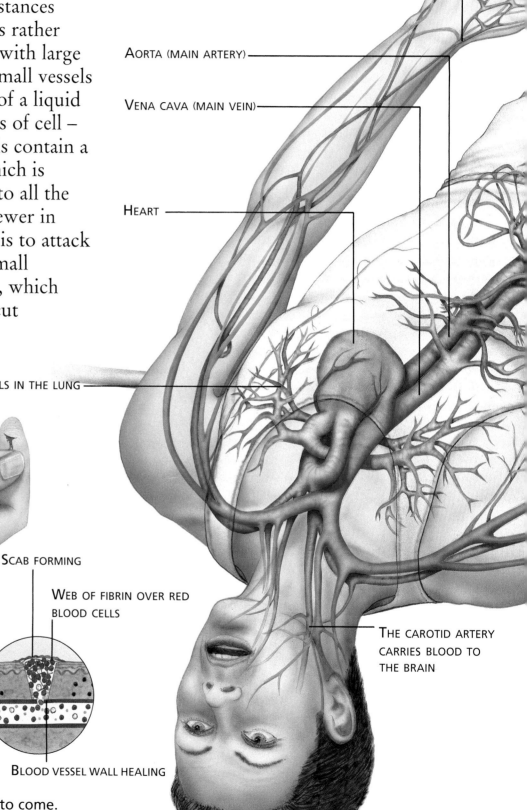

O UR BLOOD acts as a transport system, carrying substances around the body. It is rather like a road network, with large arteries as main roads and very small vessels as lanes. Blood itself is made up of a liquid called plasma and two main types of cell – red cells and white cells. Red cells contain a chemical called haemoglobin, which is responsible for carrying oxygen to all the body's cells. White cells are far fewer in number than red cells. Their job is to attack invading germs. There are also small particles in blood called platelets, which help the blood to clot when we cut ourselves.

A PERSON'S PULSE IS FELT FROM THE RADIAL ARTERY, NEAR THE SKIN SURFACE

AORTA (MAIN ARTERY)

VENA CAVA (MAIN VEIN)

HEART

BLOOD VESSELS IN THE LUNG

THE CAROTID ARTERY CARRIES BLOOD TO THE BRAIN

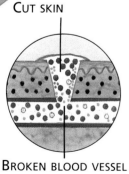

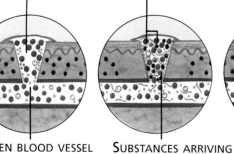

SCAB FORMING

WEB OF FIBRIN OVER RED BLOOD CELLS

CUT SKIN

PLATELETS GATHERING

BROKEN BLOOD VESSEL

SUBSTANCES ARRIVING

BLOOD VESSEL WALL HEALING

Forming a scab
When we cut ourselves, blood vessel walls break. The bleeding stops when enough platelets have stuck to the broken walls and signalled other substances to come. These substances form strands called fibrin, which form a web over the red blood cells to create a clot. The scab is the clot on the skin.

ALL ARTERIES (EXCEPT THE
PULMONARY ARTERY) ARE
SHOWN IN RED

ALL VEINS (EXCEPT THE
PULMONARY VEIN) ARE SHOWN
IN BLUE

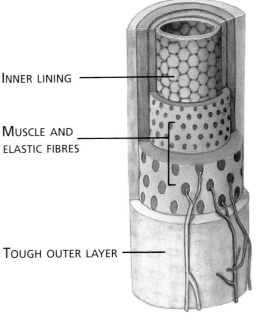

INNER LINING

MUSCLE AND
ELASTIC FIBRES

TOUGH OUTER LAYER

Blood vessels

The walls of arteries and
veins are made up of
three layers (*see above*).
Arteries carry blood
away from the heart and
are thicker than veins
because they must
withstand the heavy
pumping action of the
heart. Veins carry blood
back to the heart. Small
arteries and veins are
linked by tiny tubes
called capillaries.

The blood elements

Pictured here are the
main blood elements as
seen through a micro-
scope.

A RED BLOOD CELL – ALSO
CALLED AN ERYTHROCYTE

A COMMON WHITE CELL

ANOTHER TYPE OF WHITE CELL
– IT FORMS ANTIBODIES

BLOOD VESSELS TO AND FROM
THE KIDNEY

PLATELETS – STICKY PARTICLES

The Heart

OUR HEART is the pump at the centre of our blood system. Heart muscle is very strong as it has to pump blood through networks of small blood vessels around the body. Heart muscle contracts automatically; the number of times it contracts, or beats, in a minute is known as the heart rate. An adult normally has a heart rate of about 70 beats a minute. At birth our heart rate is much faster than this – sometimes twice as fast. Even as children our heart rate is usually about 100 beats per minute. Everyone's normal heart rate will increase if they exercise, because more oxygen, carried by the blood, is needed by hard-working muscles.

You can measure your heart rate by feeling your pulse. Your wrist is the best place to find it. If you put two fingers across the underside of your wrist, where the artery lies close to the surface of your skin, you can count the number of beats felt in one minute.

THE AORTA IS THE BIGGEST ARTERY IN THE BODY

SUPERIOR VENA CAVA

PULMONARY ARTERIES TAKE BLOOD TO THE LUNGS TO BE RE-OXYGENATED

The flow of blood
The diagrams below show the direction that blood flows through the heart. The pulmonary veins carry blood rich in oxygen from the lungs to the left atrium (1). The blood then flows through the left ventricle (2) into the aorta (3). After this it is pumped around the body. At the same time that blood is leaving the heart, more blood is arriving at the right atrium through the large vein called the vena cava (1). This blood contains little oxygen because it has already been used by the body. Blood flows to the right ventricle (2) and then into the pulmonary artery to pick up more oxygen in the lungs (3). This cycle is repeated (4).

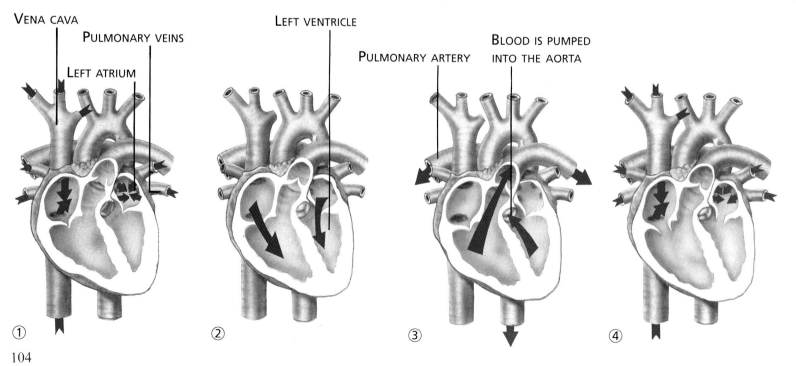

VENA CAVA

PULMONARY VEINS

LEFT ATRIUM

LEFT VENTRICLE

PULMONARY ARTERY

BLOOD IS PUMPED INTO THE AORTA

① ② ③ ④

Inside the heart
The heart is made up of four sections known as chambers. These chambers are the right and left atria, and the right and left ventricles. The ventricles are separated from the atria by valves, which are like one-way swing doors. Valves ensure that blood flows through the chambers in the right direction.

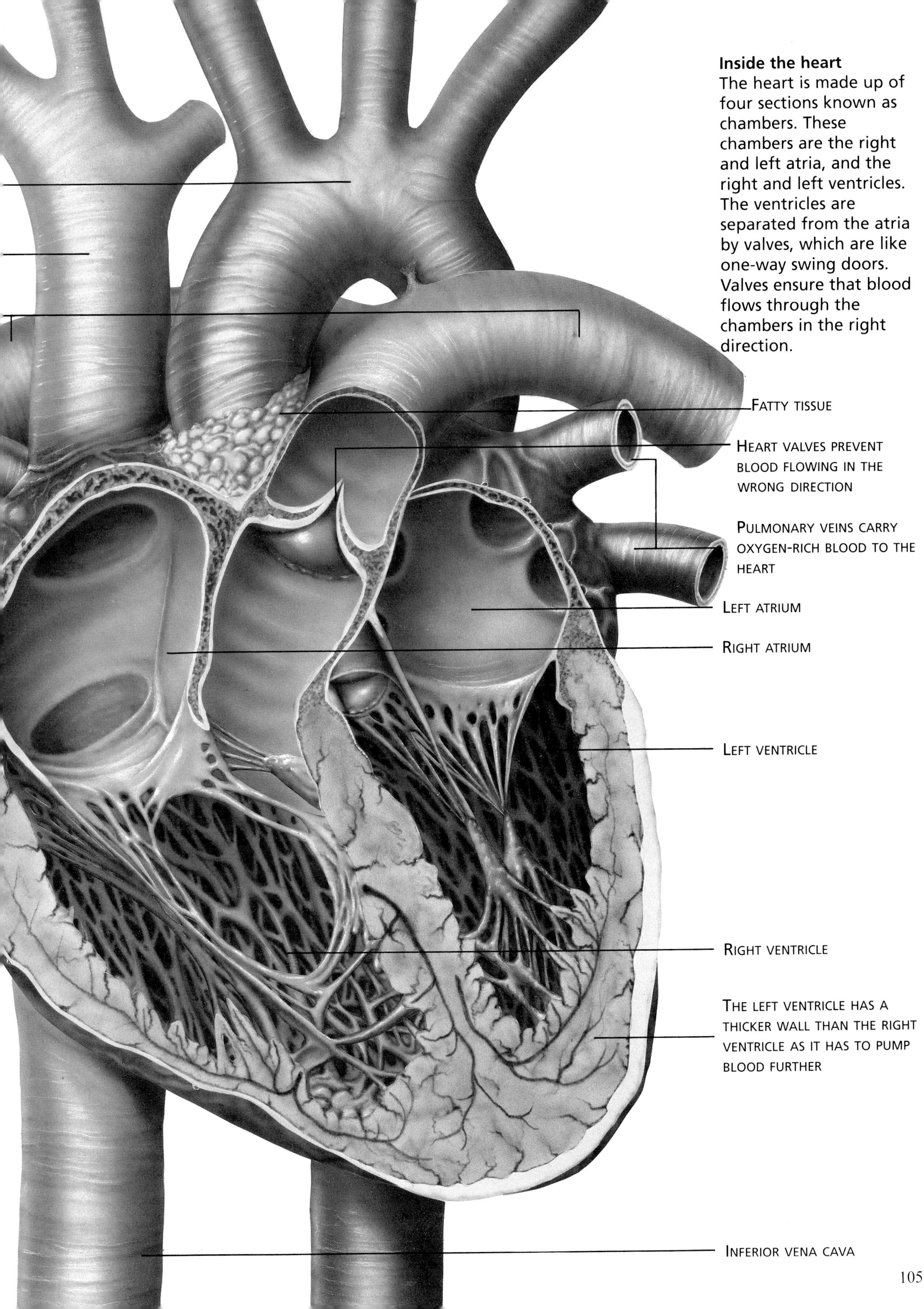

FATTY TISSUE

HEART VALVES PREVENT BLOOD FLOWING IN THE WRONG DIRECTION

PULMONARY VEINS CARRY OXYGEN-RICH BLOOD TO THE HEART

LEFT ATRIUM

RIGHT ATRIUM

LEFT VENTRICLE

RIGHT VENTRICLE

THE LEFT VENTRICLE HAS A THICKER WALL THAN THE RIGHT VENTRICLE AS IT HAS TO PUMP BLOOD FURTHER

INFERIOR VENA CAVA

Breathing

EVERY time you breathe, you draw in air containing a gas called oxygen, which makes your body work. Most adults breathe 18 times a minute – children breathe faster. When you breathe in, hairs in your nose, and mucus in your nose and throat, stop harmful particles of dust or bacteria from entering your lungs. The air then travels down the trachea (windpipe) and into your lungs through the left and right bronchi. Your ribs move outward and your diaphragm muscle moves down, allowing your lungs to expand and fill with air. The opposite happens when you breathe out.

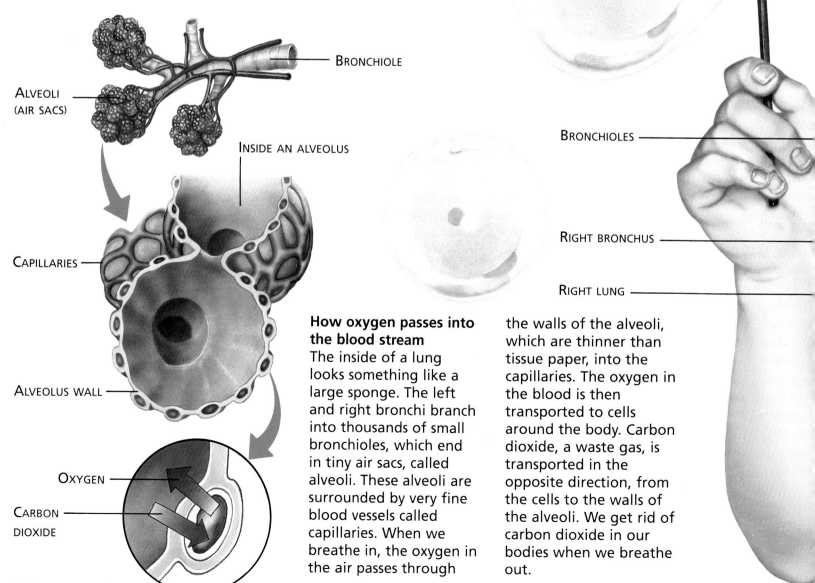

AIR BREATHED OUT (EXHALED)

BRONCHIOLE

ALVEOLI (AIR SACS)

INSIDE AN ALVEOLUS

CAPILLARIES

ALVEOLUS WALL

OXYGEN

CARBON DIOXIDE

BRONCHIOLES

RIGHT BRONCHUS

RIGHT LUNG

How oxygen passes into the blood stream
The inside of a lung looks something like a large sponge. The left and right bronchi branch into thousands of small bronchioles, which end in tiny air sacs, called alveoli. These alveoli are surrounded by very fine blood vessels called capillaries. When we breathe in, the oxygen in the air passes through the walls of the alveoli, which are thinner than tissue paper, into the capillaries. The oxygen in the blood is then transported to cells around the body. Carbon dioxide, a waste gas, is transported in the opposite direction, from the cells to the walls of the alveoli. We get rid of carbon dioxide in our bodies when we breathe out.

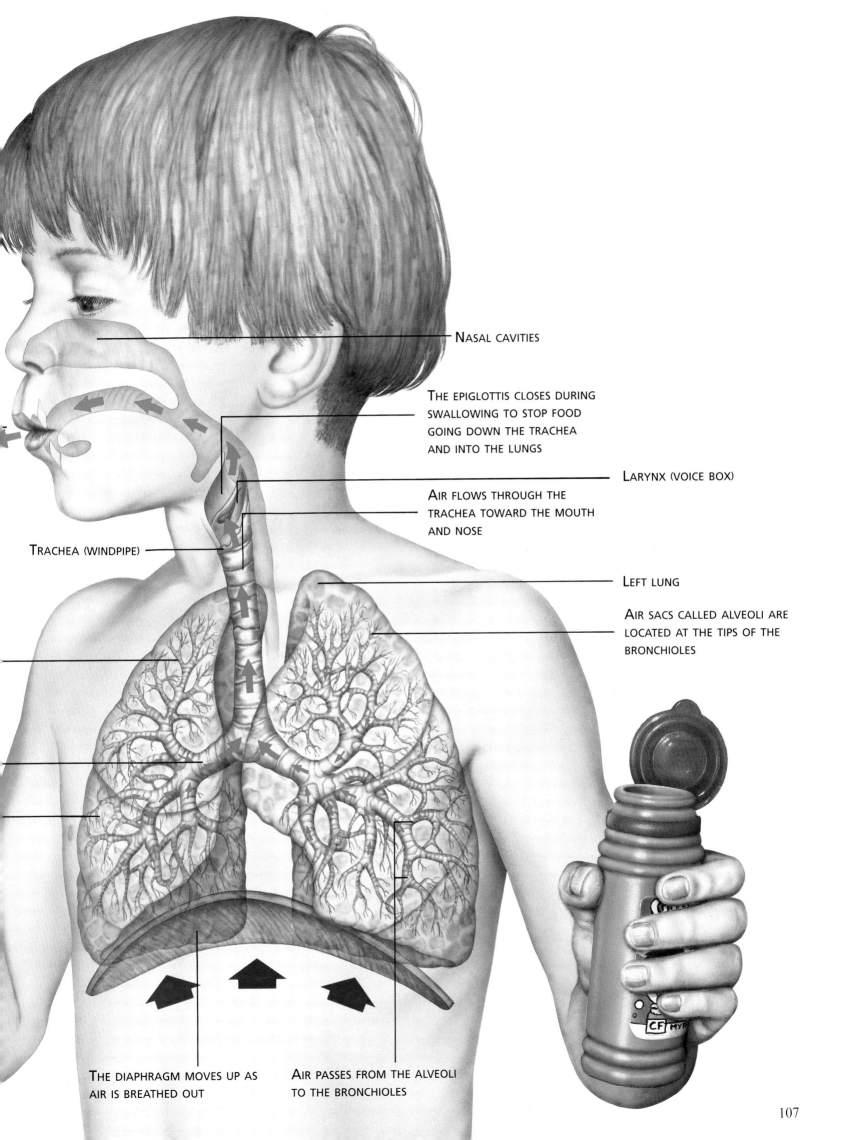

NASAL CAVITIES

THE EPIGLOTTIS CLOSES DURING
SWALLOWING TO STOP FOOD
GOING DOWN THE TRACHEA
AND INTO THE LUNGS

LARYNX (VOICE BOX)

AIR FLOWS THROUGH THE
TRACHEA TOWARD THE MOUTH
AND NOSE

TRACHEA (WINDPIPE)

LEFT LUNG

AIR SACS CALLED ALVEOLI ARE
LOCATED AT THE TIPS OF THE
BRONCHIOLES

THE DIAPHRAGM MOVES UP AS
AIR IS BREATHED OUT

AIR PASSES FROM THE ALVEOLI
TO THE BRONCHIOLES

107

The Skeleton

THE HUMAN skeleton is made up of more than 200 bones. It gives our muscles a firm place to anchor themselves and also protects our body's more fragile organs. For example, the brain is protected by the skull and the lungs are protected by the ribs. The bones of our skeleton vary in shape and size to fit their function. The spine has 33 separate bones. It is shaped to protect the spinal cord, which travels through it, while also giving the spinal muscles a place for attachment.

The male skeleton is different to the female skeleton. For example, the female pelvis is specially designed to allow a baby's safe journey down the birth canal.

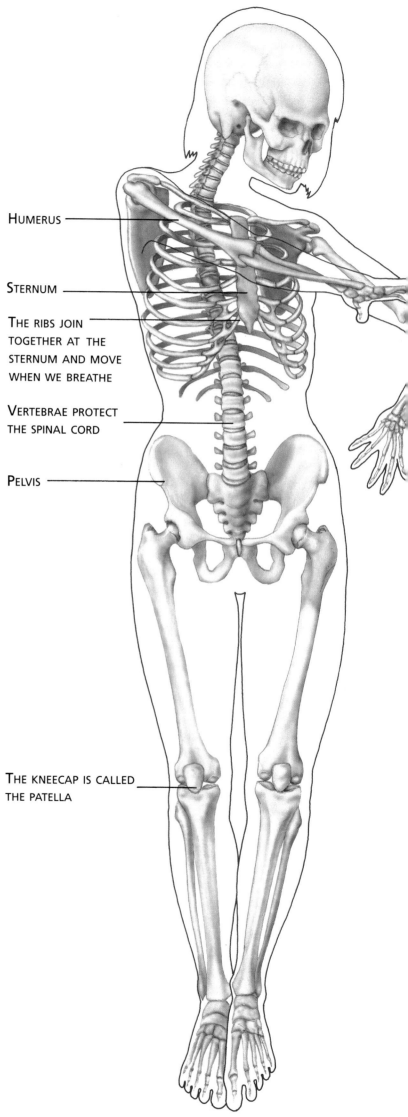

HUMERUS

STERNUM

THE RIBS JOIN TOGETHER AT THE STERNUM AND MOVE WHEN WE BREATHE

VERTEBRAE PROTECT THE SPINAL CORD

PELVIS

THE KNEECAP IS CALLED THE PATELLA

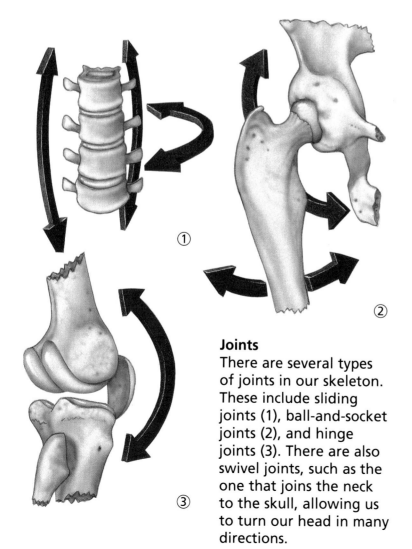

① ② ③

Joints
There are several types of joints in our skeleton. These include sliding joints (1), ball-and-socket joints (2), and hinge joints (3). There are also swivel joints, such as the one that joins the neck to the skull, allowing us to turn our head in many directions.

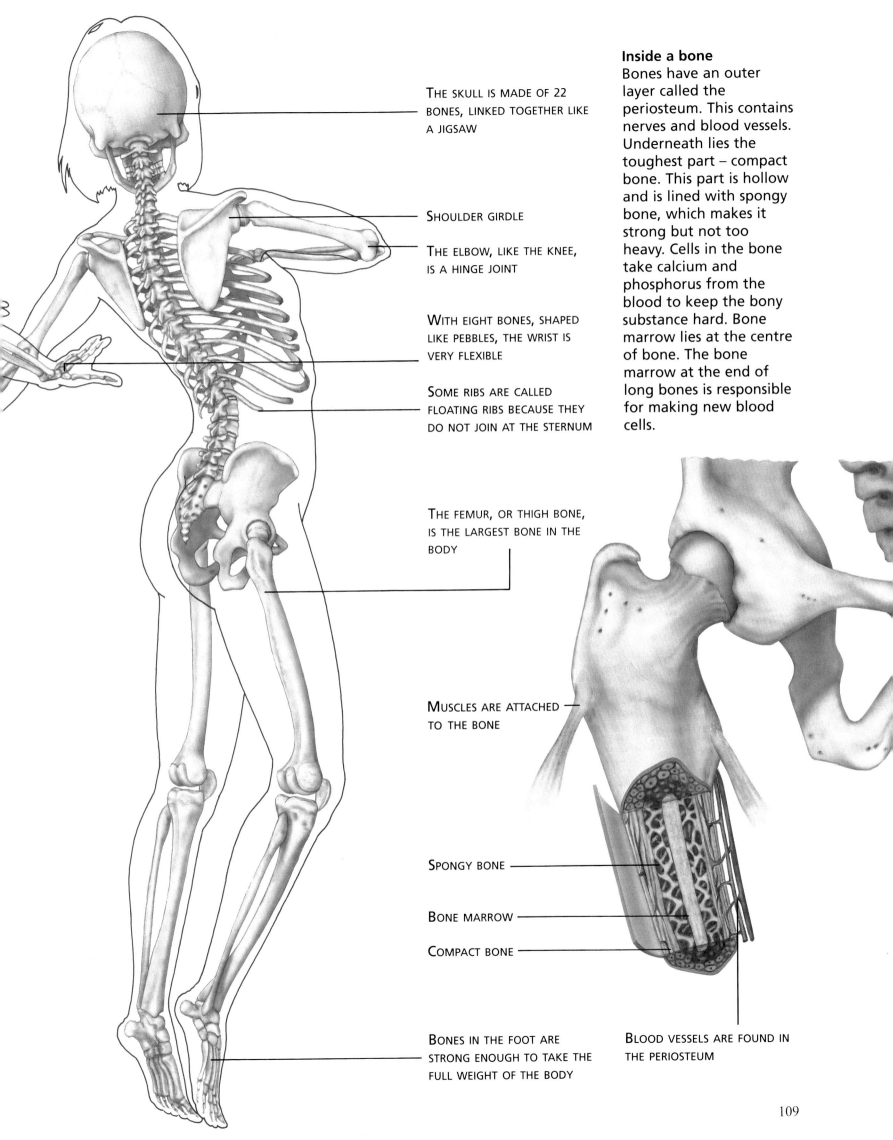

THE SKULL IS MADE OF 22 BONES, LINKED TOGETHER LIKE A JIGSAW

SHOULDER GIRDLE

THE ELBOW, LIKE THE KNEE, IS A HINGE JOINT

WITH EIGHT BONES, SHAPED LIKE PEBBLES, THE WRIST IS VERY FLEXIBLE

SOME RIBS ARE CALLED FLOATING RIBS BECAUSE THEY DO NOT JOIN AT THE STERNUM

THE FEMUR, OR THIGH BONE, IS THE LARGEST BONE IN THE BODY

MUSCLES ARE ATTACHED TO THE BONE

SPONGY BONE

BONE MARROW

COMPACT BONE

BONES IN THE FOOT ARE STRONG ENOUGH TO TAKE THE FULL WEIGHT OF THE BODY

BLOOD VESSELS ARE FOUND IN THE PERIOSTEUM

Inside a bone
Bones have an outer layer called the periosteum. This contains nerves and blood vessels. Underneath lies the toughest part – compact bone. This part is hollow and is lined with spongy bone, which makes it strong but not too heavy. Cells in the bone take calcium and phosphorus from the blood to keep the bony substance hard. Bone marrow lies at the centre of bone. The bone marrow at the end of long bones is responsible for making new blood cells.

109

Muscles

WE HAVE lots of muscles of different shapes and sizes, ranging from the large gluteus maximus on which we sit, to the tiny muscles that control the movements of our eyes. Many of our movements – when riding a bicycle, for example – involve a number of muscles that have to work together, and these are controlled by the brain. Every muscle in our body is made up of muscle fibres. Messages from the brain can make muscle fibres contract, making them shorter. As they shorten they become more powerful and are able to pull the bones to which they are attached. This causes movement.

FACIAL EXPRESSIONS ARE MADE BY TINY MOVEMENTS OF MUSCLES IN THE FACE

PECTORALIS MAJOR

TRAPEZIUS

DELTOID

LATISSIMUS DORSI

GLUTEUS MAXIMUS

HAMSTRING MUSCLES

SARTORIUS

CALF MUSCLES

SOME MUSCLES ARE VISIBLE AND BULGE WHEN TENSE

ALTHOUGH MUSCLES LOOK SOLID THEY ARE ACTUALLY MADE UP OF FIBRES

FINGER BONES ARE CONNECTED TO MUSCLES IN THE FOREARM – WHEN THE MUSCLES CONTRACT THEY HELP THE FINGERS TO BEND

Automatic muscles
Although we can control many of our muscles, we also have muscles in our body that work automatically. These include the muscles that make our heart beat and the muscles in our intestine that help us to digest food.

WITHOUT MUSCLES THE BODY COULD NOT MOVE – HERE, MUSCLES ARE USED TO STRETCH THE LEGS

Muscle-building
Muscles often work in pairs. A male gymnast illustrates this when he lifts his body to the rings. His biceps muscles shorten and stiffen, while his triceps muscles lengthen and relax. Regular training and frequent use of these muscles will increase their size and strength. This explains why many athletes have muscles you can easily see.

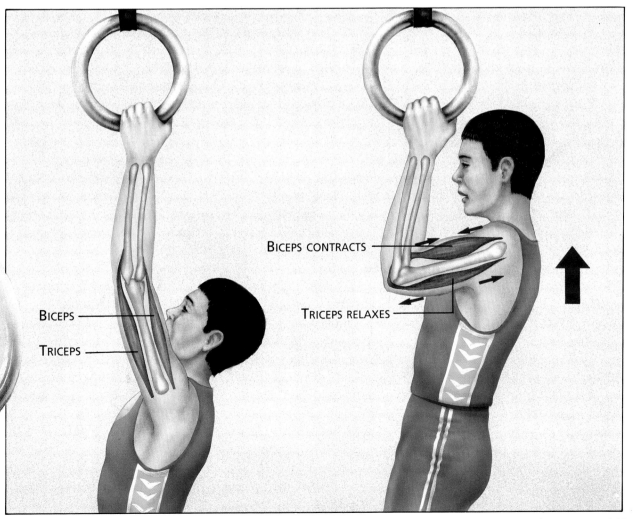

BICEPS

TRICEPS

BICEPS CONTRACTS

TRICEPS RELAXES

The Digestive System

VILLI

MUSCLE

CAPILLARIES

WE NEED food in order to live; it is the fuel for our body's energy and growth. There are three main kinds of food: protein (found in meat, cheese, and nuts, for example), carbohydrates (found in bread and potatoes), and fat (found in oils and butter). Proteins are used for repairing the body and for growing; carbohydrates and fats are needed for providing energy.

Digestion is a process that begins when we put food in our mouths and ends when the food has been absorbed into the bloodstream. It takes up to eighteen hours for digestion to occur. This is not surprising because our food has to travel through more than eight metres of coiled-up tubing called the small intestine. On its journey food gets broken down by acid and enzymes. An enzyme is a chemical that changes food into a substance we can easily absorb.

Food's journey

When we chew, our teeth break up food into small pieces for swallowing. Food then travels down a muscular tube called the oesophagus, to the stomach, which is a bag containing acid that kills off any bacteria (1). Next, food enters the small intestine (2). There it is broken up into useful substances and waste substances by enzymes, which are produced by a gland called the pancreas.

Inside the small intestine finger-like bumps, known as villi, contain blood vessels that absorb the useful substances into the bloodstream. Waste substances remain and pass into the large intestine, where water is absorbed until the waste becomes solid (3). This waste is later expelled from the rectum.

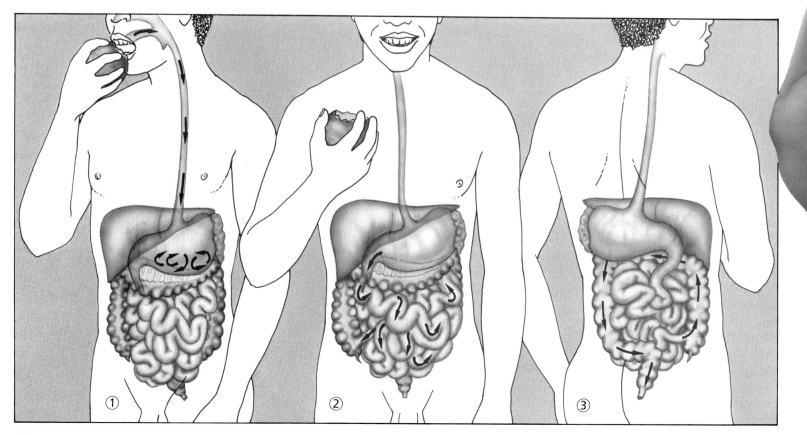

①   ②   ③

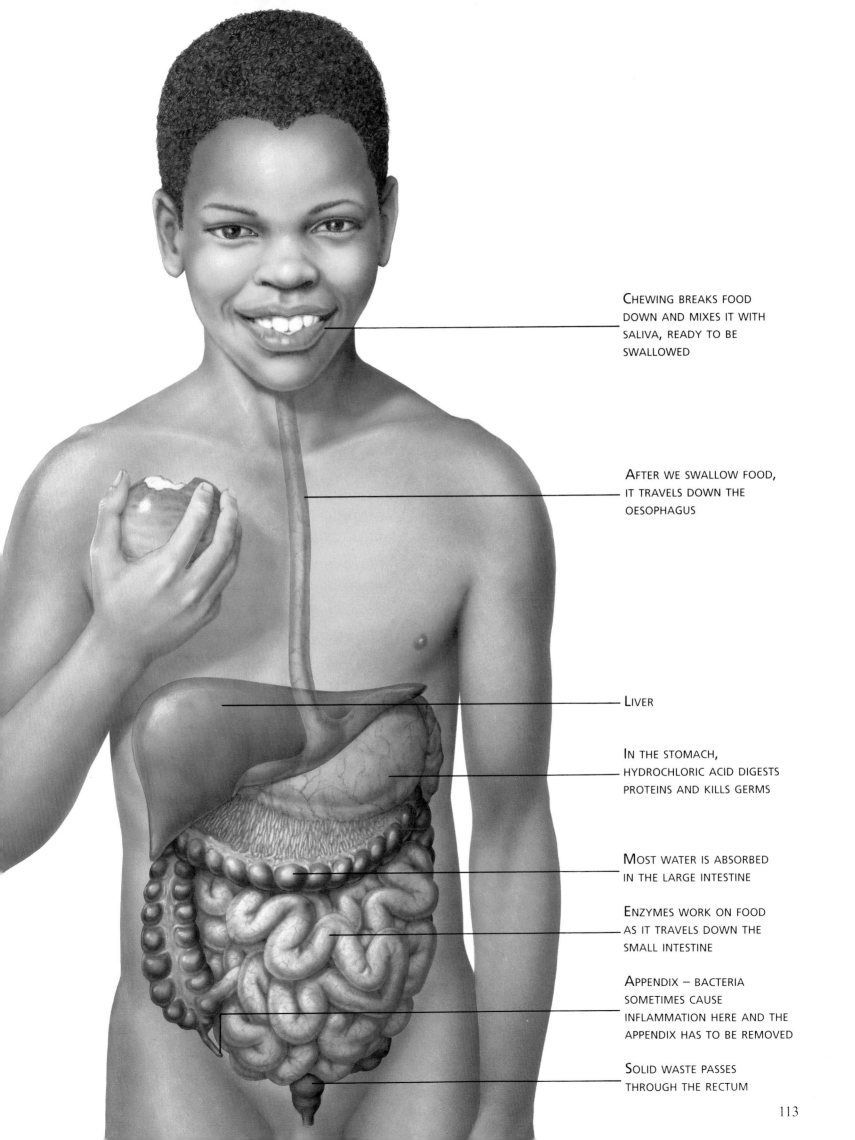

CHEWING BREAKS FOOD
DOWN AND MIXES IT WITH
SALIVA, READY TO BE
SWALLOWED

AFTER WE SWALLOW FOOD,
IT TRAVELS DOWN THE
OESOPHAGUS

LIVER

IN THE STOMACH,
HYDROCHLORIC ACID DIGESTS
PROTEINS AND KILLS GERMS

MOST WATER IS ABSORBED
IN THE LARGE INTESTINE

ENZYMES WORK ON FOOD
AS IT TRAVELS DOWN THE
SMALL INTESTINE

APPENDIX – BACTERIA
SOMETIMES CAUSE
INFLAMMATION HERE AND THE
APPENDIX HAS TO BE REMOVED

SOLID WASTE PASSES
THROUGH THE RECTUM

Teeth

TEETH are designed to break food into small, soft pieces for swallowing. The teeth at the front of the mouth, called incisors, are used for cutting. Behind these are the canine teeth, which are especially good for tearing tough food. The flatter teeth at the back are called premolars and molars; they are used for grinding and mashing.

Our first set of teeth, known as 'milk teeth', appear in infancy. The very first tooth usually appears at about seven months of age and is one of the lower incisors. The upper teeth appear two months later and the premolars appear around our first birthday. A second set of teeth grows, replacing our milk teeth, from about the age of six (*see below*). These teeth are complete when the 'wisdom teeth', which are molars at the back of the gums, come through at around the age of 20. In total an adult has 32 teeth.

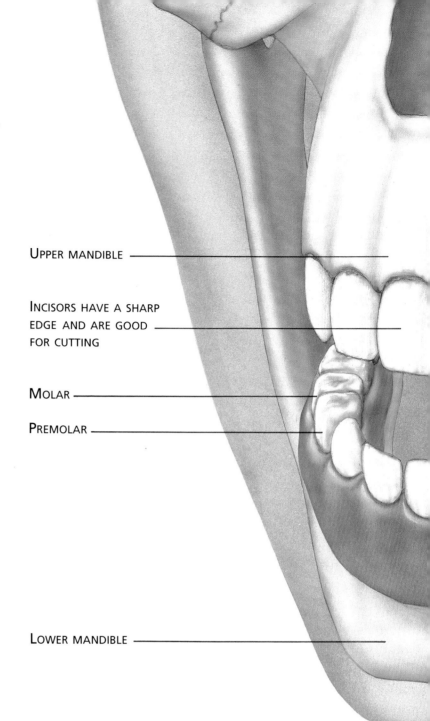

UPPER MANDIBLE

INCISORS HAVE A SHARP EDGE AND ARE GOOD FOR CUTTING

MOLAR

PREMOLAR

LOWER MANDIBLE

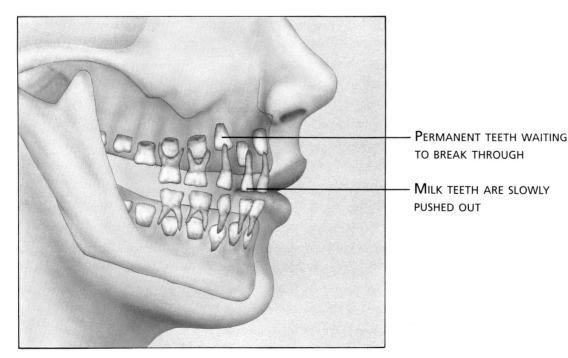

PERMANENT TEETH WAITING TO BREAK THROUGH

MILK TEETH ARE SLOWLY PUSHED OUT

Tooth decay
A tooth has two parts: the crown and the root. The crown is the visible part above the gum and the root is the part that lies hidden in the gum. The crown is covered in enamel – the hardest substance of the body – which helps to protect the fragile blood vessels and nerves that lie inside the tooth. Dentine, another hard layer, surrounds and protects

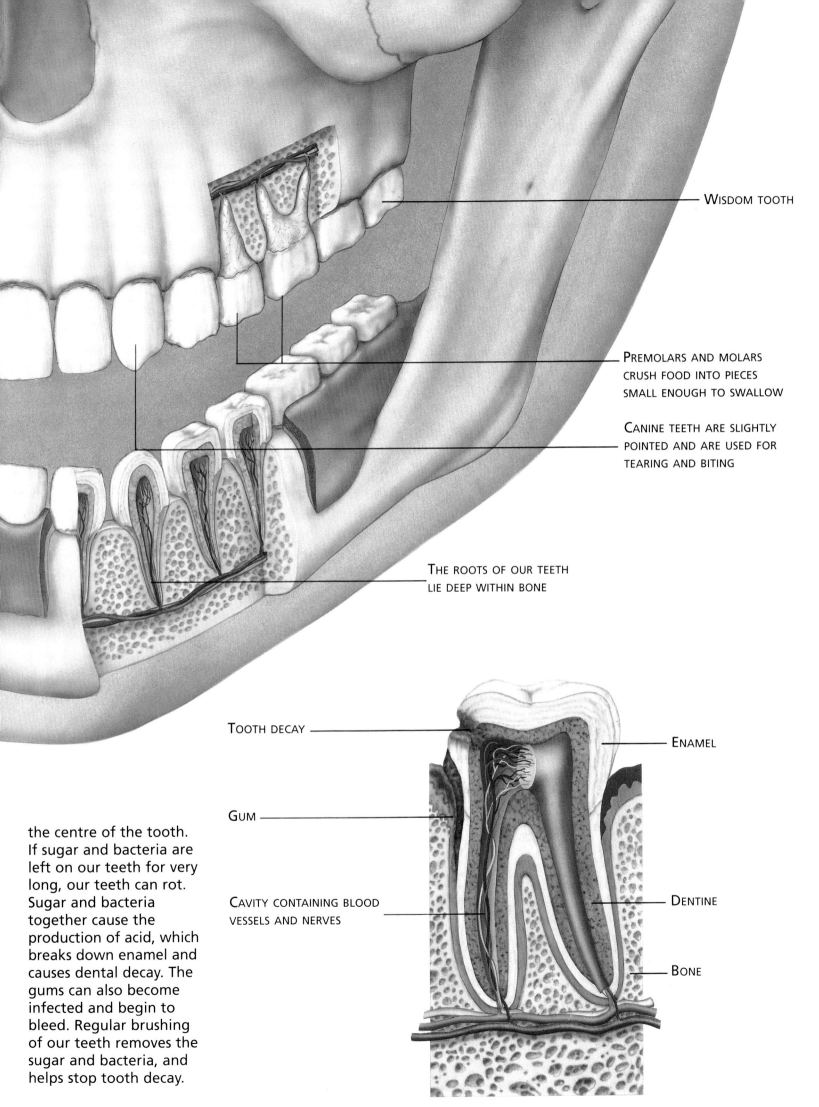

WISDOM TOOTH

PREMOLARS AND MOLARS CRUSH FOOD INTO PIECES SMALL ENOUGH TO SWALLOW

CANINE TEETH ARE SLIGHTLY POINTED AND ARE USED FOR TEARING AND BITING

THE ROOTS OF OUR TEETH LIE DEEP WITHIN BONE

TOOTH DECAY

ENAMEL

GUM

CAVITY CONTAINING BLOOD VESSELS AND NERVES

DENTINE

BONE

the centre of the tooth. If sugar and bacteria are left on our teeth for very long, our teeth can rot. Sugar and bacteria together cause the production of acid, which breaks down enamel and causes dental decay. The gums can also become infected and begin to bleed. Regular brushing of our teeth removes the sugar and bacteria, and helps stop tooth decay.

The Liver and Kidneys

THE LIVER is the blood's cleaning and sorting centre. A vein called the portal vein connects the intestines directly to the liver, bringing to the liver blood that is rich in dissolved food. The liver sorts through the blood, taking out harmful chemical waste and storing useful substances, such as sugars and vitamins.

When the kidneys receive blood containing waste substances, they filter and remove these substances together with any excess water. The kidneys pass this waste, or urine, to the bladder, and pass the filtered, clean blood back to the heart.

FLUID IS ESSENTIAL FOR THE BODY TO FUNCTION

Liver lobule

Our liver is made up of small structures called lobules. Each lobule contains spaces through which blood flows. Some of the chemical waste in the blood is removed, turned into bile, and stored in the gall bladder. Bile removes waste and makes fats soluble for absorption.

THE COMMON BILE DUCT JOINS THE GALL-BLADDER TO THE INTESTINE

THE GALL BLADDER IS A THIN-WALLED, GREEN MUSCULAR SAC THAT STORES BILE

LIVER

BLOOD FLOWS IN THROUGH THE PORTAL VEIN

BILE NETWORK

ARROWS SHOW BLOOD TRAVELLING THROUGH THE LIVER LOBULE

RENAL VEIN

RENAL ARTERY

BLOOD FLOWS OUT THROUGH THE HEPATIC VEIN

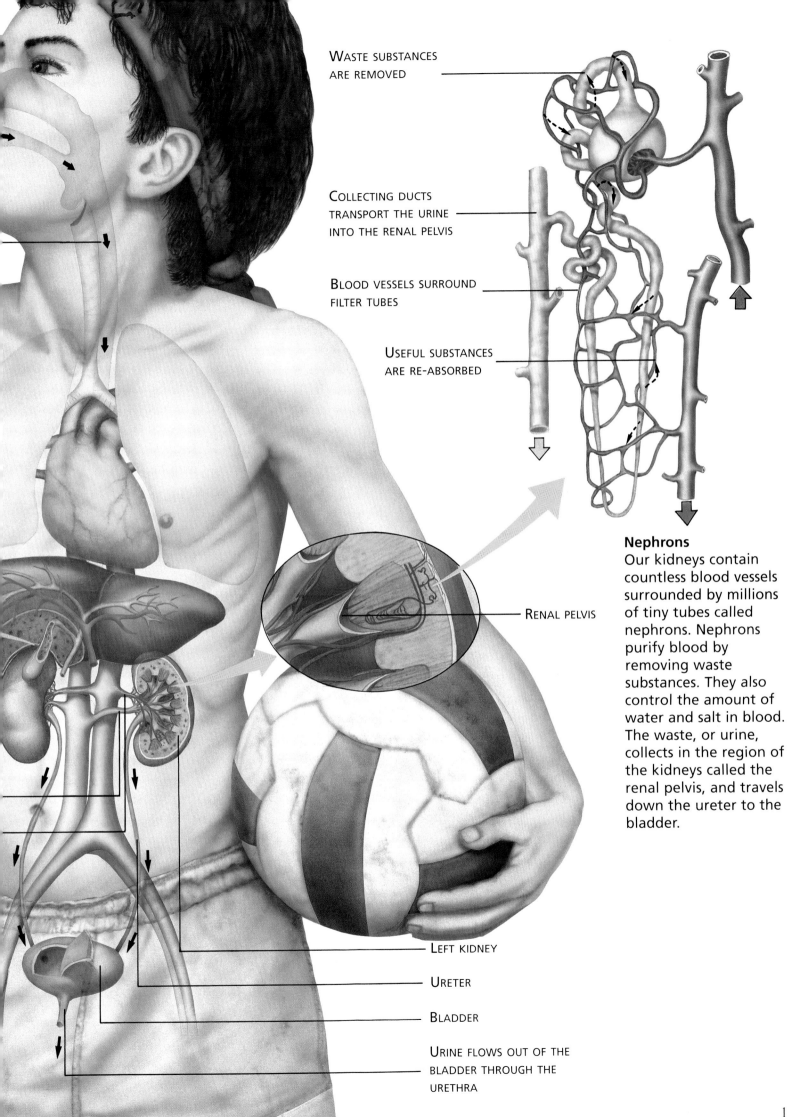

WASTE SUBSTANCES
ARE REMOVED

COLLECTING DUCTS
TRANSPORT THE URINE
INTO THE RENAL PELVIS

BLOOD VESSELS SURROUND
FILTER TUBES

USEFUL SUBSTANCES
ARE RE-ABSORBED

RENAL PELVIS

Nephrons
Our kidneys contain
countless blood vessels
surrounded by millions
of tiny tubes called
nephrons. Nephrons
purify blood by
removing waste
substances. They also
control the amount of
water and salt in blood.
The waste, or urine,
collects in the region of
the kidneys called the
renal pelvis, and travels
down the ureter to the
bladder.

LEFT KIDNEY

URETER

BLADDER

URINE FLOWS OUT OF THE
BLADDER THROUGH THE
URETHRA

The Skin

SKIN IS OUR protective coat – a complex covering of two layers. The top layer is the epidermis, which as well as being waterproof also protects us against germs. The cells in this layer are being shed all the time, with new cells growing in their place. The dermis layer beneath is much thicker, and is made up of elastic fibres. It contains blood vessels, sweat glands, and hair roots, called follicles. These all help to control our body temperature. In hot weather the blood vessels widen and allow more blood to flow near the cooler surface of the skin. Sweat glands produce salty droplets that evaporate on the body and cool it down. In cold weather muscles attached to hair follicles tighten, making our hairs stand on end. This traps a thin layer of warm air around the body. In addition, blood vessels narrow to keep the body's heat in and away from the skin's surface.

NERVE FIBRES IN THE SKIN

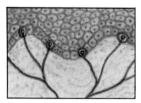

FOR PAIN

FOR COLD TEMPERATURE

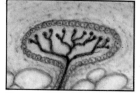

FOR HEAT

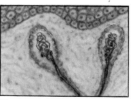

FOR TOUCH

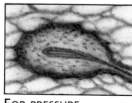

FOR PRESSURE

Sensitive skin

Nerve endings in the dermis enable us to feel heat, cold, pain, and pressure. They also help protect our bodies from damage. Our hands, lips, and the soles of our feet are the most sensitive parts of our body because the skin on them has the richest supply of nerve endings.

The sun

Our skin is delicate and very sensitive to the sun. Ultraviolet rays produced by the sun shine on our skin and can cause the skin to burn. This often results in painful blistering red skin. Sometimes the sun's rays can actually cause cells in our skin to change and skin cancer to develop.

Everybody needs to protect their skin from the sun either by staying in the shade or by using sun cream. Sun cream contains substances that help block out the harmful rays. Wearing a hat also helps to protect our face and neck, and wearing light clothing keeps the sun away from our skin.

EPIDERMIS – THIS IS THE GERMPROOF AND WATERPROOF LAYER

MELANIN – THE PIGMENT THAT GIVES SKIN A BROWN COLOUR

SENSORY NERVE ENDINGS

THE DERMIS LAYER CONTAINS FIBRES THAT MAKE THE SKIN SUPPLE AND ELASTIC

FATTY CELLS TO KEEP US WARM

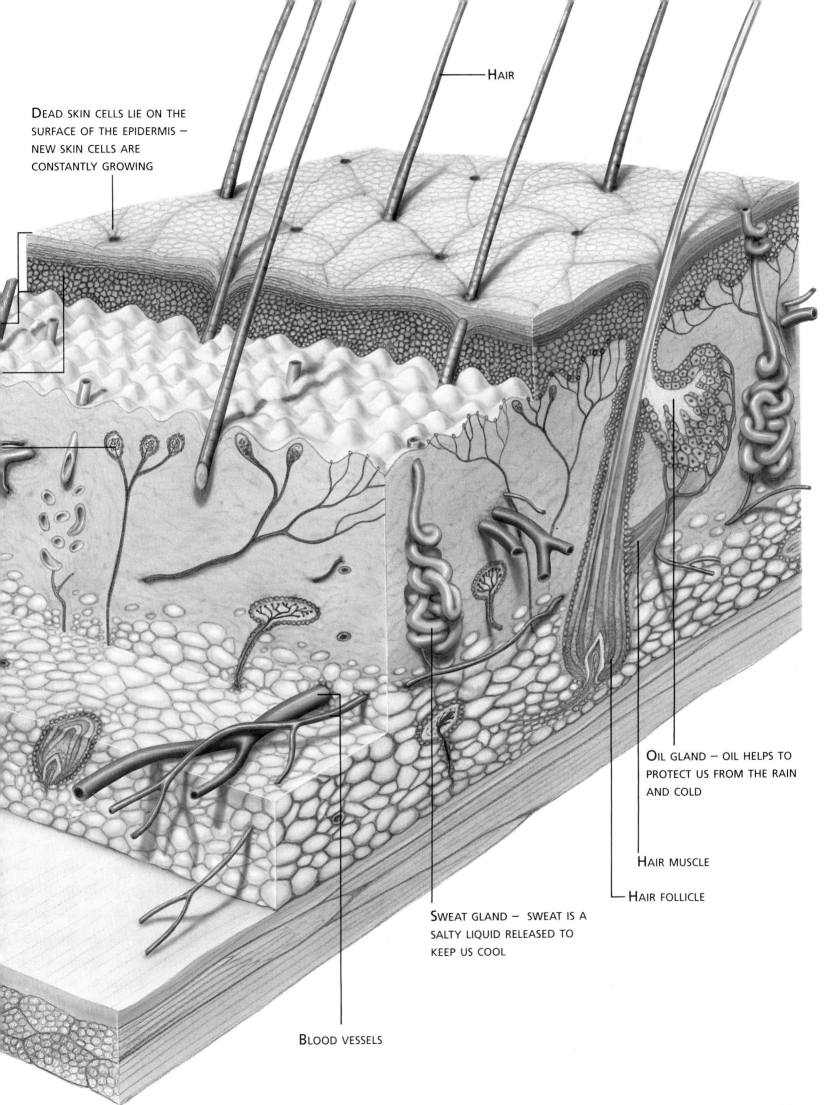

HAIR

DEAD SKIN CELLS LIE ON THE
SURFACE OF THE EPIDERMIS —
NEW SKIN CELLS ARE
CONSTANTLY GROWING

OIL GLAND — OIL HELPS TO
PROTECT US FROM THE RAIN
AND COLD

HAIR MUSCLE

HAIR FOLLICLE

SWEAT GLAND — SWEAT IS A
SALTY LIQUID RELEASED TO
KEEP US COOL

BLOOD VESSELS

The Nerves

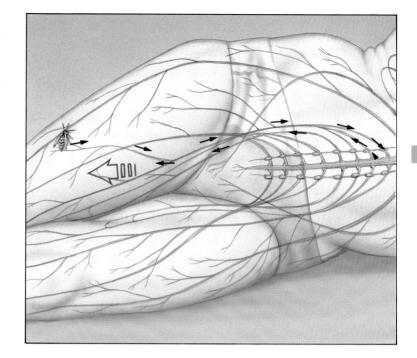

OUR NERVOUS system is a busy network of nerves. It includes the nerves in our brain and the nerves that stretch throughout our bodies. Our brain is connected to the rest of our body by the spinal cord, a thick cable that runs down the spinal column in our back.

Nerves are made up of thin strands called neurons. There are millions of these throughout the nervous system and each consists of a cell body, which has short branches called dendrites. The long arm of the neuron is called the axon. Some axons are enclosed in a fatty layer called myelin, which helps to speed up the conduction, or passing, of nerve messages along the axon. Nerve cells in our spinal cord cannot be replaced, so spinal injury can be serious.

The reflex action
The sensory impulse travels up the leg and into the spinal cord. It is then transmitted to neurons in the grey matter of the cord, which link up with motor neurons. The impulse travels back down the leg in the motor nerve, and the leg muscle tightens, making the leg jerk. The reflex action does not involve the brain.

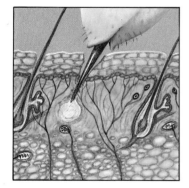

A wasp sting
When a wasp stings (*see left*), nerve endings in the area are excited and a nerve message, called an impulse, is sent along a nerve. Nerves carrying sensations, such as pain, are known as sensory nerves.

PAIN CAUSES US TO FLICK THE WASP AWAY

ARROWS SHOW NERVES TRANSMITTING PAIN – PAIN IS FELT AFTER THE REFLEX ACTION

A WASP STING CAUSES REFLEX ACTION – A RAPID LEG JERK AWAY FROM THE WASP

PERIPHERAL (OUTLYING) NERVES

DIRECTION OF NERVE MESSAGES, OR IMPULSES

IMPULSES TO THE SPINAL CORD AND BRAIN TRAVEL ALONG SENSORY NERVES

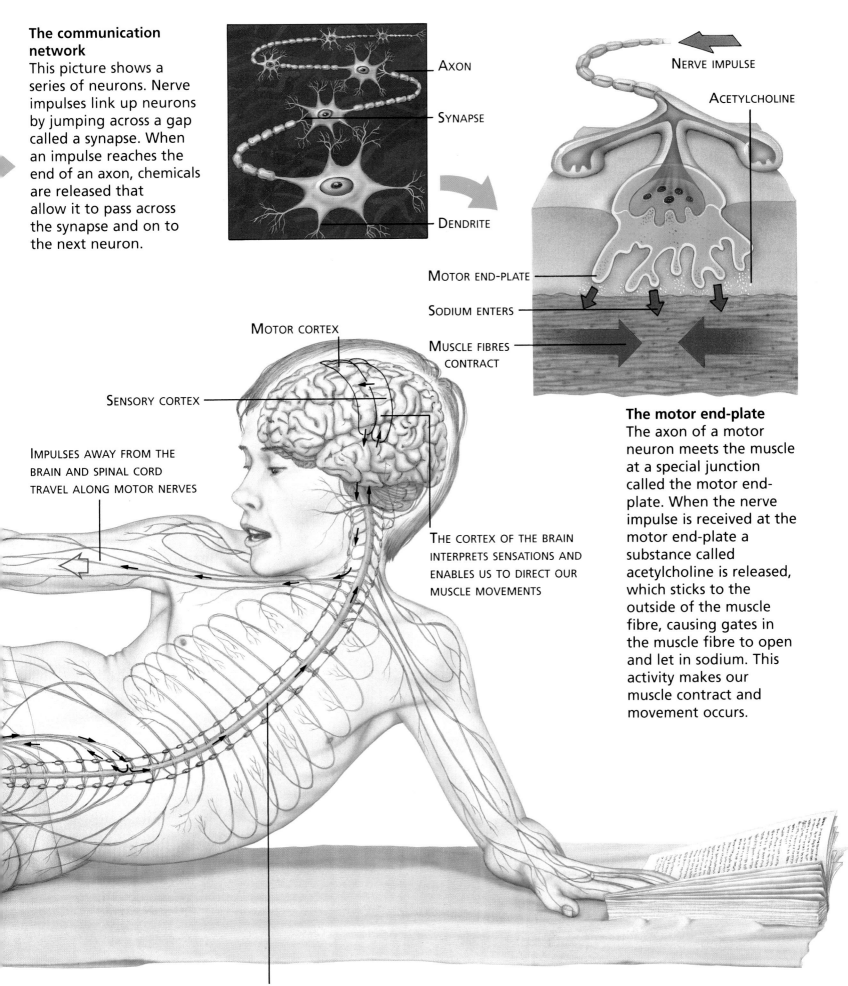

The communication network
This picture shows a series of neurons. Nerve impulses link up neurons by jumping across a gap called a synapse. When an impulse reaches the end of an axon, chemicals are released that allow it to pass across the synapse and on to the next neuron.

AXON

SYNAPSE

DENDRITE

NERVE IMPULSE

ACETYLCHOLINE

MOTOR END-PLATE

SODIUM ENTERS

MUSCLE FIBRES CONTRACT

MOTOR CORTEX

SENSORY CORTEX

IMPULSES AWAY FROM THE BRAIN AND SPINAL CORD TRAVEL ALONG MOTOR NERVES

THE CORTEX OF THE BRAIN INTERPRETS SENSATIONS AND ENABLES US TO DIRECT OUR MUSCLE MOVEMENTS

SPINAL CORD

The motor end-plate
The axon of a motor neuron meets the muscle at a special junction called the motor end-plate. When the nerve impulse is received at the motor end-plate a substance called acetylcholine is released, which sticks to the outside of the muscle fibre, causing gates in the muscle fibre to open and let in sodium. This activity makes our muscle contract and movement occurs.

121

The Brain

THE BRAIN looks like a mass of grey jelly and is very soft. It is protected in the hard, bony case known as the skull. The human brain is quite large but is wrinkled, which makes it compact.

The brain is the body's control centre. It is involved with what we do and what we think, as well as what we feel and remember. We also use our brain to learn. The left-hand side of our brain controls the right side of the body, and the right-hand side of our brain controls the left side of the body. Most people are right handed, because the left side of the brain is generally used more than the right side. It has been found that each side of our brain is responsible for different skills. The right side holds our artistic talent and imagination, and the left side is more responsible for practical abilities and logical thinking.

3-DIMENSIONAL AWARENESS

MUSICAL ABILITY

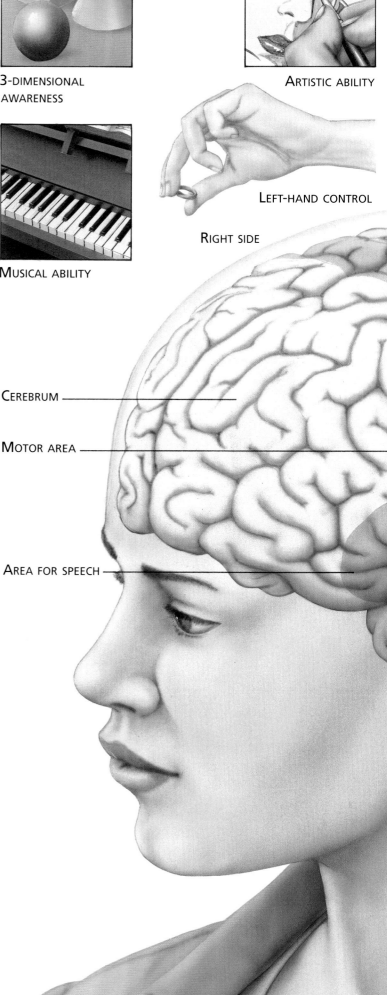

ARTISTIC ABILITY

LEFT-HAND CONTROL

RIGHT SIDE

CEREBRUM

MOTOR AREA

AREA FOR SPEECH

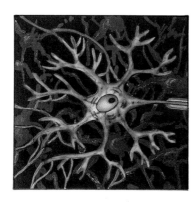

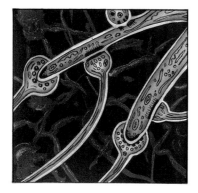

Brain cells
The cells that make up the brain are called neurons (*top left*). Branches from the cells, called dendrites, receive impulses from the nerves while axons transmit them (*bottom left*). Our brain interprets the impulses and can tell where they are coming from and to what they are referring. The brain cells can also store information. A piece of stored information is called a memory. One part of our brain stores long-term memories, another part more recent memories.

SCIENTIFIC SKILLS

RIGHT-HAND CONTROL

LEFT SIDE

LOGICAL AND
MATHEMATICAL SKILL

WRITING

SPEECH

SENSORY AREA

AREA FOR VISION

AREA FOR HEARING

CEREBELLUM

SPINAL CORD

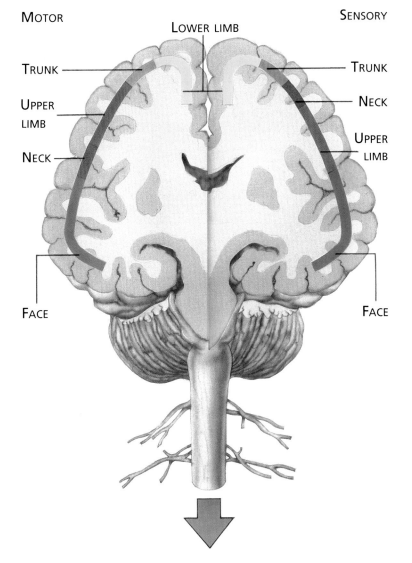

MOTOR

LOWER LIMB

TRUNK

UPPER
LIMB

NECK

FACE

SENSORY

TRUNK

NECK

UPPER
LIMB

FACE

The cerebrum

The largest part of the brain consists of two sections. Together they are known as the cerebral hemispheres or cerebrum. The cerebrum is highly organized. It is arranged in areas that relate to different parts of the body and to different needs. Vision is interpreted at the back of the cerebrum; hearing and speech at the side. The areas for sensation and movement are in the middle. The area at the front of the cerebrum, the frontal lobes, control our behaviour. Below and to the back of the cerebrum lies the cerebellum. It contains nerve cells that are mainly concerned with balance. Below this the brain is connected to the rest of the body by the spinal cord.

Seeing

O UR EYES work like cameras. Each eye has a pupil, which, similar to a camera's aperture, is a hole that allows light to enter the eye. When it is dark our pupils enlarge to let in as much light as possible. The size of each pupil is controlled by the iris, which surrounds it. When light passes through the pupil it meets the lens. The lens causes the light to bend so that it shines on an area at the back of the eye called the retina. The retina is something like the colour film in a camera in that an image can be formed on it. This image is upside down and is transmitted by the optic nerve to the brain, which enables us to interpret it right-side up.

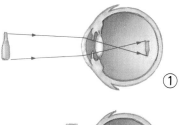

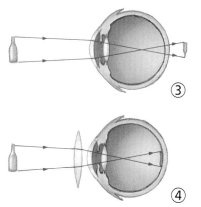

Focusing with glasses
A camera can be focused by moving the lens in and out, but the human eye focuses by making its lens thinner and longer or shorter and thicker. Some people's lenses will not focus properly, but they can be helped with glasses or contact lenses. These provide another lens through which the light can bend, allowing it to focus accurately on the retina. Short-sighted people cannot see distant images clearly because they focus them in front of the retina (1). Such people need concave lenses (2). Long-sighted people cannot see close images clearly because they focus them behind the retina (3). These people need convex lenses (4).

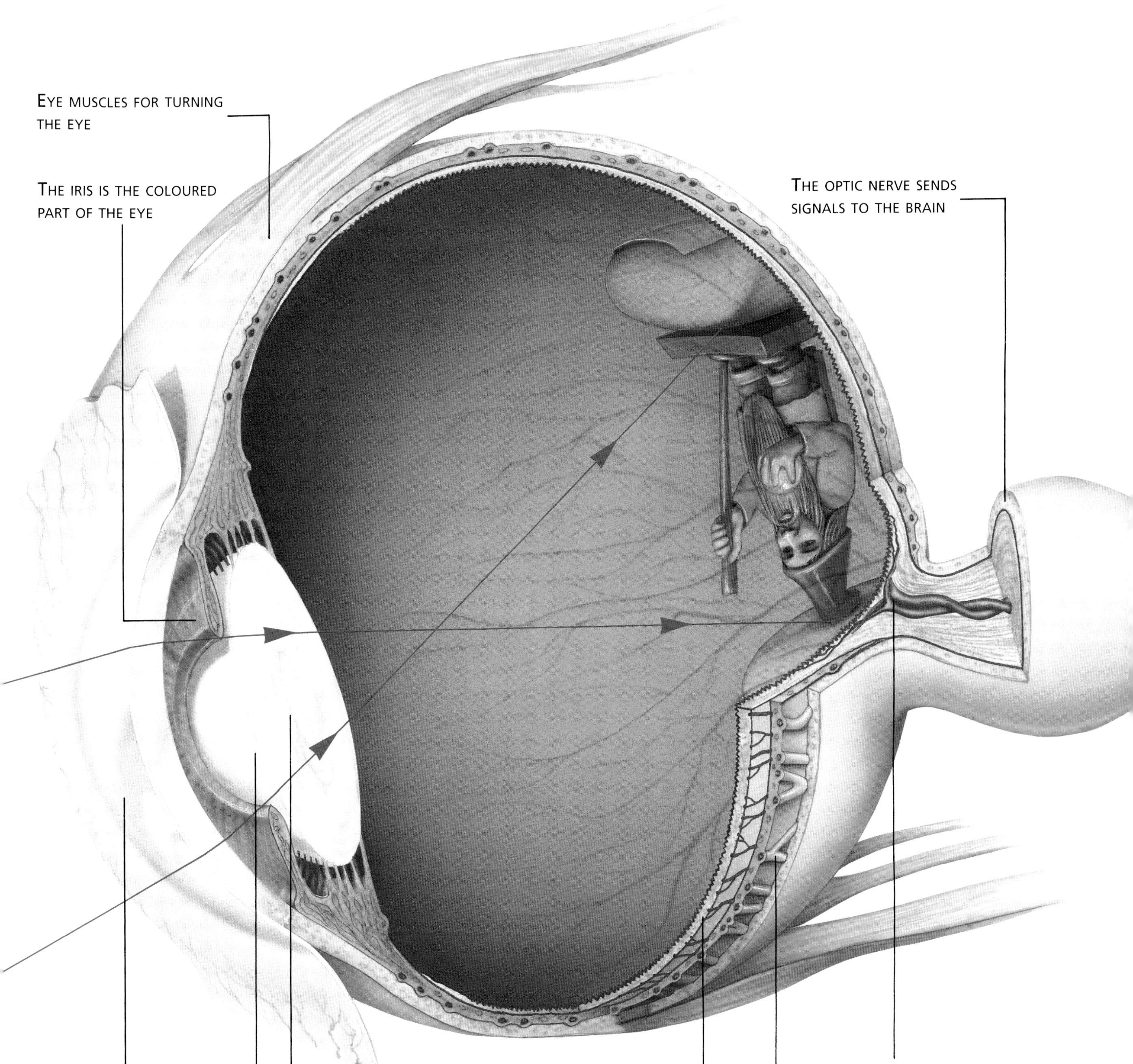

EYE MUSCLES FOR TURNING
THE EYE

THE IRIS IS THE COLOURED
PART OF THE EYE

THE OPTIC NERVE SENDS
SIGNALS TO THE BRAIN

THE CORNEA IS THE
TRANSPARENT, PROTECTIVE
LAYER OF THE EYE

WHEN IN THE DARK OUR
PUPILS ENLARGE TO ALLOW AS
MUCH LIGHT IN AS POSSIBLE

THE LENS BENDS THE LIGHT, SO
THAT IT FALLS ON THE RETINA

THE RETINA IS MADE UP
OF MILLIONS OF LIGHT-
SENSITIVE CELLS

WHERE THE OPTIC NERVE
MEETS THE RETINA THERE ARE
NO LIGHT-SENSITIVE CELLS —
THIS IS CALLED THE BLIND SPOT

BLOOD VESSELS

125

Taste and Smell

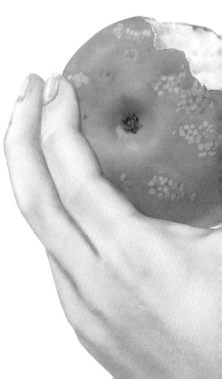

WE ARE most familiar with the senses of taste and smell for the pleasure they can bring. However, they probably were developed to protect us from eating food that could be poisonous. Our sense of smell is much stronger than our sense of taste. When we taste food we rely on the smell and texture as well as the taste. This explains why we cannot taste food very well when we have a cold.

When eating a pear, for example, scent from the fruit rises up the nose and dissolves in a mucus lining that covers the scent-sensitive cells at the top of the nose. Nerve signals are sent from the cells to the olfactory lobe in the brain, where the smell is recognized and enjoyed. The pear's sweetness is also sensed by taste buds on the tongue, and is similarly transmitted by nerve signals to the brain.

MUCUS LINING

NERVE FIBRES TO THE BRAIN

ODOUR-SENSITIVE CELLS

Odour-sensitive cells
At the top of our nose lie special odour-sensitive cells that become stimulated when vapours are released from food, drinks, and the environment. These special cells are called olfactory cells and they contain hairs on which mucus lies. Vapours dissolve in the mucus, causing nerve impulses to be sent to the brain.

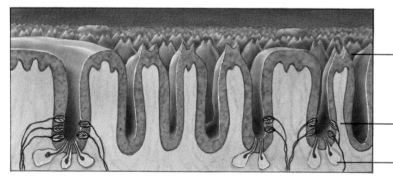

PAPILLAE COVER THE UPPER SURFACE OF THE TONGUE

TASTE BUDS

GLANDS SECRETE MUCUS

SCENT FROM THE PEAR IS BREATHED IN

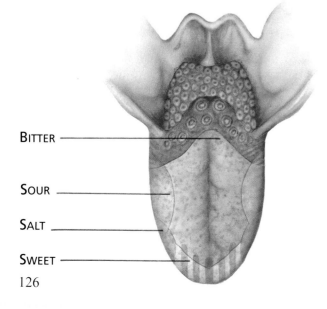

BITTER

SOUR

SALT

SWEET

Four kinds of taste
Our tongue contains about 10,000 taste buds, which pick up and respond to salt, sweet, sour, or bitter tastes. The taste buds are stimulated when chemicals from food are dissolved in the mouth's fluid – our saliva. Combined together, the four basic tastes give us a range of subtle flavours.

WE TASTE FOOD WHEN NERVE IMPULSES REACH THE BRAIN

OLFACTORY AREA OF THE BRAIN, RESPONSIBLE FOR INTERPRETING SMELL

NASAL PASSAGES

TONGUE

SENSORY NERVE FIBRES FOR TASTE

Hearing

THE PART of the ear we see is shaped to collect sound and allow it to travel along the ear canal to the eardrum. Sound causes the eardrum to vibrate. Behind the eardrum are three small bones called the hammer, anvil and stirrup, which get their names from their shapes. Vibrations from the eardrum cause the small bones to vibrate too, and these vibrations pass through an oval window to the cochlea. The cochlea is a coiled tube filled with liquid. Low-pitched sounds make the first part of the tube vibrate, while high-pitched sounds vibrate a part further up. These vibrations are picked up by nerve fibres connected to the brain. The brain can tell where the vibrations are occurring and so can tell one sound from another.

Balance and sound

Ears help us to balance. There are three semi-circular canals in the ear. They contain fluid that moves when we change our position. The moving fluid sends signals to the brain that helps our body to adjust and keep its sense of balance.

Our ears can endure very loud sounds, but if they are too loud, sounds can damage the cochlea. Soft sounds become more difficult to hear as we get older. We can hear low- and high-pitched sounds, although many animals, such as bats, can hear even higher-pitched sounds than we can.

SEMICIRCULAR CANALS CONTAIN FLUID AND NERVE CELLS THAT ARE SENSITIVE TO MOVEMENT AND HELP US TO KEEP OUR BALANCE

STIRRUP

ANVIL

HAMMER

SOUND SIGNALS TRAVEL TO THE BRAIN

NERVE

THE COCHLEA CONTAINS NERVE ENDINGS THAT PICK UP VIBRATIONS FROM SOUND

THE EARDRUM LIES AT THE END OF THE EAR CANAL

CROSS-SECTION OF
COCHLEA TUBES

THE FLESHY OUTER EAR IS
KNOWN AS THE PINNA

VIBRATIONS OF ANVIL
AND STIRRUP

THE FLUID VIBRATES HAIR
CELLS WHICH PASS A SIGNAL
TO THE NERVE THAT TRAVELS
TO THE BRAIN

VIBRATIONS ARE PASSED
ALONG A COILED TUBE IN THE
COCHLEA, WHICH CONTAINS
FLUID

ARROWS SHOW THE DIRECTION
OF SOUND TRAVELLING ALONG
THE EAR CANAL

THE OUTER EAR GATHERS
SOUND AND HELPS TELL US
THE DIRECTION FROM WHICH IT
IS COMING

EAR CANAL

Reproduction

It takes two cells for human sexual reproduction to occur: a woman's egg-cell and a man's sperm-cell. These cells have to meet and join together in order for a baby to be made. This process is called fertilization, and it normally only occurs when a couple has had sexual intercourse. When a man becomes excited his normally limp penis becomes hard and enlarged from a rush of blood. This makes him able to slide it into a woman's vagina. The penis becomes more stimulated by movements of sexual intercourse until the man has an orgasm. When this occurs a fluid called semen, which contains sperm, is released from the man's penis into the woman's vagina.

THIS OVARY, IN CROSS-SECTION, SHOWS IMMATURE EGGS AT DIFFERENT STAGES OF GROWTH

FALLOPIAN TUBE

AN EGG RIPENING, READY FOR RELEASE

OVARY

THIS TUBE CONTAINS SPERM AND IS CALLED THE SPERMATIC CORD

BLADDER

THE SEMINAL VESICLES AND PROSTATE GLAND SECRETE SEMINAL FLUID, IN WHICH SPERM TRAVEL

THE EPIDIDYMIS IS WHERE SPERM IS STORED

PENIS

SPERM ARE MADE IN THE TESTIS

Sperm
Sperm look a bit like tadpoles. About 500 million sperm are made each day in the male testes. As with the female's eggs, each sperm contains genes that will help determine an offspring's looks and personality. The sperm's tail is used to help it swim. Sperm have a long journey, up the vagina to the uterus and then on to the fallopian tube, in their search for an egg.

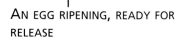

HEAD

TAIL

Eggs and fertilization

Women usually release one egg each month from one of their two ovaries. The egg is sent from the ovary down the fallopian tube, which is where fertilization occurs. One sperm penetrates the egg, by breaking through its outer wall. Other sperm are then prevented from entering. The sperm and egg join together to form a cell that divides, again and again, to form a clump that attaches to the uterine wall. This clump of cells soon forms an embryo, which grows into a foetus.

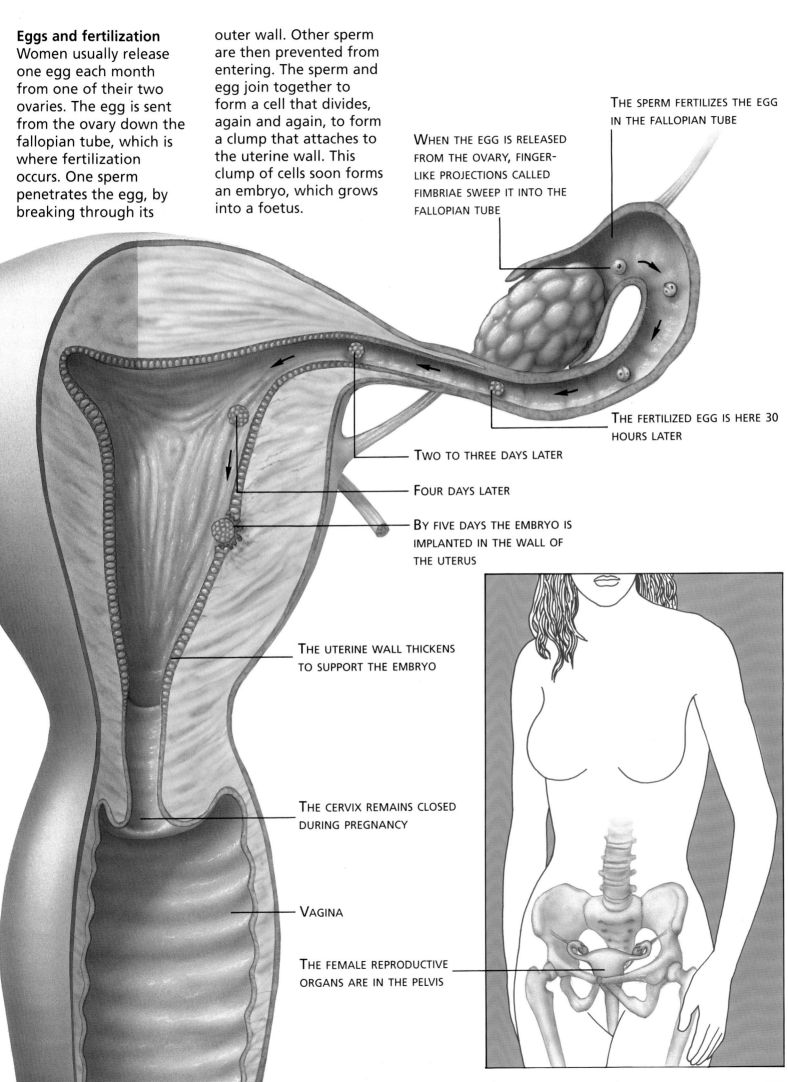

THE SPERM FERTILIZES THE EGG IN THE FALLOPIAN TUBE

WHEN THE EGG IS RELEASED FROM THE OVARY, FINGER-LIKE PROJECTIONS CALLED FIMBRIAE SWEEP IT INTO THE FALLOPIAN TUBE

THE FERTILIZED EGG IS HERE 30 HOURS LATER

TWO TO THREE DAYS LATER

FOUR DAYS LATER

BY FIVE DAYS THE EMBRYO IS IMPLANTED IN THE WALL OF THE UTERUS

THE UTERINE WALL THICKENS TO SUPPORT THE EMBRYO

THE CERVIX REMAINS CLOSED DURING PREGNANCY

VAGINA

THE FEMALE REPRODUCTIVE ORGANS ARE IN THE PELVIS

131

How a Baby Grows

EACH OF US begins life as a tiny microscopic cell. In just nine months this single cell becomes a baby, fully formed and ready to be born. First, inside the mother, the cell divides into a hollow ball of many cells. This becomes attached to the side of the mother's uterus, and grows into what we call the foetus. The head soon grows, the arms and legs appear, and the foetus begins to look like a human being. A tube, called the umbilical cord, carries the foetus's blood to and from the placenta. In the placenta the foetus's blood mixes with the mother's blood. When the baby is ready to be born, chemicals signal the mother's uterus to push the baby out. The umbilical cord is cut, leaving the new-born baby with a small scar – the belly button.

Stages of growth

To grow and survive the fetus needs nutrition and oxygen from its mother's blood. Inside the placenta there are vessels linking the mother's and fetus's blood. Waste chemicals from the fetus's blood are taken away by the mother's blood, and the mother's blood feeds the fetus. After two months the main part of the baby's body are formed. At this stage it looks rather strange as its head seems too big for its body. At five months the toenails, fingernails, and all the main organs have formed. Even the eyelashes have appeared. By seven and a half months it looks almost like a new-born baby. It is about 38 cm long, while at birth a baby is usually 50 cm. If the baby were born at this earlier stage, it would still be able to survive if given special care and attention. When a baby is born early it is called premature.

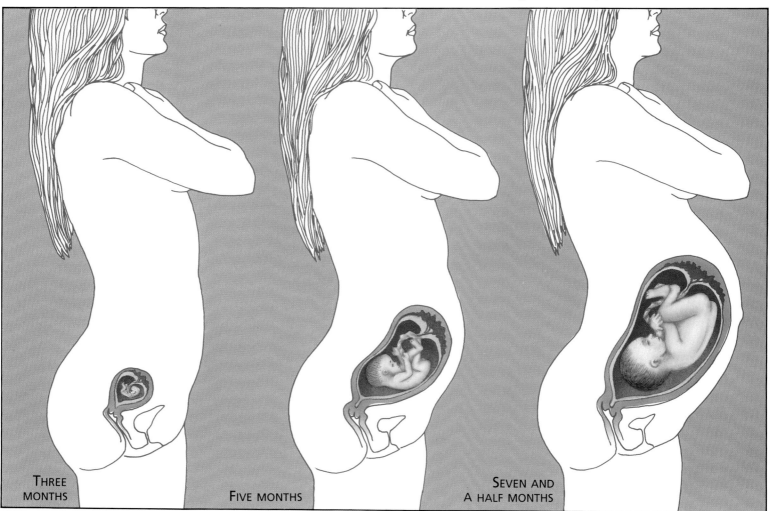

THREE MONTHS

FIVE MONTHS

SEVEN AND A HALF MONTHS

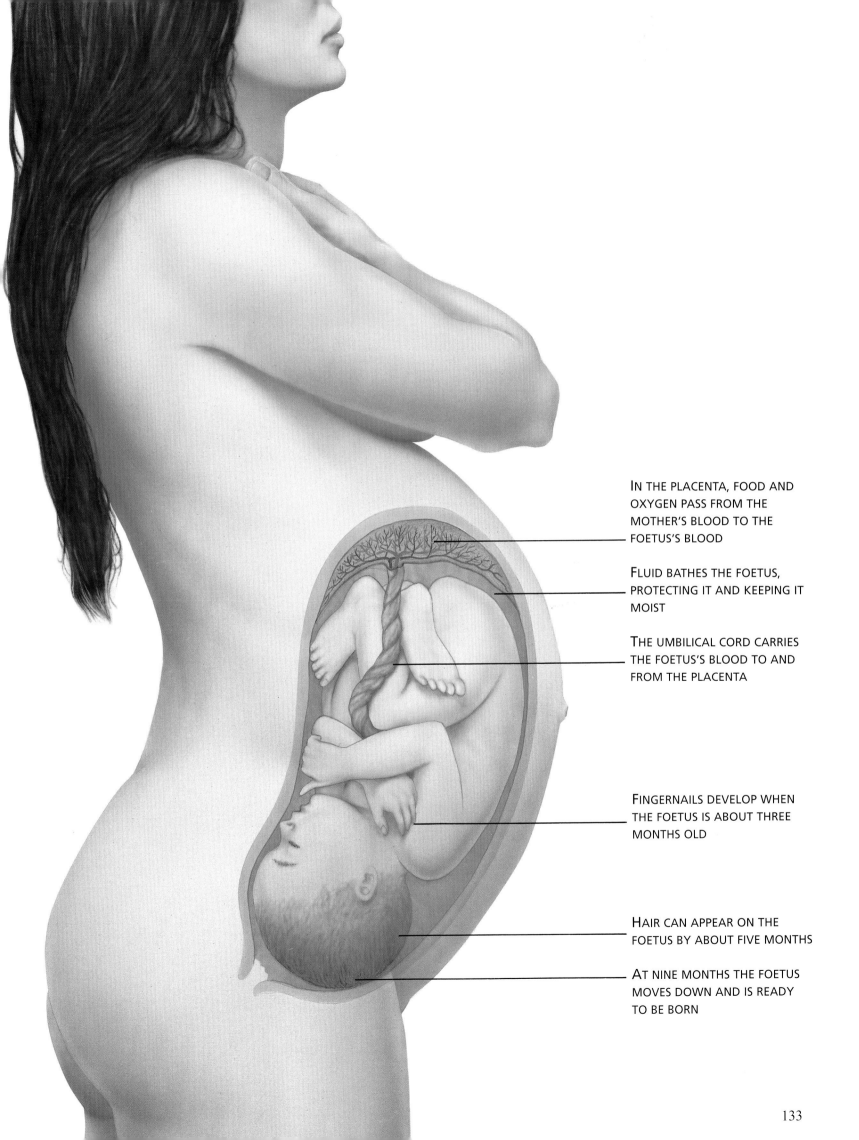

IN THE PLACENTA, FOOD AND OXYGEN PASS FROM THE MOTHER'S BLOOD TO THE FOETUS'S BLOOD

FLUID BATHES THE FOETUS, PROTECTING IT AND KEEPING IT MOIST

THE UMBILICAL CORD CARRIES THE FOETUS'S BLOOD TO AND FROM THE PLACENTA

FINGERNAILS DEVELOP WHEN THE FOETUS IS ABOUT THREE MONTHS OLD

HAIR CAN APPEAR ON THE FOETUS BY ABOUT FIVE MONTHS

AT NINE MONTHS THE FOETUS MOVES DOWN AND IS READY TO BE BORN

Fighting Germs

MILLIONS of germs, known as bacteria and viruses, lie on and in our body. They don't usually harm us because they cannot easily pass through our skin or the acid in our stomach. However, if they do get past these barriers an army of white cells is called in to protect us. Most white cells are contained in lymph tissue, such as the tonsils and spleen, as well as in our blood. There are several different types of white cell that make up the immune system. The most common are the polymorphs, which destroy germs. Sometimes germs have protective coatings to help them avoid capture by polymorphs. When this happens specially-shaped structures called antibodies are produced that lock into the germ's coating, breaking the germ apart.

 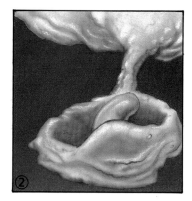

Destroying a germ
The first picture (1) illustrates how a polymorph white cell works. On receiving a chemical message saying that a bacterium is invading, it moves to the area of invasion and makes part of its cell longer. This elongated part moves towards the bacteria and swallows it (2). The bacterium is actually sucked into the polymorph, surrounded

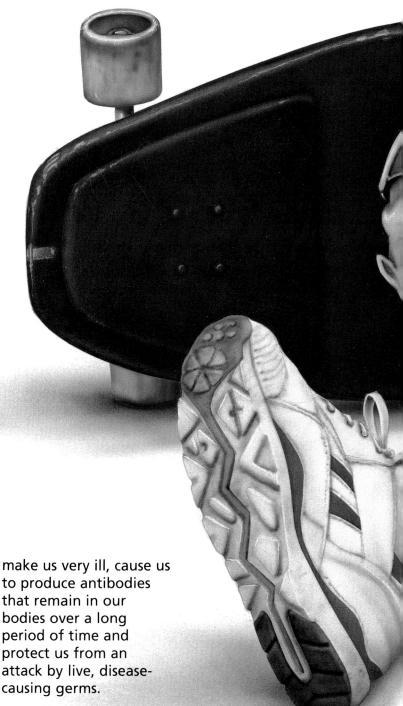

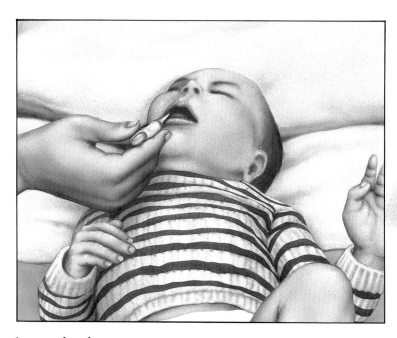

Immunization
Many diseases that were very common 40 or 50 years ago are rare in developed countries today. This is mainly because most of the people receive vaccines against these diseases.

Nowadays, we are given vaccinations when we are children, either by injection or by mouth. Vaccinations put dead or weakened germs into our bodies. These germs, not harmful enough to make us very ill, cause us to produce antibodies that remain in our bodies over a long period of time and protect us from an attack by live, disease-causing germs.

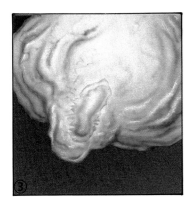

by its cell membrane (3). Next, powerful chemicals are released by the cell to destroy the invader. Eventually the cell moves on, leaving the bacterial remains behind.

The white cell army
When you cut your skin, you have broken the skin's defence barrier and bacteria get in. Within a short time chemicals released around the cut attract an army of white cells from the blood. These cells are able to cover the germs and destroy them. Many white cells die in the process and together with the germs they form yellow pus.

Spare Parts

FORTUNATELY, today many people with diseases can be helped by organ transplants. Patients with organs – such as a heart or kidney – that are badly diseased can have healthy organs surgically transplanted to replace their own. These operations rely on the goodwill of people who say their organs can be used for this purpose after they die.

Some people do not need organ transplants, but may be helped by artificial implants. For example, artificial limbs have been developed for people who have lost a leg or an arm. Surgeons can also use parts of the patient's own body to treat his or her disease. Veins from a patient's leg, for example, can be used to replace a damaged artery in their heart.

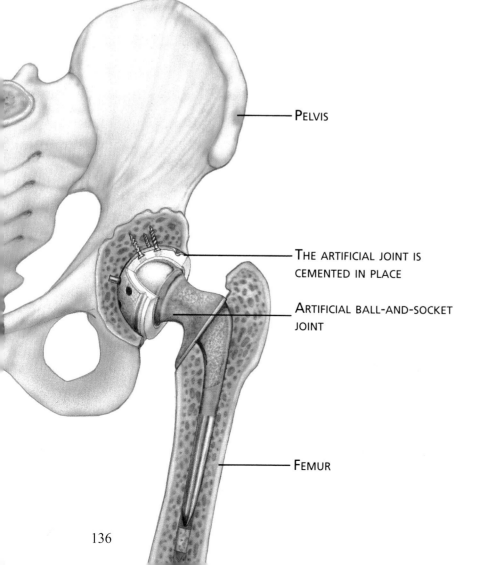

PELVIS

THE ARTIFICIAL JOINT IS CEMENTED IN PLACE

ARTIFICIAL BALL-AND-SOCKET JOINT

FEMUR

Joint replacements
One of the most common artificial replacements is of the hip joint. Hip replacements are normally given to people who have developed osteoarthritis. This is a condition caused by wear and tear on joints that happens as we get older. When it affects the hip it causes a lot of pain and difficulty in getting about. The artificial hip joint is usually made of metal and is cemented into the bone in the upper leg once the old joint has been removed.

THE KNEE MECHANISM USES
ENGINEERING TECHNOLOGY TO
RECREATE MUSCLE POWER

BLOCKED CORONARY
ARTERIES

THIS KNEECAP IS MADE OF
PLASTIC

AN ARTIFICIAL KNEE JOINT
ALSO WORKS LIKE A HINGE

VEIN FROM LEG STITCHED INTO
THE HEART

THIS FALSE LEG IS MADE OF
CARBON FIBRE – IT IS LIGHT
BUT STRONG ENOUGH TO
WALK ON

A SPECIAL FOAM OUTER LAYER
FEELS LIKE SKIN

Heart problems
As we age, our arteries
may become blocked
with fat that has entered
the bloodstream. By not
smoking and by
following a sensible diet
we can help to stop this
happening. The coronary

arteries are the most
serious arteries to
become blocked because
they supply blood rich in
oxygen to the heart.

Coronary artery bypass
The dangerous condition
shown (*above right*) can

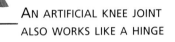

VEIN IN LEG

now be treated by an
operation called a
coronary artery bypass.
Blocked blood vessels in
the heart are passed-by
after a new circulation
route is stitched into the
heart, using a vein from
somewhere else in the
patient's body.

137

EXPLORING THE
OCEANS

Stephen Hall

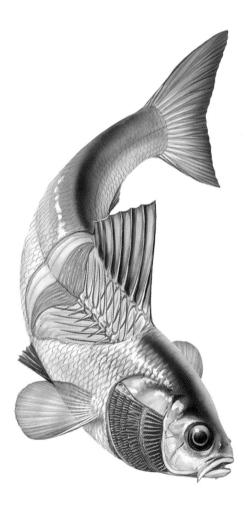

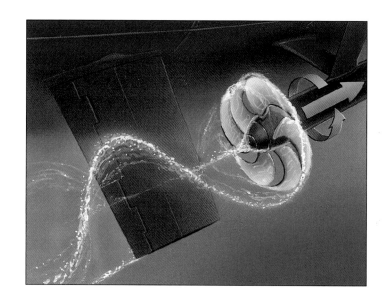

EXPLORING THE
OCEANS
CONTENTS

The Ocean Floor

THE EARTH'S thin surface layer is known as the crust. It is split into several pieces, called plates, that drift slowly on a lower layer of molten, denser rock. Two types of rock form these plates: continental and oceanic. Continental rock is about 40 kilometres thick, increasing to 70 kilometres under high mountain ranges. Oceanic rock is only about 6 kilometres thick. Beneath the oceans, oceanic rock is constantly forming at 'spreading ridges' where plates are pulling apart. Oceanic rock is always being destroyed in 'subduction zones', where it dips under a continental plate and melts.

Water fills up the great oceanic basins, but the amount of water varies over time. Today, sea levels are high enough to cover the lower parts of the continents. These submerged parts are called continental shelves.

AS MOUNTAINS ARE WORN DOWN BY THE WEATHER, MATERIAL IS CARRIED BY RIVERS INTO THE OCEAN

A SLOPE DOWN TO THE DEEP OCEAN FLOOR LIES AT THE EDGE OF A CONTINENT

LOW LYING LAND IS FLOODED BY THE OCEAN WHEN SEA LEVELS RISE

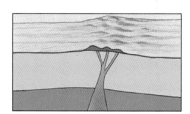
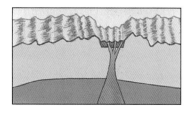
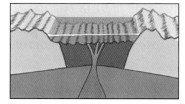

The birth of an ocean
Volcanic activity starts along a weak point in the Earth's crust (*top left*). As the crust splits and two or more plates drift apart a steep-sided valley is formed, like the Rift Valley of East Africa (*middle*). The valley floods, and over millions of years widens into an ocean (*bottom*). Long ago Africa and America split apart and the Atlantic Ocean filled the gap.

MOLTEN ROCK RISES AND THEN SETS HARD TO FORM THE CORE OF MOUNTAINS

OCEANIC CRUST SOMETIMES CONTINUES BELOW THE THICKER CONTINENTAL CRUST

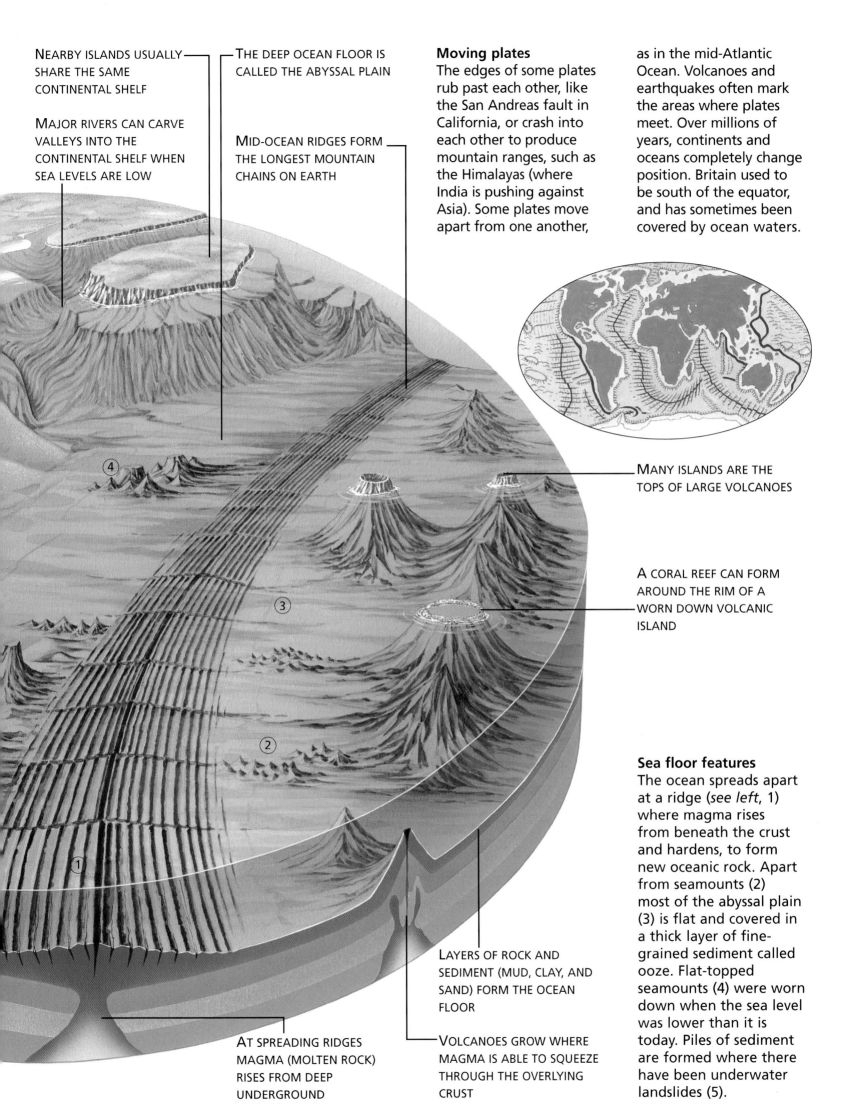

NEARBY ISLANDS USUALLY SHARE THE SAME CONTINENTAL SHELF

THE DEEP OCEAN FLOOR IS CALLED THE ABYSSAL PLAIN

MAJOR RIVERS CAN CARVE VALLEYS INTO THE CONTINENTAL SHELF WHEN SEA LEVELS ARE LOW

MID-OCEAN RIDGES FORM THE LONGEST MOUNTAIN CHAINS ON EARTH

Moving plates

The edges of some plates rub past each other, like the San Andreas fault in California, or crash into each other to produce mountain ranges, such as the Himalayas (where India is pushing against Asia). Some plates move apart from one another, as in the mid-Atlantic Ocean. Volcanoes and earthquakes often mark the areas where plates meet. Over millions of years, continents and oceans completely change position. Britain used to be south of the equator, and has sometimes been covered by ocean waters.

MANY ISLANDS ARE THE TOPS OF LARGE VOLCANOES

A CORAL REEF CAN FORM AROUND THE RIM OF A WORN DOWN VOLCANIC ISLAND

LAYERS OF ROCK AND SEDIMENT (MUD, CLAY, AND SAND) FORM THE OCEAN FLOOR

AT SPREADING RIDGES MAGMA (MOLTEN ROCK) RISES FROM DEEP UNDERGROUND

VOLCANOES GROW WHERE MAGMA IS ABLE TO SQUEEZE THROUGH THE OVERLYING CRUST

Sea floor features

The ocean spreads apart at a ridge (see left, 1) where magma rises from beneath the crust and hardens, to form new oceanic rock. Apart from seamounts (2) most of the abyssal plain (3) is flat and covered in a thick layer of fine-grained sediment called ooze. Flat-topped seamounts (4) were worn down when the sea level was lower than it is today. Piles of sediment are formed where there have been underwater landslides (5).

Tides

THE MOON orbits (travels around) the Earth, and together the Earth and Moon orbit the Sun. While this happens the gravitational forces of the Moon and Sun pull on the oceans, causing tides. The Moon has a more powerful effect on the tides as it is much closer to the Earth. It stretches the Earth's ocean waters into an oval shape, creating a tidal bulge on each side of the Earth. These tidal bulges are where high tides occur.

The usual tidal range, or difference between high- and low-water level, is 2–3 metres on open coastlines. Many things can affect the tidal range, including severe weather, the presence of land such as islands, friction of the tide against the sea floor, and wind direction. Complicated multiple tides can also occur when tidal cycles affect one another. The largest tidal ranges are where the shape of the coastline strengthens the tidal effects. Seas that are enclosed, such as the Mediterranean Sea, show a much smaller tidal range than the open oceans.

The effects of the Sun and Moon

Below you can see how the oceans bulge outward towards the Moon and Sun (the effects are exaggerated to make them clearer). When the Moon and Sun are at right angles (*pictures 1 and 3*) you can see the stronger pull of the Moon on the oceans. Because the Sun is pulling from a different direction the tidal bulges are less extreme and 'neap' tides occur. When the Moon and Sun are in line their forces combine and more extreme 'spring' tides occur (*2 and 4*). The greatest tides occur during the spring and autumn equinoxes, when the Sun is directly over the equator and most perfectly aligned with the Moon. Many plants and animals have adapted to take advantage of the tidal ranges.

SPRING TIDE WITH FULL MOON VISIBLE FROM EARTH

AS THE EARTH SPINS, AN OCEAN RISES AND FALLS ROUGHLY EVERY 12 HOURS

LOW SPRING TIDE

②

HIGH SPRING TIDE

THE SUN IS 130 MILLION KILOMETRES AWAY FROM EARTH BUT HAS A POWERFUL GRAVITATIONAL FIELD

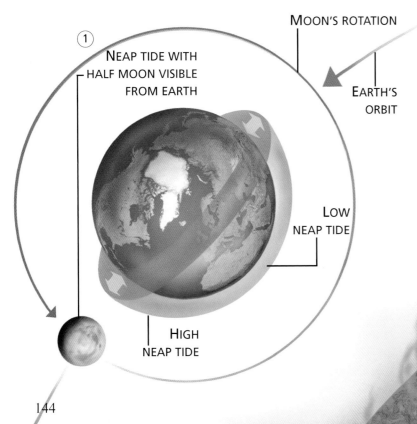

MOON'S ROTATION

①

NEAP TIDE WITH HALF MOON VISIBLE FROM EARTH

EARTH'S ORBIT

LOW NEAP TIDE

HIGH NEAP TIDE

LOW NEAP TIDE   LOW SPRING TIDE   HIGH NEAP TIDE   HIGH SPRING TIDE

Tidal range and plant growth

Because of the regular rise and fall of the oceans, plants and animals live at particular heights along the shoreline. Only salt-resistant lichens live in the splash zone. To stay alive, green seaweeds and barnacles need to be low enough to get a covering of water at high tide.

Tidal ranges

The positions of the boat and views of the Moon show the differences between spring and neap tides.

At Full and New Moon, we get spring tides, when the tidal difference is great. At Half Moon the tidal difference is small.

LICHENS LIVE ABOVE THE HIGH TIDE MARK, IN THE SPLASH ZONE

HIGH TIDE WATERS REACH GREEN SEAWEED, LIMPETS, AND BARNACLES

BROWN SEAWEEDS LIVE NEAR THE LOW TIDE MARK, SO THEY ARE UNDERWATER MOST OF THE TIME

RED SEAWEEDS OFTEN GROW BELOW THE LOW TIDE MARK

NEAP TIDE WITH HALF MOON VISIBLE FROM EARTH

③

SPRING TIDE WITH CRESCENT OR NEW MOON VISIBLE FROM EARTH

THE TIDAL RANGE IS SMALL WHEN THE SUN AND MOON ARE AT RIGHT ANGLES

THE TIDAL RANGE IS LARGE WHEN THE SUN AND MOON PULL FROM THE SAME DIRECTION

④

Waves and Wind

THE EARTH is like a huge spinning ball, with a heat lamp – the Sun – shining over the equator. At the equator, ocean waters get warmer and move out towards the extreme northern and southern parts of the Earth (the North and South Poles). At the poles the water becomes cooler and flows back towards the equator to begin the cycle again. This is how currents of water move deep in the oceans. Surface currents are caused by winds, the spin of the Earth, and the position of land masses (*see below, right*).

Winds also cause waves as they blow over the surface of the sea. As shown below, the water itself does not move forward in a wave. The water particles only go round in a circle. It is the energy that this movement makes that moves forward with a wave.

The Beaufort Scale

The Beaufort Scale is used to describe the strength of the wind at sea. This system relies on signs that can be seen with the eye, rather than on scientific instruments, but is still a valuable warning of stormy seas.

0 calm, sea like a mirror
1 light air, small ripples
2 light breeze, small wavelets
3 gentle breeze, wave crests begin to break
4 moderate breeze, small waves and some 'white horses'
5 fresh breeze, frequent waves, many 'white horses'
6 strong breeze, large waves 3 metres high begin to form
7 near gale, rough sea with spray
8 gale, waves up to 6 metres high
9 strong gale, rough waves, up to 9 metres high
10 storm, visibility difficult, waves up to 12 metres high
11 violent storm, sea covered in foam, small ships lost to view between wave crests
12 hurricane, waves over 14 metres high, air filled with foam/spray.

WAVE PEAKS ARE WHIPPED INTO FOAM BY A STRONG FORCE 8 GALE

WAVES WITH HEIGHTS OF MORE THAN 30 METRES HAVE BEEN RECORDED

A WELL-MAINTAINED AND PROFESSIONALLY CREWED SHIP CAN WITHSTAND THE MOST VIOLENT STORMS

IN A FORCE 11 STORM THE SEA IS COVERED IN FOAM

THE 'EYE' OF THE STORM

COOL, DESCENDING AIR

WARM, ASCENDING AIR

THUNDERCLOUDS

WALLS OF DENSE CLOUD

WINDS OF MORE THAN 150
KM PER HOUR ARE FOUND
BELOW THE STORM

AIR SPIRALS IN TOWARDS THE
'EYE' OF STORM

Great storms

Tropical revolving storms
(known as typhoons,
hurricanes or cyclones)
form over warm water
and can reach 560–800
kilometres in diameter.
Walls of dense cloud
form rings around the
centre of the storm as
warm, moist air is drawn
in and spirals rapidly
upwards. The 'eye'
(centre) of the storm is a
calm area of cool,
descending air. These
storms cause
tremendous damage if
they pass over land, but
soon die out as they
move in from the coast.

LIGHT BREEZES CAUSE SMALL
WAVELETS

AT THE END OF EACH WAVE,
WATER PARTICLES ARE BACK
WHERE THEY STARTED

AS WAVE HEIGHT INCREASES
THE ANGLE OF THE CREST
GETS STEEPER

IN A FORCE 8 GALE
WAVES ARE UP TO
6 METRES HIGH

DEEP BELOW A WAVE THE
CIRCULAR MOTION OF THE
WATER PARTICLES IS SMALLER

Surface waters

The colours on the map
below show the
temperatures of land
and ocean surface
waters. The
temperatures were
picked up by a satellite
as it orbited the Earth.
Warm equatorial
temperatures are shown
in orange; cool polar
temperatures are shown
in green and blue.
   The arrows on the
map show the flow of
surface currents (warm

currents are in red; cold
are in blue). These wind
driven currents are
swung to one side by the
spin of the Earth,
creating large circular
currents in the oceans.
All oceans are connected
by currents at various
depths. The currents
have a great effect on
climate. For example,
warm waters from the
Indian Ocean enter the
Atlantic and move north,
helping to keep northern
Europe warm.

THE WATER PARTICLES IN THE
WAVE MOVE IN A CIRCULAR
PATTERN, BUT THE ENERGY
OF THE WAVE MOVES
FORWARDS

THE EQUATOR IS AN
IMAGINARY LINE AROUND
THE EARTH, LYING HALFWAY
BETWEEN THE POLES

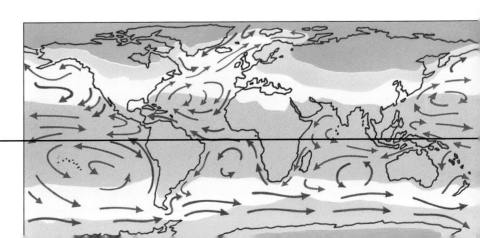

Coastlines

COASTS ARE where the land and sea do battle. Without humans becoming involved, the sea usually wins. The coastal land that survives the pounding of storm waves best is made of hard, volcanic rock; soft sandstone, on the other hand, is easily worn away. The slope of coastal rocks and any weaknesses in them that the ocean can make use of also influence the shape of the coastline.

Coasts are the most popular places for people to live, work, and take vacations. To preserve rapidly eroding coastlines engineers build sea defence works such as walls of concrete or stone. Beaches are sometimes preserved with walls or jetties called groynes. In some countries whole areas of low-lying land have been reclaimed from the sea by building walls called dykes, and then pumping away the seawater.

Large rivers preserve the coast because as they enter the sea, rivers deposit many tonnes of mud, stone, and sand onto the sea floor, building up natural sea defences.

Speed of erosion

How long can a coastline last? There are several things to take into account. In particular, the hardness of the rock, the fierceness of the sea, and the presence of sea-defences are critical.

Over many years sea levels change and this also effects how coastlines are eroded (worn down). For example, thousands of years ago areas of land were covered in ice that eventually melted. Since the weight of the ice was lifted, the land has slowly sprung back upwards. This accounts for the ancient beaches found high above the present sea level in many places. Where rocks under a coastline are now sinking, the sea can flood an area that was once dry land.

COVES ARE FORMED WHEN THE SEA OPENS A GAP THROUGH A NECK OF HARD ROCK INTO SOFTER ROCK BEHIND

LIKE THE SEA, A RIVER WILL FLOW THROUGH ROCK WEAKENED BY A GEOLOGICAL FAULT

IN SHELTERED AREAS SAND DUNES FORM

ABANDONED HOUSES ARE LOST OVER A RAPIDLY ERODING CLIFF

DEBRIS WILL SOON BE WORN DOWN INTO SAND BY WAVES

Coastal waves

Waves become shorter and steeper as they approach the coast. This is because the circular motion of water particles within the wave gets pushed upwards as the wave is influenced by the sloping sea floor. Once it has reached its maximum height, the wave breaks. The water then sweeps back out to sea, as backwash.

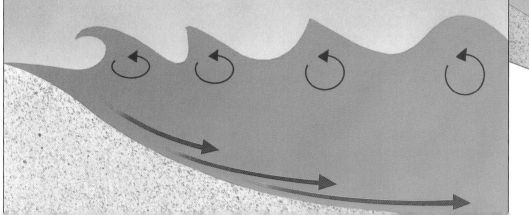

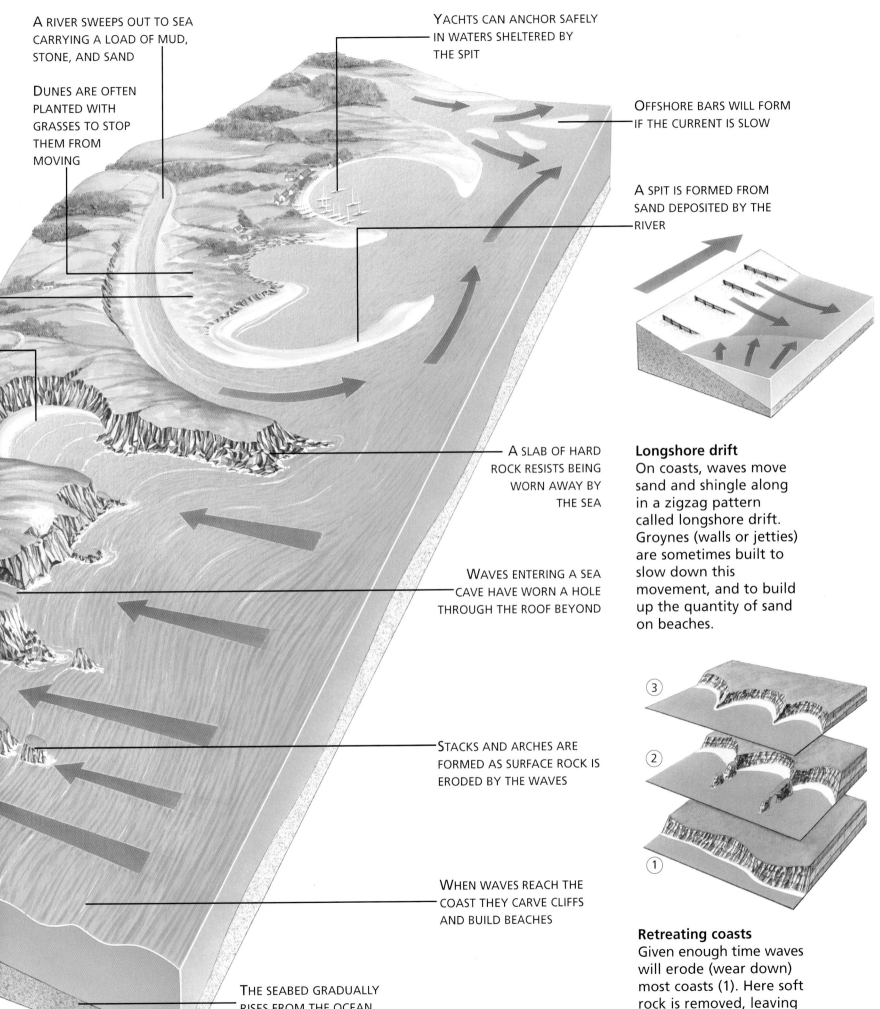

A RIVER SWEEPS OUT TO SEA CARRYING A LOAD OF MUD, STONE, AND SAND

DUNES ARE OFTEN PLANTED WITH GRASSES TO STOP THEM FROM MOVING

YACHTS CAN ANCHOR SAFELY IN WATERS SHELTERED BY THE SPIT

OFFSHORE BARS WILL FORM IF THE CURRENT IS SLOW

A SPIT IS FORMED FROM SAND DEPOSITED BY THE RIVER

A SLAB OF HARD ROCK RESISTS BEING WORN AWAY BY THE SEA

WAVES ENTERING A SEA CAVE HAVE WORN A HOLE THROUGH THE ROOF BEYOND

STACKS AND ARCHES ARE FORMED AS SURFACE ROCK IS ERODED BY THE WAVES

WHEN WAVES REACH THE COAST THEY CARVE CLIFFS AND BUILD BEACHES

THE SEABED GRADUALLY RISES FROM THE OCEAN DEPTHS TO THE COAST

Longshore drift

On coasts, waves move sand and shingle along in a zigzag pattern called longshore drift. Groynes (walls or jetties) are sometimes built to slow down this movement, and to build up the quantity of sand on beaches.

Retreating coasts

Given enough time waves will erode (wear down) most coasts (1). Here soft rock is removed, leaving headlands (2). Then these too are eroded away (3).

149

Frozen Seas

THE EXTREME northern and southern regions of our planet are very cold. The Arctic, in the north, is an ice-covered ocean, surrounded by Greenland and the northern continents. Antarctica, in the south, is a huge continent surrounded by the Southern Ocean.

Glaciers (huge masses of moving ice) have built up to form the ice sheets that cover much of Greenland and Antarctica. In places the ice sheets extend down to the coast and out to sea. Cold winds cause other parts of the sea to freeze, while warmer currents or winds can sometimes melt the sea ice (*see right*).

Few creatures live on the surface of the frozen seas, but near the ice edges there is a rich variety of fish and plankton that provide food for larger animals such as seals and whales.

Melting ice
The amount of ice on Earth varies over time – 25,000 years ago glaciers extended across much of the northern hemisphere. So much water was used up as ice that the sea level was 200 metres lower than it is today.

If all of the ice that rests on land such as Antarctica and Greenland could be melted the sea level would be well over 100 metres higher than it is now, because extra water would be added to the oceans.

RISING WARM WATER MELTS AN AREA OF ICE

ICEBERGS FROM ICE SHEETS CAN BE LARGE ENOUGH TO LAND AN AIRCRAFT ON

RIDGES OF ICE APPEAR WHERE SHEETS OF PACK ICE BUMP INTO EACH OTHER

THE SEA BEGINS TO FREEZE, FORMING PANCAKE ICE – THESE SHEETS GRADUALLY MERGE TOGETHER TO FORM PACK ICE

AN ICEBREAKER BATTERS ITS WAY INTO THE PACK ICE

AT THE BOUNDARY WITH WARMER WATER, THE ICE EDGE THINS OUT AND GRADUALLY DISAPPEARS

UPWELLING OCEAN CURRENTS BRING NUTRIENTS TO FEED PLANKTON (TINY PLANTS AND ANIMALS)

FOR SIX MONTHS OF THE YEAR THE SUN DOES NOT RISE IN THE FAR NORTH OR SOUTH

GLACIERS BUILT UP TO FORM THE VAST ANTARCTIC ICE-SHEET OVER MANY YEARS

AN ICE SHEET CREEPS DOWN-HILL UNDER ITS OWN WEIGHT, AND IS FORMED FROM SNOW AND ICE THAT HAS BUILT UP OVER MANY YEARS

FREEZING WINDS GUST OUT TO SEA FROM THE ICE-BOUND LAND

Seasonal changes

At the poles during the summer, ice melts and daylight returns. In the Arctic, cargo ships can sail along the Siberian coastline. As the ice edge retreats, icebergs drift into the open ocean, gradually melting as they move south. In Antarctica, too, the arrival of the warmer months causes the pack ice to retreat. Migrating birds and animals also move with the seasons, arriving in spring to feast on abundant sea food.

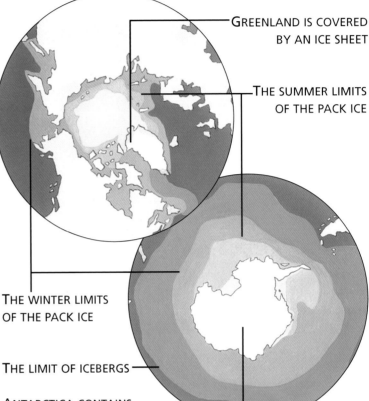

GREENLAND IS COVERED BY AN ICE SHEET

THE SUMMER LIMITS OF THE PACK ICE

THE WINTER LIMITS OF THE PACK ICE

THE LIMIT OF ICEBERGS

ANTARCTICA CONTAINS OVER 80 PER CENT OF THE WORLD'S ICE

ICE SHEETS CAN EXTEND OUT TO SEA FOR SEVERAL KILOMETRES

WHEN SEAWATER FREEZES, SALT IS LEFT BEHIND – THE SALTY WATER SINKS, SETTING UP A CIRCULATION OF WATER

WARM, LESS SALTY WATER FLOWS UP TOWARDS THE SURFACE WHERE IT WILL COOL AND FREEZE, CONTINUING THE CYCLE

ICEBERGS (GIANT LUMPS OF ICE) BREAK AWAY FROM THE ICE EDGE IN A PROCESS CALLED CALVING, THEN DRIFT OUT TO SEA

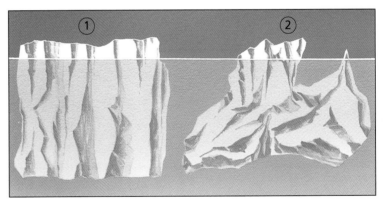

Icebergs

Some icebergs break off immense ice sheets and are as large as an island, taking months or even years to melt (1). They are called 'tabular' (table-like) because of their flat tops. Icebergs that break off glaciers are much smaller (2).

They carry rocky debris, have a more ragged or angular shape, and are mostly found in the Arctic.

Nine-tenths of an iceberg is underneath the water. As it melts, it may become unstable and capsize in a spectacular manner.

Mapping the Sea

TO TAKE measurements at the bottom of the ocean, scientists called oceanographers use sonar (*so*und *na*vigation and *r*anging) because sound waves travel well in water. They measure depth using a downward-pointing echo sounder, and build up a picture of the ocean floor using a side-scan sonar system. To find out what the ocean floor is made of, columns of earth are pulled up using coring devices. Oceanographers also need to measure the temperature, saltiness, and chemistry of the ocean. They use devices that are lowered or towed from research ships, and take water samples to analyse in the laboratory. Satellites look at sea surface temperature, winds and wave heights, and even plankton cover. Subsurface drifters and pilotless submarines roam the depths, radioing back their findings whenever they surface.

SPECIAL RADAR EQUIPMENT CAN LOOK THROUGH CLOUD TO MEASURE THE OCEAN BELOW

WAVE HEIGHTS CAN BE MEASURED BY SATELLITE ALTIMETERS, WHICH ARE VERY ACCURATE EVEN FROM A HEIGHT OF 800 KILOMETRES

A BATHYSONDE RECORDS TEMPERATURE, SALINITY (SALT CONTENT), AND PRESSURE

THE GIANT PISTON CORER IS USED FOR REMOVING LONG, DEEP SAMPLES OF OCEAN FLOOR

Towed instruments
An undulator is shaped like a small plane, and is towed behind a research ship. It travels down from the surface for 500 metres then travels back up, all the time gathering data such as water temperature. A side-scan sonar is also towed. It gathers data to map the shape of the seabed.

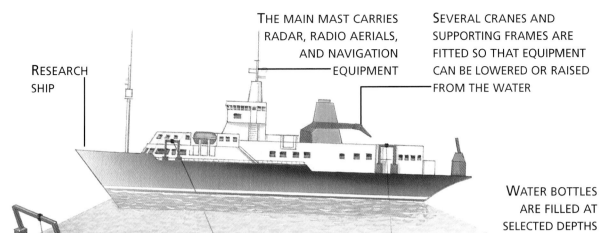

RESEARCH
SHIP

THE MAIN MAST CARRIES
RADAR, RADIO AERIALS,
AND NAVIGATION
EQUIPMENT

SEVERAL CRANES AND
SUPPORTING FRAMES ARE
FITTED SO THAT EQUIPMENT
CAN BE LOWERED OR RAISED
FROM THE WATER

WATER BOTTLES
ARE FILLED AT
SELECTED DEPTHS
TO TEST THE
SALINITY

Research ships

Research ships carry scientists and technicians for several weeks at a time, to gather information about the ocean. Because these ships are extremely expensive to operate there are not that many of them. Robot explorers like the one pictured left (1), are being developed to measure the oceans when ships are not available, or to go on dangerous missions such as exploring under ice caps. Moored buoys (2) are left to measure ocean currents and temperature. They emit radio signals so that they can be found again.

What lives at the bottom?

Over 2000 metres down in the North Atlantic Ocean, a sea cucumber swims above the ocean floor. Pictures are taken with special time-lapse cameras.

Charts and maps

Computers help produce maps of the sea floor by turning sonar images into three-dimensional pictures. Engineers use the maps to plan where to lay cables and pipelines, or to navigate submarines with safety.

Plankton recorder

This device is towed behind ships to measure how much plankton lives near the sea surface. Seawater and plankton enter through the front and a fine silk mesh inside catches the plankton. The plankton is then stored in a cylinder, ready to be analysed later at a laboratory.

Computer models

Information about the ocean is fed into special computer programmes called 'models', which can show how the ocean works. Models can help predict the route of accidental oil spills or how the ocean responds to climate change.

Grab sampler

As its name implies, the grab sampler 'grabs' a sample of the ocean floor and brings it up.

Early Ships

UNTIL THE invention of steam power, the only way ships could move forwards was by using oars or sails. Wind power enabled explorers to travel all over the oceans for hundreds of years, but only in the last hundred years has sail finally given way to other forms of propulsion.

Some of the earliest ships relied on oars – it took many centuries before people learned how to build ships that could move without having the wind behind them. The Vikings and Polynesians rowed for days if the wind was not behind them, and ancient Greeks and Romans relied upon slaves to row their warships and trading ships.

In the 19th century, steam power began to take over from the sail. In ship-building, steel began to replace wood, and in the early 20th century oil began to replace coal as fuel. Steam piston engines were followed by steam turbines, which are still used today by some military vessels and ice-breaking ships, with a nuclear reactor providing the steam.

Developments since steam

Ships like the *Titanic* were built to cross oceans quickly, carrying business-men, immigrants, and mail. After the Second World War, aircraft took over these roles, so large passenger ships were used as cruise liners instead. Steam ships are being retired because, at low speeds, diesel engines are cheaper to run. Gas-turbine (jet-engine) ships were built from the 1970s but they use up a lot of fuel. Today, gas turbines power warships, for which acceleration and speed are important.

Ancient ships

Long-distance voyages were made by the Egyptians in boats built of reeds, palm fibre, and tar. Modern copies have crossed the Atlantic and northern Indian Ocean. Other early ships were built of animal skins and wood, and all of them were used to cross open oceans, though we do not know how many sailors were lost in the attempt.

AN EGYPTIAN REED BOAT, FROM AROUND 2000 BC

SS GREAT BRITAIN WAS THE FIRST OCEAN-GOING SHIP TO BE BUILT OF IRON AND THE FIRST PROPELLER-DRIVEN STEAM SHIP TO CROSS THE ATLANTIC

THE CROW'S NEST WHERE LOOKOUTS WATCHED OUT FOR ICEBERGS

A TOTAL OF 1503 PEOPLE DIED WHEN *TITANIC* SANK ON 14 APRIL 1912

TITANIC HAD THREE ENGINES (TWO STEAM PISTON ENGINES AND ONE STEAM TURBINE ENGINE)

MAYFLOWER CARRIED THE PILGRIM FATHERS TO THE NEW WORLD (AMERICA) IN 1620

MAYFLOWER WAS TINY (180 TONNES) AND TOOK 63 DAYS TO CROSS THE ATLANTIC

From sail to steam

The development of the sailing ship was slow until about the 15th century, when the Americas began to attract voyagers from the other side of the Atlantic. By the 19th century the sailing ship was perfected, but at the same time the invention of steam power meant that ships could travel in any direction, whatever the wind. Some journeys that had taken months to complete now only took a few weeks.

THREE FUNNELS WERE REAL, ONE WAS A DUMMY

TITANIC HAD THREE PROPELLERS AND ONE HUGE RUDDER

TITANIC DID NOT CARRY ENOUGH LIFEBOATS FOR EVERYONE – NOW THE LAW MAKES SURE SHIPS DO

LENIN WAS A RUSSIAN ICEBREAKER AND THE FIRST SURFACE SHIP TO BE DRIVEN BY NUCLEAR POWER

THREE NUCLEAR REACTORS GAVE A MAXIMUM SPEED OF 18 KNOTS

Nuclear power at sea

Only a small number of nuclear-powered civilian (non-military) ships have been built. The Russians chose nuclear power for their large ice-breaking ships because the ships could clear the sea lanes off their northern coasts without having to constantly return to base for refuelling.

LENIN COULD CLEAR A 30-METRE WIDE CHANNEL THROUGH PACK ICE 2.4 METRES THICK

155

Modern Ships

MOST MODERN ships are built of steel and powered by diesel engines. They are usually equipped with a lot of automated machinery so that only a small crew is needed. Satellites and computers control navigation, backed up with traditional instruments such as the sextant.

Running ships cheaply is now more important than travelling at top speed, except for specialist ships such as express ferries, which commonly use twin-hull designs. In the future there will be more ships using two or three small, streamlined hulls as they give high speed without needing a lot of expensive fuel. Their narrow, smooth shapes cut more easily through the water. Any water resistance can slow a ship down, so a streamlined shape helps a ship to go faster.

Luxury cruise liner
Ocean liners no longer carry passengers travelling from one port to another. Today, people take their holidays on board ocean liners. Instead of high speed, comfort has become the priority, so the ships have smooth-running diesel engines, stabilizers to help keep the ship steady, and full air-conditioning.

Why do ships float?
The metal hull of a ship encloses a vast amount of air. This means a cubic metre of ship weighs much less than a cubic metre of water, so a ship floats. If the hull was solid metal the ship would sink like a stone.

THE FUNNEL OR STACK CARRIES EXHAUSTS AND AIR INTAKES FOR THE MAIN ENGINES

THERE ARE MANY SWIMMING POOLS, INDOOR AND OUTDOOR, ON BOARD

SATELLITE COMMUNICATIONS EQUIPMENT PROVIDES CONSTANT CONTACT WITH THE MAINLAND

CASINOS, SHOPPING MALLS, AND HAIRDRESSERS ARE ALL AVAILABLE ON BOARD

PASSENGERS RELAX ON THE AFT DECK

ROPES CAN BE USED TO HELP THE SHIP TO DOCK

TWIN RUDDERS STEER THE SHIP – CROSS WINDS CAN EASILY BLOW SUCH A HIGH-SIDED SHIP OFF COURSE

LIFEBOATS AND RAFTS ARE CARRIED SO PASSENGERS CAN ESCAPE IN EMERGENCIES

Stabilizers

Most passenger ships use stabilizers to reduce roll (*see left*). These are often in the form of fins, like small wings. They use gyroscopes, computer software, and hydraulic jacks to react quickly to the ship's roll, and provide lift or down-force so the ship is kept on an even keel. When the sea is calm, they are retracted to prevent damage.

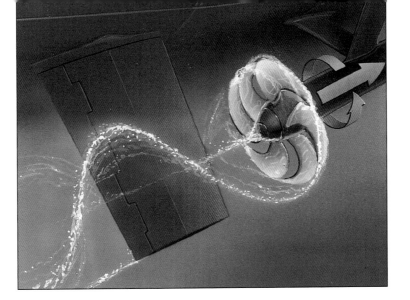

Propeller design

Great care goes into the design and manufacture of propellers. If just one blade is out of balance the smooth propulsion of a ship can be ruined. Modern designs use several curved blades, and on some ships the blades can be rotated to provide reverse thrust.

NAVIGATION, RADIO, AND RADAR EQUIPMENT ARE CARRIED ON THE MAIN MAST

THE MOST EXPENSIVE CABINS ARE HIGH UP

THE BRIDGE HOUSES THE SHIP'S MAIN CONTROLS

THE FORWARD AUDITORIUM IS A FULL-SIZE THEATRE

THE FORWARD WEATHER DECK CAN WITHSTAND HEAVY WAVES

A BOW THRUSTER HELPS THE SHIP TURN

STABILIZER FINS ENSURE A COMFORTABLE CRUISE

HEAVY EQUIPMENT, FUEL, AND STORES IN THE LOWEST PART OF THE SHIP AID STABILITY

ELECTRIC MOTORS TURN THE PROPELLER SHAFTS

POWERFUL DIESEL ENGINES TURN GENERATORS TO PROVIDE ELECTRICITY FOR ALL THE SHIP'S NEEDS

Satellite navigation

Global Positioning System (GPS) satellites carry highly accurate atomic clocks and send time and position data to GPS receivers fitted to ships and aircraft. The receiver compares signals from two or more satellites and can work out its position to within a few metres. Buoys fitted with radio beacons also help to confirm a ship's position.

Fishing

ACROSS THE WORLD there is a high demand for fish and squid, so there are always large fleets of fishing vessels on the ocean. Because the demand for fish is so high, nations are able to monitor and control fishing up to 200 nautical miles from their coasts. Governments use aircraft or satellites to watch out for illegal fishing. Inspectors can go aboard fishing vessels to check that regulations are being followed.

A fishing crew lives and works aboard ship 24 hours a day and is often paid according to the value of the catch. Even today, deep-sea fishing remains a tiring and physically dangerous job.

Factory ship
Fishing grounds can be a long way from the country where the fish will be eaten. Some ships are equipped like factories so they can turn fish into products that can be sold at the end of the voyage, perhaps several months' journey away. On board the fish are gutted and the quality fish fillets are sorted and deep frozen. The organs are stored or processed into fish oils and chemicals, and the offcuts, heads, and bones turned into fishmeal, pastes, and cheaper foods. Nothing is wasted, and the ship will stay at sea until the hold is full or fuel runs low.

THE A-FRAME HOLDS THE NET AND CABLES CLEAR OF OBSTRUCTIONS ON THE STERN

WINCHES (REELS) ARE COMPUTER CONTROLLED TO KEEP THE NET AT THE RIGHT DEPTH

AS THE CATCH ARRIVES, THE CREW SET TO WORK – GUTTING AND PROCESSING

THE CREW CAN HARNESS THEMSELVES TO RAILS SO THAT THEY ARE NOT SWEPT OVERBOARD IN ROUGH SEAS

CRANES ARE USED TO HANDLE THE CABLES AND NETS

THE NET IS HAULED BACK ON BOARD UP THE SLOPING STERN RAMP

A POWERFUL PROPELLER AND DOUBLE-HINGED RUDDER MAKE THE SHIP EASIER TO MANOEUVRE

THE ENGINE ROOM PROVIDES POWER FOR WINCHES AND THE SHIP'S ELECTRICAL SUPPLY

THE MAIN DIESEL ENGINE IS HEAVY AND SITS DEEP IN THE HULL, HELPING STABILITY

ABOVE THE BRIDGE IS A FULL SET OF NAVIGATION, COMMUNICATION, AND RADAR AERIALS

ACCURATE NAVIGATION EQUIPMENT KEEPS THE VESSEL WITHIN THE LEGAL BOUNDARIES FOR FISHING

ALL OF THE VESSEL'S OPERATIONS CAN BE CONTROLLED FROM THE BRIDGE

LIGHTS ON THE FOREMAST WARN OTHER SHIPS TO STAY CLEAR OF THE NETS

THE FOREDECK HOUSES LIFEBOATS, ANCHOR CHAINS, CAPSTANS, AND THE FOREMAST

Sonar on fishing boats
Sonar works by sending pulses of sound through the water which bounce back off anything solid. Sonar has several functions on fishing boats. It measures the depth of the water by reflecting off the seabed and 'sees' where fish are. Trawlers use sonar to track the position and depth of the net, and sonar fitted to the otterboards (holding the net open) detects how wide the mouth of the net is. A sonar at the end of the net alerts the boat when the net is full.

BUNKS FOR THE CREW, WHO WORK VERY HARD BOTH NIGHT AND DAY

Fishing methods
Some fish and squid are caught using bright lights (1). The lights attract them to the surface at night, where they are caught on baited hooks. Drift nets (2) can be several

kilometres long. Trawl nets (3) are towed at a set depth by a fishing boat and hauled in when full. Purse seine nets (4) surround a shoal (group) of fish at once, and then scoop them from the water.

PROCESSED FISH IS DEEP-FROZEN IN THE HOLD

THE STRONG STEEL HULL ALLOWS THE BOAT TO OPERATE IN ICY WATERS

NETS HAVE MESH SIZES THAT ALLOW YOUNG FISH TO ESCAPE

DRIFT NETS CAN BE DANGEROUS, TRAPPING DOLPHINS, TURTLES, AND BIRDS – THEY ARE BANNED FROM EUROPEAN WATERS

Submarines

THERE ARE many submarines operating in the world's oceans. A few are small, carrying just two or three people. They are used by people doing scientific research or construction work, and stay underwater for only a few hours at a time.

Military submarines are much larger. There are three basic types: missile-carrying (*right*), hunter-killer, and diesel-electric. The main reason why missiles are carried by submarines is that submarines are hidden underwater and are hard for the enemy to find. However, the hunter-killer submarine is designed to find and destroy the missile-carrying submarines of enemies as well as the enemies' own hunter-killer submarines. The diesel-electric submarine is the quietest type. It is used for missions where stealth is important, such as secretly landing soldiers near an enemy coast.

Ballistic-missile submarine

Some countries use massive ballistic-missile submarines, which carry nuclear weapons. The submarines remain deep under the ocean or under ice caps for several months at a time. The idea behind them is known as 'deterrence': if a country was ever attacked and destroyed by a nuclear weapon, its submarines would survive to launch a revenge attack on the enemy country. The belief is that if an enemy country knows this threat of revenge exists, they will be deterred (put off) from launching an attack in the first place.

Staying hidden

The most important thing for military submarines is to avoid being found, so they rarely surface, raise periscopes, or use radio to speak to base. Because sound carries easily underwater, submarines are built to be as quiet as possible. Mechanics are taught to be careful not to drop their tools, and if necessary the submarine will sit motionless for days. However, it is impossible to be completely silent, and trailing hunter-killer submarines will listen out for the slightest hint that there might be a target nearby.

THE NAVIGATION BRIDGE IS USED WHEN THE SUBMARINE HAS SURFACED

FORWARD FINS CAN BE RAISED VERTICALLY TO HELP THE SUBMARINE SURFACE THROUGH ICE

THE UPPER SURFACES ARE STRENGTHENED TO COPE WITH SURFACING THROUGH ICE

EMERGENCY ESCAPE HATCH

BALLAST TANKS

THE STREAMLINED NOSE AIDS SPEED AND REDUCES NOISE

INSIDE THE NOSE IS THE SONAR DOME WHICH EMITS SOUNDS TO DETECT OTHER SOLID OBJECTS IN THE SEA

LAUNCH TUBE FOR TORPEDOES

A COVERING OF SOFT TILES ABSORBS SOUND

SOME OF THE CREW HAVE BUNKS NEXT TO THE TORPEDOES

THE HULL, MADE FROM STEEL, TITANIUM, OR CERAMIC MATERIALS, IS STRONG ENOUGH TO DIVE OVER 600 METRES

Detection by sound

A submarine uses sonar (sound *n*avigation and *r*anging) to detect solid objects. Sonar can be active, where the submarine emits sounds which are reflected back from the target, or passive, where the submarine just listens to the noises that other vessels or large animals are making.

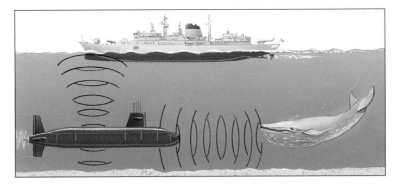

LARGE RUDDERS KEEP THE SUBMARINE STEADY

THE PROPELLER IS DESIGNED TO MAKE LITTLE NOISE AND NO BUBBLES

THE MISSILE IS LAUNCHED FROM THE TUBE WITH A PUFF OF GAS – ITS ROCKET ENGINE LIGHTS AS IT REACHES THE SURFACE

THE NUCLEAR REACTOR CAN OPERATE FOR SEVERAL YEARS WITHOUT REFUELLING

THIS TOWER CARRIES THE RADAR, PERISCOPES, AND COMMUNICATIONS EQUIPMENT

EACH MISSILE CARRIES SEVERAL NUCLEAR WARHEADS

MISSILE HATCHES

BALLAST TANKS

STEAM IS GENERATED AS WATER PASSES THROUGH THE REACTOR, AND IT DRIVES A TURBINE

THE TURBINE GENERATES ELECTRICITY FOR THE MAIN MOTOR AND ALL THE SUBMARINE'S SYSTEMS

MISSILES HAVE SOLID-FUEL ROCKET ENGINES

Diving and surfacing

In order to sink, a submarine has to become heavier. It does this by filling large tanks, called ballast tanks, with seawater (1). If it has to surface, compressed air is blown back into the ballast tanks to push out the water (2). This makes the submarine lighter again, and more buoyant (able to float). Some submarines have been lost at sea when something has gone wrong with the ballast tank system.

EMERGENCY BATTERIES IN CASE OF MAIN POWER FAILURE

THE MISSILES ARE CARRIED IN TUBES – THEY CAN BE LAUNCHED WHILE THE SUBMARINE IS UNDERWATER

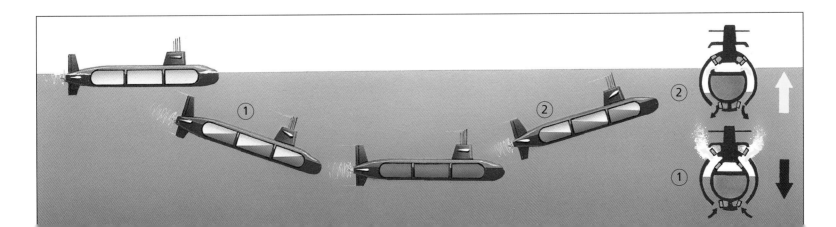

Scuba Diving

SCUBA (self-contained underwater breathing apparatus) has enabled people to explore the ocean to a depth of about 30 metres, and deeper, using special air mixtures. At greater depths the water pressure has dangerous effects on the diver (the water pressure increases with depth).

Pioneers like Jacques Cousteau and Hans Hass made scuba diving very popular, and today people dive all over the world. In fact diving is so popular that it has become a problem in some places because too many divers can damage fragile corals and affect the normal behaviour of fish.

Although diving is quite safe, training is essential. Divers learn safety drills and calculate how long they have been at depth, so that they can surface without getting the bends, a painful condition where air bubbles form inside the body.

Breathing apparatus
The tank strapped to the diver's back contains air for the diver to breathe. At the top of the air tank, level with the diver's lungs, is a valve called a regulator. Air passes through the regulator down a tube to the mouthpiece. The regulator reduces the pressure of the air that comes out of the tank. The pressure is further reduced by the demand valve in the mouthpiece. This ensures the air

THE REGULATOR CONTROLS THE FLOW OF AIR FROM THE AIR TANK AND REDUCES THE AIR'S PRESSURE

PIPE TO THE MOUTHPIECE

THE FACE MASK ENABLES THE DIVER TO SEE UNDERWATER

FLASH UNIT FOR CAMERA

ELECTRICAL ITEMS MUST BE WATERPROOF

UNDERWATER PHOTOGRAPHY IS OF GREAT INTEREST TO MANY SPORTS DIVERS

DEMAND VALVE

A DIAPHRAGM IN THE VALVE EQUALIZES AIR AND WATER PRESSURE

DIVER BREATHES THROUGH VALVE

AIR TUBE TO THE BC JACKET

FLOW OF EXHAUST AIR WHEN BREATHING OUT

breathed is at the same pressure as that of the water around. Divers must breathe smoothly all the time and not hold their breath, because as they travel up to the surface, air expands and could burst their lungs!

THE AIR TANK CARRIES HIGHLY COMPRESSED (SQUEEZED) AIR MIXTURES

DIVERS MUST TAKE CARE NOT TO DAMAGE CORALS WITH THEIR FINS

SWIM FINS ARE USED TO PROPEL THE DIVER

NEOPRENE WET SUIT, HAT, GLOVES, AND SOCKS KEEP THE COLD OUT

DIVERS WEAR A KNIFE TO USE IF THEY GET TANGLED UP IN NETS, LINES, OR SEAWEEDS

THE WETSUIT'S BRIGHT COLOURS MAKE THE DIVER EASIER TO SEE

A BC (BUOYANCY COMPENSATOR) IS A JACKET THAT CAN BE INFLATED WITH AIR TO HELP THE DIVER RISE TO THE SURFACE

WEIGHT BELT SO THAT THE DIVER CAN SINK EASILY

COMPASS, AND GAUGES THAT SHOW DEPTH AND AMOUNT OF AIR LEFT IN TANK

THE COMPASS IS ESSENTIAL IN MURKY WATERS

MANY DIVERS USE A DIVE COMPUTER TO KEEP TRACK OF TIME AND CALCULATE THE SPEED AT WHICH THEY ARE RISING TO THE SURFACE

'OK' – EVERYTHING IS ALL RIGHT ON THE SURFACE

'NOT OK' – HELP NEEDED ON THE SURFACE

'ARE YOU OK?'/'I AM OKAY'

'HELP!'

Wetsuits

In a wetsuit a layer of neoprene foam rubber insulates against cold, and can be bought in various thicknesses depending upon water temperature. The wetsuit is designed so that water leaks into it through the neck, leg, and armholes. The body then warms up the thin layer of water between the wetsuit and skin, keeping the diver warm for hours.

Hand signals

Although there are gadgets that enable you to speak underwater, most divers don't have them so they rely on hand signals. There is an international code of hand signals so that divers can work safely anywhere in the world. Divers never dive alone. They always have a fellow diver to keep an eye on them and watch out for distress signals.

Submersibles

SUBMERSIBLES are small, deep-diving vehicles that were first used in the search for wreckage of lost aircraft, ships, and weapons. Today, they are most often used by scientists exploring mysterious features of the deep ocean floor, such as trenches and volcanic ridges. Compared with military submarines, submersibles cannot stay under the surface of the water for very long – usually a few hours, or a day or two at the most. However, they are more useful to scientists. They can dive far deeper than any military submarine, some to 6000 metres or more. They also have windows, camera systems, and mechanical hands so that the crew can view and handle things at the bottom of the sea.

Today, rigid diving suits can almost do the same job as submersibles and some, such as the *Newt* suit, use small propellers to move about.

UNDERWATER TELEPHONE TRANSMITTER

THE TOWER IS BRIGHTLY COLOURED SO THAT IT CAN BE EASILY SEEN WHEN THE CRAFT HAS SURFACED

THE SONAR SCANNER CAN FIND HIDDEN OBSTACLES

TV CAMERAS RECORD EVERYTHING GOING ON OUTSIDE. PLENTY OF LIGHTS PENETRATE THE DARKNESS

THE CABIN IS LIKE A METAL BALL

MECHANICAL ARMS COLLECT OBJECTS FROM THE OCEAN FLOOR

WITH THE HELP OF LASER TECHNOLOGY, ARM CONTROL IS PRECISE

A COLLECTING CAGE CARRIES SAMPLE BOTTLES, ROCK SPECIMENS, AND ITEMS FROM SHIPWRECKS

Trieste

Trieste 1 was designed to reach the greatest depths possible. On 23 January 1960 she carried Jacques Piccard and Don Walsh to a record depth of 10,912 metres at the bottom of a gorge in the Pacific Ocean.

Trieste had two ballast tanks filled with heavy iron shot. To surface, the iron shot was released, making *Trieste* lighter and able to rise. A large tank filled with petrol gave buoyancy. The crew sat below in a steel sphere.

A LARGE TANK, CALLED THE FLOAT, PROVIDED BUOYANCY

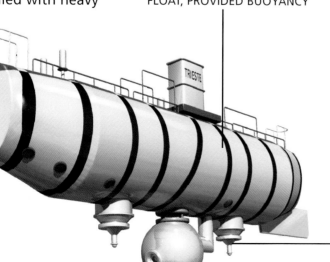

TWO TANKS CONTAINED METAL BALLAST

BALLAST TANKS FOR
SEAWATER AND AIR

SIDE THRUSTERS CONTROL
UP-AND-DOWN MOVEMENT

SEVERAL THRUSTERS DRIVE
AND STEER THE CRAFT

THE OUTSIDE HULL IS MADE
OF COMPOSITE MATERIALS

Rigid diving suit
A rigid (armoured)
diving suit resists water
pressure at depths of
over 800 metres. The
pressure inside the suit
remains the same as it is
at the surface, enabling
the diver to work in
comfort inside. The suit
weighs just 22 kilograms
underwater and is
flexible enough for the
diver to walk up ladders,
roll on the seabed, and
get up again.

ELECTRIC CONTROLS ARE
KEPT IN PROTECTIVE TANKS

BATTERIES PROVIDE
POWER TO RUN
THE MOTORS AND
ELECTRICAL
EQUIPMENT

TANK CONTAINING AIR FOR
THE CREW TO BREATHE

PORTHOLE

STRONG TITANIUM
FRAME AND LANDING SKIDS

IRON WEIGHTS CAN BE
RELEASED IN AN EMERGENCY
SO THAT THE CRAFT WILL RISE

DIFFERENT TOOLS CAN BE
FITTED TO THE HANDS

THE *NEWT* SUIT IS MADE OF
METAL, GLASS FIBRE, AND
CERAMICS

Alvin
Alvin has been used
since 1964 to explore the
ocean floor. After many
modifications it can now
reach a depth of 4500
metres. Alvin gained
fame in 1966 when it
found a lost nuclear
bomb, which was then
safely recovered. In the
1970s Alvin took the
first pictures of deep-sea
volcanic vents – hot
water springs that are
rich in oceanic chemicals
(see page 168). In 1986
Alvin explored the
wreck of the *Titanic*
(see page 154).

165

Shipwrecks

IN AN average year about 150 ships sink because of accidents, severe storms, and, most commonly, human error. Some of these wrecks cause major pollution problems, but the ocean's natural forces are able to cope with most types of waste. Iron-eating bacteria start working on the hull, worms eat up the wood, and chemical action sorts out what is left. After a few hundred years a lot of the shipwreck has gone, leaving behind fewer clues for explorers.

As diving technology has advanced, getting valuable items from shipwrecks has become easier. At first, only recovering treasure and cannons was considered worth the risk involved. Later it became possible to raise the wrecks by patching up holes and pumping in air.

The development of deep-ocean exploration systems was encouraged by the need to find missing submarines and nuclear weapons during the Cold War years. It has resulted in spectacular findings including Dr Bob Ballard's discovery of the *Titanic* and *Bismarck*.

Wreck hunting

Finding deep wrecks is not easy because the ocean is so big. First there is a survey of the area where the wreck might be, using side-scan sonar and cameras mounted on sledges. When the wreck is found, detailed exploration can begin using TV cameras attached to remote-operated vehicles (ROVs). A submersible like *Alvin* may be used so the explorers can examine the wreck close-up.

Viewing the remains

An ROV camera travels inside the wreck to bring back images of familiar objects. There are no dead bodies – they were eaten long ago by fish.

What a side-scan sees

A side-scan sonar gives a one-colour image of shadows. Computers help to improve the picture quality, but recognizing what the image shows still requires skill and experience.

THE CREW WORK IN A TITANIUM SPHERE WITH THICK WINDOWS – WATER PRESSURE AT 3000 METRES IS 300 TIMES GREATER THAN ATMOSPHERIC PRESSURE

THE SUBMERSIBLE'S PROPELLER IS PROTECTED BY A LIGHT COVERING SO THAT PIECES OF RIGGING, WIRE, OR ROPE WILL NOT TRAP THE VESSEL ON THE SEA FLOOR

A REMOTE MANIPULATOR ARM LIFTS ITEMS FROM THE OCEAN FLOOR – SOME PIECES MAY BE BROUGHT TO THE SURFACE FOR CLOSER EXAMINATION

IT MAY TAKE A SURVEY SHIP WEEKS OF SEARCHING TO FIND THE WRECK

A CURIOUS WHALE IS ATTRACTED BY SONAR SOUNDS

THE SIDE-SCAN SONAR GENERATES FAN-SHAPED BEAMS OF SOUND ENERGY WHICH WILL BOUNCE OFF GOOD REFLECTING SURFACES

A CAMERA SLEDGE IS TOWED NEAR THE SEA FLOOR TO TAKE PICTURES OF THE WRECK

The first images
The bow of the wreck is pictured surrounded by the darkness of the deep ocean. The wreck may be draped with a rust-like crust, produced by iron-eating bacteria.

ALVIN SENDS A SMALL ROV THROUGH A HOLE IN THE WRECK TO TAKE PICTURES OF THE INTERIOR

Looking for ancient wrecks
In the warm, clear waters of the Mediterranean, marine archaeologists hunt for the wrecks of ancient Greek, Roman, and Persian ships. The wooden parts will have been eaten away unless well buried, but metal remains can be found by a submersible metal detector.

A diver photographs the cargo of a Roman shipwreck. A survey grid enables the position of items to be accurately recorded.

A cannon is raised using lifting bags that were filled with air at the sea-bed. The diver releases air pressure to control ascent speed. Larger bags can raise aircraft, ships, and submarines.

Ocean Life

THE OCEANS teem with a wide variety of life, from tiny bacteria to huge whales. Scientists believe that life on earth first began in the oceans. Today, land animals still have salty blood – perhaps this is a sign of their ancient connection to the oceans.

Life exists throughout the ocean, even in the deepest, darkest trenches of the ocean floor and in icy polar waters. At the surface, phytoplankton (tiny floating plants) use the energy of the Sun to make food. Animals graze on the plankton, and are in turn eaten by larger hunters and scavengers. In very deep water where there is no light for plants to grow, and in the thick mud of the ocean floor, worms, bacteria, and other creatures feed on the material that has sunk all the way down from above.

There is one very unusual group of creatures on the ocean floor which feed on chemicals rather than animal or plant matter. They live near hot water springs.

Something for everyone
In the ocean, every possible niche (living space) is taken up by one or more life form. New creatures are constantly being discovered as researchers learn more about the deep oceans. Scientists were amazed to discover that life could exist around deep-sea hot water vents. From these volcanic vents water gushes up at temperatures of 400°C carrying a dissolved mixture of strong chemicals. The source of energy for most animals stems from the Sun: animals eat plants which use sunlight to make their food energy. But the creatures living near the volcanic vents get their energy from eating bacteria which change the chemicals they have absorbed into energy.

IN WARM SUNLIT WATERS, PLANTS AND ANIMALS THRIVE

THE PORTUGESE MAN-OF-WAR CATCHES ITS PREY WITH LONG STINGING LINES

MOST OF THE DRIFTING 'PLANKTON' IS MADE UP OF PHYTOPLANKTON (TINY PLANTS) AND ZOOPLANKTON (TINY ANIMALS) INCLUDING LARVAE (YOUNG FORMS OF ANIMALS)

THE DIM TWILIGHT ZONE (TO 1000 METRES) IS HOME TO MANY FISH LIKE THESE HATCHET FISH

FEW ANIMALS LIVE IN THE DARK, COLD BATHYPELAGIC ZONE (TO 4000 METRES)

TRIPOD FISH AND SEA CUCUMBER

MINERALS FROM THE HOT WATER FORM CHIMNEYS AROUND THE VENTS

GIANT TUBE WORMS GROW UP TO 3 METRES LONG

DEEP-SEA CRABS AND FISH THRIVE NEAR A HOT WATER VENT

SUNLIGHT PROVIDES THE
ENERGY THAT STARTS OFF
THE FOOD CHAIN

SMALL FISH EAT PLANKTON

Food chains
In the open ocean, tiny
floating plants
(phytoplankton) are
eaten by tiny animals

ALL THE OCEAN'S PLANTS
AND MANY OF ITS ANIMALS
LIVE IN THE SUNLIT ZONE
(DOWN TO 200
METRES)

(zooplankton), which in
turn are eaten by small
fish. The small fish are
eaten by larger fish and
squid, which are eaten
by sharks and toothed
whales (*see left*). This is
called a food chain,
where each group of
animals is an important
link in the chain as food
for another group.

SQUID
EAT SMALL
FISH

SPERM
WHALES
EAT SQUID

SHARKS HAVE EXISTED FOR
MILLIONS OF YEARS

OCTOPUSES ARE INTELLIGENT
CREATURES FOUND IN DEEP
AS WELL AS SHALLOW WATER

A BRITTLE STAR
IS ABLE TO LIVE
AT GREAT DEPTHS

GULPER EELS CAN DISLOCATE
THEIR JAWS TO SWALLOW
LARGE PREY

ANGLER FISH ATTRACT PREY
WITH A LIGHT-EMITTING
'ROD' ABOVE THEIR HEAD

THE ABYSSAL ZONE IS DARK
AND VERY COLD

GILL ARCHES

How fish breathe
Fish do not have lungs,
but breathe using similar
organs called gills, which
can extract the oxygen
dissolved in seawater.
The fish gulps water into
its mouth, then pushes it
out between the gill
arches, which are lined
with blood-filled cells.
Here, oxygen passes
from the seawater into
the fish's blood, and
waste gases flow out of
the fish back into the
seawater. Some of the
gas which the fish
extracts from the water
inflates a swim bladder,
which helps to stop the
fish from sinking.

169

Coastal Life

ANIMALS AND plants that live on the coast need to be hardy and adaptable as they have to cope with periods in and out of the water as the tides change the sea level. Some seaweeds produce slime to help stop them from drying out at low tide. Many animals burrow into the wet sand, hide under seaweed, or close up their shells while the tide is out. Coastal plants and animals in exposed places also need to be strong enough to stand up to the waves, and be able to put up with changes in the saltiness of the water when it rains.

A much greater variety of animals and plants live in rockpools, where they do not suffer from drying out as the tide goes down. But they still have to cope with large changes in temperature as the pool warms up in the sun or cools down in winter, and with freshwater when it rains.

Burrowing on the beach
In the sand many animals burrow with skill. With its hind flippers, the female loggerhead turtle digs a hole in which to lay her eggs (1). Razors (2) have a long shell – a powerful 'foot' at the bottom helps them to move up or down. The sand gaper (3) has an oval shell and feeds through two tubes that stretch up to the surface. Sea potatoes (4) are burrowing sea urchins. The sea mouse (5) is actually a worm covered in fine hairs. Lugworms (6) swallow sand to feed, passing out what's left as a worm cast.

Coastal life zones
The splash zone lies above high tide but is regularly sprayed with salt water. It's a hard place to live, and few species are seen here. Typical ones are yellow, orange and black lichens, and snails.

The intertidal zone, between high and low tide, is home to creatures such as barnacles, limpets, mussels, sea anemones, and crabs. Plants include brown, green, and red seaweed.

Below low-tide level live many more kinds of plants and animals. In colder waters, great forests of large brown seaweeds, called kelp, live on rocks, sheltering delicate red seaweeds, fish, and many other animals, while in warm waters coral reefs thrive.

SEAWEEDS SECURELY ATTACH THEMSELVES TO ROCKS

SAND, GRAVEL, MUD, AND ROCK FORM THE SEABED

THE LEAVES OF THIS GIANT KELP STRETCH UP TOWARDS THE SURFACE WATERS TO RECEIVE SUNLIGHT

SEAWEEDS CLING FIRMLY TO ROCKS SO THAT THEY ARE NOT SWEPT OUT TO SEA

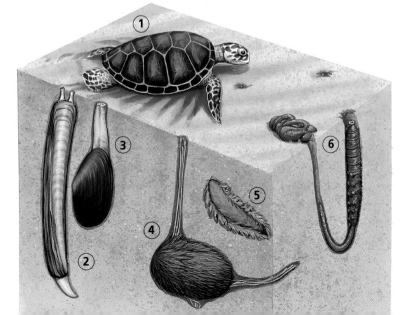

SEA BIRDS OFTEN NEST ON CLIFFS NEAR TO THEIR FOOD SUPPLY

LICHENS ARE FORMED BY A FUNGUS AND AN ALGAE LIVING TOGETHER

SEA SLATERS FEED ON SEA-WEED AND DEAD ANIMALS

PERIWINKLES CAN BE ROLLED BY WAVES WITHOUT BEING DAMAGED

Limpets
When the tide goes out, limpets clamp their shells firmly to the rock, stopping their body from drying out. A sucker-like foot allows it to crawl along.

A CROSS-SECTION OF A LIMPET REVEALS ITS STOMACH AND OTHER ORGANS

AIR-FILLED SACS KEEP SOME BROWN SEAWEEDS AFLOAT

A CRAB'S SOFT UNDER-BODY IS PROTECTED BY THE HARD SHELL ON ITS BACK

Crabs
Crabs of several types are found on the coast. They are well protected by their shells. The pincers are used to crush the shells of their prey.

AT THE CENTRE OF THE SEA URCHIN, ABOVE FIVE SHARP TEETH, LIES ITS GUT

Sea urchins and starfish
Sea urchins have a protective outer covering of spines, and a shell made of layers of interlocking plates. The spines and sucker-like feet allow urchins to move around on the seabed and shore. Five teeth under the body scrape food off the rocks.
Starfish are in the same family as sea urchins. Under the arms of a starfish are rows of tube-like feet, used for moving and feeding.

Mangroves
Mangrove trees are unusual in that they can live in salty seawater. The mass of tangled roots of a mangrove swamp provide homes to many young fish, the salt-water crocodile, and sea snake. The mudskipper (*above*) is a small fish that can walk on its front fins and climb up the mangrove roots. It feeds on small animals in the mud at low tide.

171

Seabirds

THE BROWN PELICAN FLIES SEVERAL METRES ABOVE THE SURFACE LOOKING FOR FISH

SEABIRDS LIVE in all of the world's oceans, from the freezing waters of the Antarctic to the warmth of tropical lagoons. Some, such as the albatross and storm petrel, spend most of their lives at sea, returning to the land only once a year to breed and moult (shed old feathers).

Seabirds eat fish, squid, or plankton and they may travel thousands of kilometres to find them. To stay warm in cold seawater most birds have a lot of fat under their skin, and they have feathers which are oiled to keep them waterproof. An exception to this is the cormorant, which has to rest out of the water with its wings outstretched to dry in the sun.

While seabirds have few natural enemies, many are killed accidentally by humans – by becoming tangled in fishing nets, or by pollution.

AS IT SPOTS A GROUP OF FISH CLOSE TO THE SURFACE, IT DIVES INTO THE SEA, FOLDING AWAY ITS WINGS

THE STORM PETREL HOVERS JUST ABOVE THE SURFACE

ONCE IN THE WATER THE PELICAN SCOOPS UP AS MANY FISH AS POSSIBLE

THE AUK USES ITS STUMPY WINGS TO FLY UNDERWATER

The brown pelican

Brown pelicans live in coastal areas of the USA. They have a large baggy pouch on the underside of their beak with which they catch lots of small fish.

The pelican flies about looking for fish which are swimming near the water surface. When a shoal of fish is spotted, the bird dives gracefully into the water, taking the fish by surprise. The pelican swims around, scooping the fish into its pouch, then returns to the surface to swallow them.

FISH SLIDE HEAD FIRST DOWN THE PELICAN'S GULLET

THE FISH THEN TRAVEL ON TOWARDS THE STOMACH

172

Feeding

There are many ways to catch seafood. Skimmers fly low over the surface at night using the tip of their beak to scoop up small fish and shrimps.

The storm petrel hovers over the sea surface, picking up individual fish. The auk, from the family that includes the puffin, guillemot, and razorbill, dives under the sea to chase fish using its powerful, stumpy wings and webbed feet. The albatross glides effortlessly, landing occasionally to catch fish or squid from the surface.

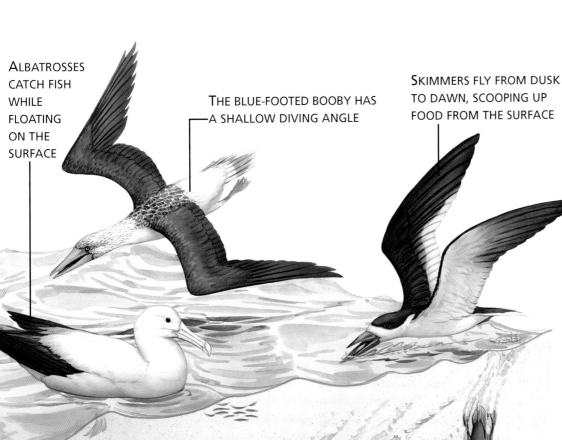

ALBATROSSES CATCH FISH WHILE FLOATING ON THE SURFACE

THE BLUE-FOOTED BOOBY HAS A SHALLOW DIVING ANGLE

SKIMMERS FLY FROM DUSK TO DAWN, SCOOPING UP FOOD FROM THE SURFACE

THE CORMORANT HAS A STEEP, STREAMLINED DIVE AND USES ITS FEET TO PUSH IT THROUGH THE WATER

PENGUINS CATCH FISH AND SQUID BY SWIMMING QUICKLY UNDERWATER

FISH, SQUID, AND PLANKTON ARE FOOD FOR SEABIRDS

Puffin nest
Puffins live in noisy groups on isolated islands away from land predators like rats and foxes. They nest inside tunnels, amongst rocks, or in abandoned rabbit burrows. Puffins can dig their own burrows, using their sharp claws and feet.

Kittiwake nest
Kittiwakes attach their cup-shaped nests into narrow cliff-side ledges using droppings as a kind of glue.

Guillemot nest
Guillemots nest on rock ledges, with a sheer drop to the sea below. They lay pointed eggs which are less likely to fall off if they are accidentally knocked.

Coral Reefs

CORAL LOOKS and feels like rock but is made by tiny animals related to jellyfish and sea anemones. These animals, called polyps, build a stony cup-shaped skeleton around them. As the polyps multiply, new polyps grow on the skeletons of dead polyps. Thousands of these polyps together form a clump of coral. Corals are highly sensitive to pollution and to rapid changes in sea level and temperature. They mainly grow in clear, shallow, tropical waters.

Coral reefs form walls along coastlines, often with a calm, shallow lagoon inside. Life flourishes in these sheltered, food-rich lagoons. Thousands of brightly coloured fish make use of the coral reef in different ways, some grazing there, others hiding from predators (creatures that hunt them).

YOUNG ANGEL FISH

BUTTERFLY FISH RECOGNIZE EACH OTHER BY THEIR MARKINGS

SEA CUCUMBERS ARE IN THE SAME ANIMAL GROUP AS THE STARFISH AND SEA URCHINS

GIANT CLAMS GROW SLOWLY AND MAY LIVE FOR A HUNDRED YEARS

DELICATE SEA FANS ARE FOUND IN DEEPER WATER AWAY FROM DAMAGING WAVES

CLOWN FISH ARE ABLE TO HIDE IN ANEMONES, WHICH STING OTHER FISH

A GROUPER LETS A CLEANER WRASSE REMOVE PARASITES LIVING IN ITS MOUTH

THE CROWN OF THORNS STARFISH ATTACKS CORAL

174

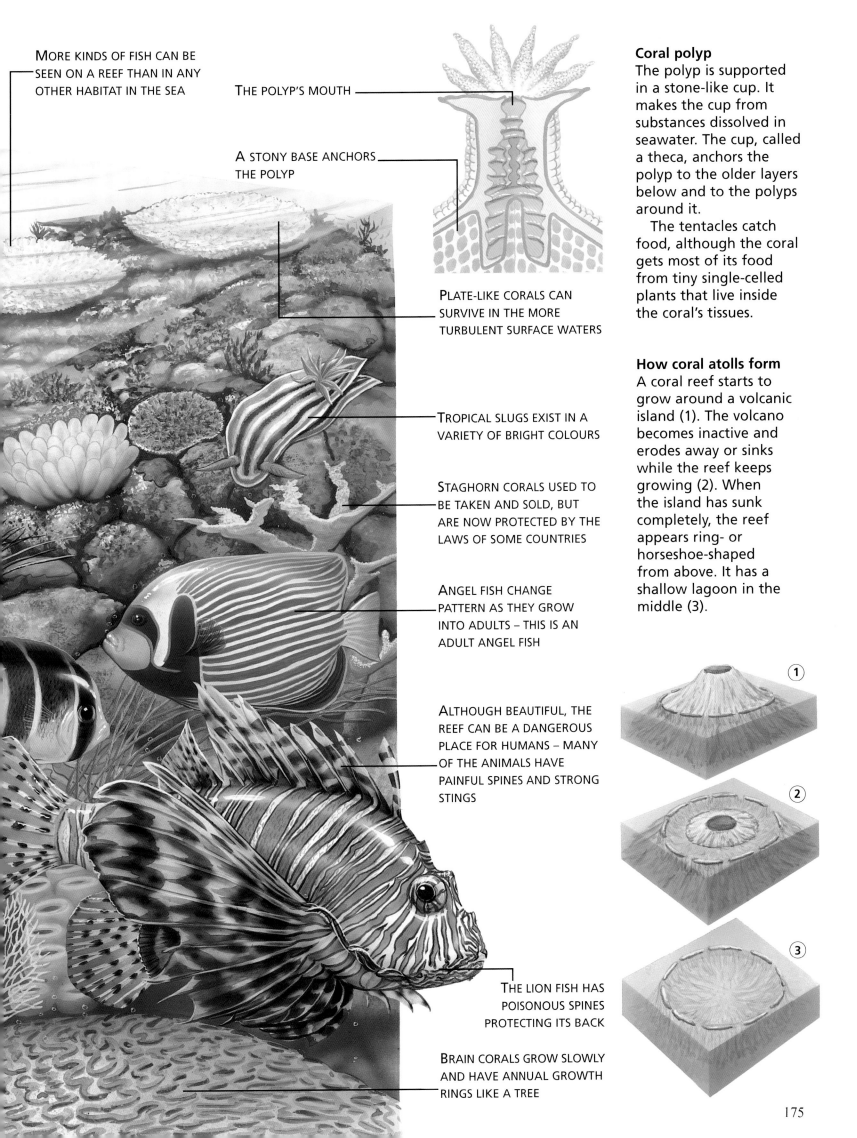

MORE KINDS OF FISH CAN BE SEEN ON A REEF THAN IN ANY OTHER HABITAT IN THE SEA

THE POLYP'S MOUTH

A STONY BASE ANCHORS THE POLYP

PLATE-LIKE CORALS CAN SURVIVE IN THE MORE TURBULENT SURFACE WATERS

TROPICAL SLUGS EXIST IN A VARIETY OF BRIGHT COLOURS

STAGHORN CORALS USED TO BE TAKEN AND SOLD, BUT ARE NOW PROTECTED BY THE LAWS OF SOME COUNTRIES

ANGEL FISH CHANGE PATTERN AS THEY GROW INTO ADULTS – THIS IS AN ADULT ANGEL FISH

ALTHOUGH BEAUTIFUL, THE REEF CAN BE A DANGEROUS PLACE FOR HUMANS – MANY OF THE ANIMALS HAVE PAINFUL SPINES AND STRONG STINGS

THE LION FISH HAS POISONOUS SPINES PROTECTING ITS BACK

BRAIN CORALS GROW SLOWLY AND HAVE ANNUAL GROWTH RINGS LIKE A TREE

Coral polyp

The polyp is supported in a stone-like cup. It makes the cup from substances dissolved in seawater. The cup, called a theca, anchors the polyp to the older layers below and to the polyps around it.

The tentacles catch food, although the coral gets most of its food from tiny single-celled plants that live inside the coral's tissues.

How coral atolls form

A coral reef starts to grow around a volcanic island (1). The volcano becomes inactive and erodes away or sinks while the reef keeps growing (2). When the island has sunk completely, the reef appears ring- or horseshoe-shaped from above. It has a shallow lagoon in the middle (3).

① ② ③

Ocean Pollution

ALMOST ALL rivers and drainage systems eventually flow into the ocean, carrying waste products from human activities out to sea. The ocean has become an enormous sink for chemicals, sewage, and rubbish as a result of wars, accidents, and deliberate dumping. Of course the ocean is very large, and not all pollutants (polluting substances) cause major problems. Bacteria exist which will eat up oil spills, or even digest steel, and over many years the ocean can clean itself very well. But where pollutants are concentrated, a great deal of damage can be done. Coastal waters beside large cities, intensively farmed land, or heavy industries can become so polluted that natural systems cannot cope. The result can be death for marine life, ugly pollution along coastlines, and damage to the health of the human population.

Today, research is being done to find out how much waste can be safely allowed into the oceans. Many countries are trying to control pollution.

Poisonous waters

There are so many sources of pollution that it is difficult to know exactly what is being poured into the sea. Chemicals that are harmless on their own get mixed with others and produce dangerous mixtures that can have unexpected effects, such as turning male fish into females. Nutrients (food) in sewage and fertilizers (crop sprays) can make poisonous plankton grow at an alarming rate, causing plankton blooms, or red tides.

SOME OF THE CHEMICALS SPRAYED ON CROPS END UP IN RIVERS AND OCEANS

HOUSING DEVELOPMENTS NEAR THE COAST INCREASE LOCAL POLLUTION LEVELS

SEWERS CAN LEAK INTO GROUNDWATER AND SPOIL WATER SUPPLIES

Fertilizer damage

Farmers use large quantities of artificial fertilizer so that they can grow as many crops as possible. Some of the fertilizer gets washed into rivers by rainfall, and carried into coastal waters where the local marine plants start growing at a greater rate. The fast-growing plants can choke the spaces where other animals and plants would normally live, and when the plants start to rot they begin to smell and attract many insects.

POISONOUS PLANKTON THRIVES IN SOME POLLUTED SEAS, COLOURING THE WATER

SEWAGE SLUDGE DUMPED FROM A SHIP IS POISONOUS TO MARINE LIFE

DUMPED MINING WASTE CAN POISON THE WATER, SMOTHER THE SEA FLOOR, AND KILL MARINE LIFE

OLD WATERWAYS THAT ARE
NO LONGER USED CAN
BECOME HEAVILY POLLUTED,
ESPECIALLY WHERE THE
FLOW IS SLOW

THE WIND MAY BLOW
SMOKE FROM FACTORIES
OUT TO SEA

HEAVY PARTICLES FROM
FACTORY SMOKE FALL, OR
ARE CARRIED BY THE WIND
AND RAIN, INTO THE OCEAN

DANGEROUS CHEMICALS
FROM RUBBISH TIPS LEAK
INTO THE WATER OVER
MANY YEARS

SOME MICROSCOPIC PLANTS
(PLANKTON) ARE VERY
POISONOUS AND CAN
CONTAMINATE THE SEA-
FOOD WE EAT

OBJECTS ON THE
SEA FLOOR CAN
BECOME BURIED
UNDER A LAYER OF SILT

Dumping at sea
Coastal seas have been
used as a dumping
ground for sewage (1),
old ships (2), chemical
wastes (3), and even
disused weapons. Oil
rigs (4) may be dumped
at the end of their
working lives, too. Oil is
washed from ships or
accidentally leaks out
when oil tankers run
aground. Oil slicks (5)
and the chemicals used
to clean them up can kill
sea life. Even the special
paint used on yachts (6)
can harm sea life if spilt.

SOME SHIPS DISCHARGE
BALLAST WATER, LEAKING
WASTES AND MARINE LIFE
FROM OTHER WATERS

A SHIPWRECK CAN CAUSE
POLLUTION BUT IT MAY ALSO
PROVIDE SHELTER FOR
YOUNG FISH, PROTECTING
THEM FROM FISHING NETS

Mining the Sea

BENEATH THE ocean floor there are vast reserves of oil, gas, and coal, as well as other minerals and metals that are of value to humans. The ocean floor has valuable reserves of sand and gravel which can be used in road building and construction. Occasionally the sand and gravel contains diamonds or other precious substances.

Where a resource is in plentiful supply on land, like coal for example, there is not much point in mining it from beneath the sea. However, oil and gas are so valuable that the difficulty and cost of drilling exploration wells, building offshore platforms, and sending reserves to the shore are thought to be worth while.

In the future, as reserves of raw materials run out on the land, other products will be mined from the sea.

FLARE STACK BURNS OFF EXCESS GAS

Oil platform
The superstructure is built of several modules, which are lifted onto the jacket by cranes. There are modules for power, engineering, pump rooms, accommodation, catering, medical services, and entertainment.

GAS TURBINE EXHAUSTS

THE STEEL JACKET (FRAMEWORK) IS REGULARLY MAINTAINED BY DIVERS AND UNDERWATER ROBOTS

⑤

A PIPE FROM THIS DERRICK CARRIES OIL AND GAS TO THE SURFACE

④

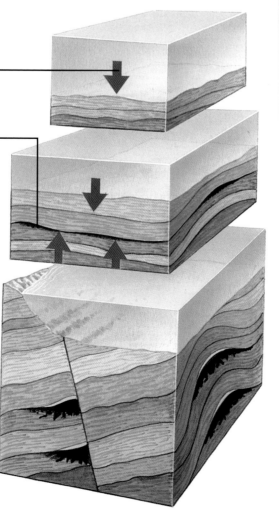

CONSTANT RAIN OF ORGANIC MATERIAL ONTO SEABED

INCREASING PRESSURE AND TEMPERATURE GRADUALLY CAUSE HYDROCARBONS TO FORM

Formation of oil and gas
Organic matter such as plankton drifts to the seabed and gets buried (*top right*). Over time the layers of decomposing matter deepen, and their temperature and pressure increase. Chemical reactions and bacteria slowly change the organic matter into hydrocarbons such as oil and gas (*middle*). Along geological faults the oil and gas may get trapped behind layers of rock (*bottom*).

178

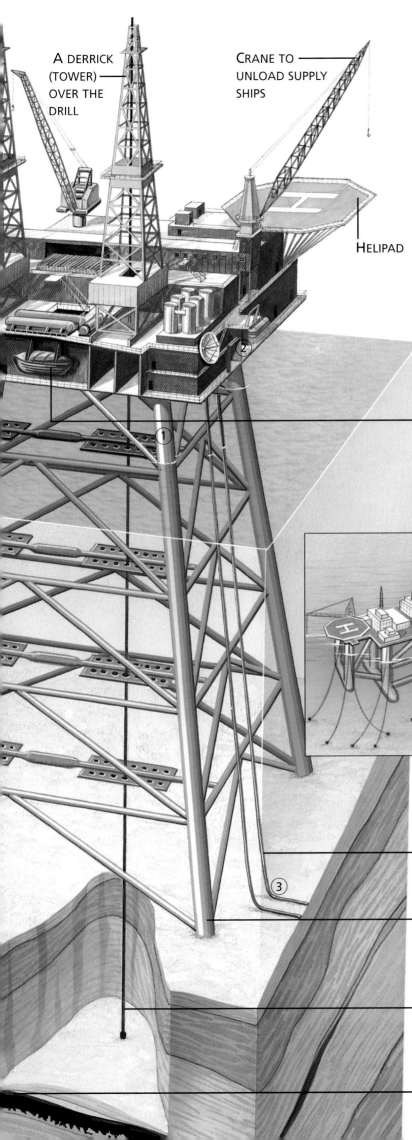

A DERRICK (TOWER) OVER THE DRILL

CRANE TO UNLOAD SUPPLY SHIPS

HELICOPTERS ARE USED TO TRANSFER CREW TO AND FROM THE PLATFORM

HELIPAD

Oil production platform

The basic oil production platform consists of a metal jacket or frame-work (1) extending from the sea floor up to a height above the highest possible waves, upon which is built a super-structure (2). This carries all of the equipment needed to safely drill holes in the seabed, suck oil out of the reservoir,

carefully control the rate of flow, and pump it either along a pipeline to a shore base (3) or load directly onto oil tankers. The platform is powered by gas turbines (4) which provide electricity and pressurize the oil well to get the oil to rise faster.

Gas comes up with the oil – some is injected back into the reservoir, some is used to fuel the turbines, and if there is enough it is separated and sent to the shore for use. Any excess gets burnt off at the end of a long boom (5).

LIFEBOATS DESIGNED FOR ESCAPE THROUGH BURNING SEAS

PIPELINES TO THE SHORE AND NEARBY WELLS

THE PLATFORM IS ANCHORED IN PLACE WITH LONG STEEL PINS

THE DRILL PENETRATES THE OIL RESERVOIR

OIL TRAPPED BEHIND DENSE ROCKS

Platform types

As well as the steel jacket rig, other platforms include: a floating platform held by anchors (*above left*), and used in deep water or for smaller oil fields; a very large concrete platform (*above centre*), able to withstand severe weather, with storage tanks built in the base; sea floor well-head (*above right*), used in deep waters, installed by a drilling ship, and then left to automatically pump oil ashore.

179

Ocean Power

THE SEA provides huge amounts of energy which can be used to generate electricity in ways that do not cause pollution or release any gases which can change the climate. And power from the sea will never run out. So why has it taken so long to develop this power? The answer is that people have thought that the cost of setting up the machinery is too high. Large, complex machines need to be built, then towed out to rough waters and moored in position. It would be many years before the sale of power would cover the cost of building and installing the machines, and even longer before any profit was made. But now the threat of pollution is being taken much more seriously and alternative forms of energy, such as sea power, are being used.

Thermal power
Ocean Thermal Energy Conversion (OTEC) uses the difference in temperature between warm surface water and deep cold water to evaporate liquid ammonia and spin a turbine electrical generator. It works best in the tropics where the cold water can be piped to nearby islands after use.

The picture (*right*) and diagram (*below, right*) show how the system works. Warm surface water boils liquid ammonia to make it into a vapour (1). The ammonia vapour spins a turbine to make electricity (2). Very cold water is drawn up from deep in the ocean (3), and condenses the ammonia back into liquid (4). The liquid travels back to the tank (5) to be used over and over again.

CROSS-SECTION OF A THERMAL POWER PLANT

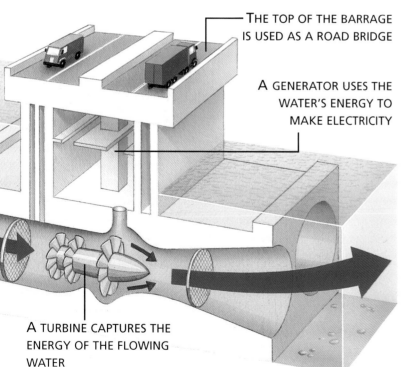

THE TOP OF THE BARRAGE IS USED AS A ROAD BRIDGE

A GENERATOR USES THE WATER'S ENERGY TO MAKE ELECTRICITY

A TURBINE CAPTURES THE ENERGY OF THE FLOWING WATER

WARM SURFACE WATER (OVER 25°C) BOILS AMMONIA

LIQUID RETURNS TO THE TANK AND IS USED OVER AND OVER AGAIN

Tidal power barrage
People first used sea power by building dams across estuaries. At high tide the estuary would fill up. At low tide the water was released, passing across a water wheel geared to a mill for grinding grain. In today's version, called a tidal power barrage, the water spins a turbine to make electricity.

COLD WATER (BELOW 5°C) IS DRAWN UP FROM OVER 500 METRES DEPTH

WAVES ENTERING A BAY ARE
FUNNELLED TOWARDS A CLIFF

A SURGE GENERATOR
OPERATES WITHIN A CLIFF

FLOATING POWER STATIONS
TRANSMIT ELECTRICITY
BACK TO SHORE

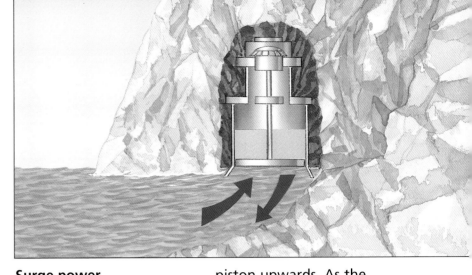

Surge power

A few power plants use power generated from the up-and-down movement of a piston. Waves entering a bay force the piston upwards. As the waves retreat the piston falls back into position ready for the next wave. A surge generator extracts power from every wave.

A ROW OF SALTER DUCKS
EXTRACTS POWER FROM
PASSING WAVES

②

④

⑤

③

COLD WATER CONDENSES
THE AMMONIA BACK
INTO LIQUID

AFTER USE THE
WARM WATER IS
RETURNED TO
THE OCEAN

AFTERWARDS THE
COLD WATER CAN
BE PIPED TO
NEARBY ISLANDS
FOR FARMERS
TO USE

WAVE FORCES THE DUCK'S
SHELL UPWARDS

THE ROCKING MOTION IS
USED TO GENERATE
ELECTRICITY

Wave power

Offshore, the constant rise and fall of the sea can be harnessed by devices such as Salter's Nodding Ducks. These use hollow concrete floats, each about 33 metres long and 20 metres across. Incoming waves tilt the duck, transferring the power to a system of electricity generation. Fifty or more ducks connected together form a very efficient generation system.

THE WORLD OF
PLANT LIFE

Text by Gerald Legg
Illustrated by Steve Weston

THE WORLD OF
PLANT LIFE
CONTENTS

Plant Cells

PLANTS ARE made up of many different kinds of tiny cells. Each cell has a different job to do but all plant cells have certain parts in common. Cells are held in shape by a tough cell wall made of cellulose, which is very strong. Each cell is controlled by a nucleus, which holds all the instructions needed for the plant to live and grow. A large vacuole (storage area) holds a watery fluid under pressure, keeping the cell rigid and storing chemicals. Proteins, which are vital for carrying out many tasks, are made by ribosomes found on the endoplasmic reticulum (a network of folded membranes). Mitochondria are the cell's power stations. They convert energy stored in foods into energy which the cell can use. Chloroplasts, made of layers of membranes, contain a green pigment (colouring) called chlorophyll. Chlorophyll catches sunlight and turns it into food and energy which the plant can use.

THE GOLGI BODY PACKS UP PROTEINS MADE BY RIBOSOMES, READY TO BE STORED OR TRANSPORTED

MICROBODIES HOLD ENZYMES WHICH BREAK DOWN SUBSTANCES IN THE CELL

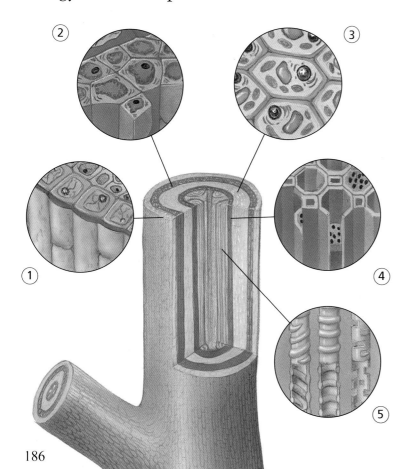

Different cell types
Epidermis cells (1) form the skin. Their outside walls are covered in a waterproof cuticle. Collenchyma cells (2) have cell walls heavily thickened with cellulose to support the plant. Parenchyma cells (3) contain chloroplasts for photosynthesis. Phloem cells (4) are thin and transport food through the plant. Xylem cells (5) are woody and joined together, forming long tubes which carry water throughout the plant.

THE VACUOLE, A LARGE BAG-LIKE AREA, HOLDS A WATERY FLUID OF DISSOLVED SALTS, SUGARS, AND PROTEINS

THE NUCLEUS, SURROUNDED
BY A THIN MEMBRANE, IS THE
CELL'S CONTROL CENTRE

NUCLEUS PORE

THE NUCLEOLUS, A SMALL
STRUCTURE INSIDE THE
NUCLEUS, PRODUCES
CHEMICALS TO MAKE
PROTEINS

THE ENDOPLASMIC
RETICULUM MOVES
SUBSTANCES AROUND
INSIDE THE CELL

RIBOSOMES (ON THE
ENDOPLASMIC RETICULUM)
MAKE PROTEINS

TINY STRANDS THAT PASS
THROUGH OPENINGS IN EACH
CELL WALL LINK CELLS
TOGETHER

MITOCHONDRIA PROVIDE
ENERGY TO DRIVE THE CELL

THE CELL WALL HOLDS THE
CELL TOGETHER

PIT FIELDS LINK CELLS

CHLOROPLASTS CONTAIN THE
GREEN PIGMENT, CALLED
CHLOROPHYLL, WHICH TRAPS
ENERGY FROM SUNLIGHT

THE PLASMA MEMBRANE
SURROUNDS THE CELL
BENEATH THE CELL WALL

MICROTUBULES ARE HOLLOW
TUBES THAT HELP SUPPORT
THE CELL SO THAT IT KEEPS
ITS SHAPE

Diatoms
The smallest plants live in
water and consist of a
single cell only visible
through a microscope. For
protection diatoms have a
hard skeleton of silica, the
same substance that sand
is made from. They form
a variety of shapes and
patterns *(right)*. Diatoms
living in the sea produce
a large amount of the
oxygen we breath.

Parts of a Plant

ALTHOUGH there are many different kinds of flowering plants they are all built in a similar way. Each plant is made of millions of cells which are organized to do different jobs. Some produce food, others store it, some provide strength, and others protect the plant from pests. Groups of cells form tissues, such as wood. Different tissues work together too, forming organs. These include stems, flowers, and roots. An important set of tissues forms the vascular system, which transports food and water throughout the plant, allowing it to grow. Most plants have stems, which hold a plant up. Flowers enable plants to reproduce, and leaves make food in the form of sugars. Nearly all plants have roots that anchor them into the ground.

THE MALE AND FEMALE PARTS OF A FLOWER PRODUCE SEEDS

PETALS ARE OFTEN COLOURFUL AND ATTRACTIVE

LEAVES, FULL OF GREEN CHLOROPHYLL, MAKE FOOD USING PHOTOSYNTHESIS

VEINS CARRY FOOD FROM THE LEAVES

SIDE ROOTS GROW OUT FROM THE MAIN ROOT

MOTOR CELLS GET BIGGER AS THEY EXPAND

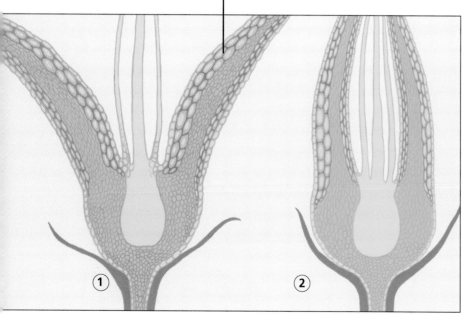

① ②

Opening flowers

Plants are not completely still – they can move parts of their bodies. Many have flowers that open during the day and close at night. Special motor cells on opposite sides of the petals can change their size. During the day those on the upper side of the petals expand while those on the lower side (1) shrink. In the evening the opposite occurs (2). These movements make flowers open and close.

188

A YOUNG BUD WITH SEPALS
THAT GROW TIGHTLY ROUND
THE PETALS

GREEN SEPALS PROTECT THE
DELICATE EXPANDING PETALS

PETALS, ALMOST READY
TO UNFOLD

Buds
Buds grow at the tip of branches and where leaves join the stem. Most buds form new stems and leaves, but some develop into flowers. A flower bud grows as the petals and other parts expand. Once the flower is fertilized its petals, stamens, and stigma are not needed anymore. They shrivel, die, and fall to the ground.

AS SEEDS DEVELOP, PETALS
WITHER AND DIE, READY TO
DROP OFF

LEAVES TAKE IN CARBON
DIOXIDE TO MAKE SUGARS

A STRONG STEM CARRIES
LEAVES AND FLOWERS

VASCULAR TISSUES CARRY
FOOD AND WATER THROUGH-
OUT THE PLANT

ROOTS GROW DOWN AND
HOLD THE PLANT FIRMLY IN
PLACE

ROOTS ABSORB WATER AND
MINERALS

ROOTS GROW FINER
AND FINER

Food flow
Inside the green parts of a plant sunlight is used to make sugars from water and carbon dioxide (a gas). This and other foods are carried in the vascular tissue throughout the plant.

Water and mineral nutrients are absorbed by the roots and carried up the plant. The water keeps the plant rigid and continually flows from the roots and out through tiny holes in the leaves.

Plant Leaves

THE LEAVES of plants vary in size from the tiny 2 millimetre leaves of duckweeds to the 4 metre leaves of banana plants. The main part of a leaf is the thin blade or lamina. Some leaves are a single blade while others are divided into small parts. A stalk joins the leaf blade to a stem on the plant. Veins are visible on the surface of the blade. These are tubes which carry water to and food from the leaf. Underneath the leaf tiny holes called stomata let carbon dioxide in, and oxygen and water out. The leaves act as the plant's factory. Their green colouring, called chlorophyll, traps sunlight and turns water and carbon dioxide into food. This process is called photosynthesis.

DROUGHT, DISEASE, AND WEATHER CHANGES MAKE LEAVES CHANGE COLOUR

SUNLIGHT FALLS ON THE SURFACE OF THE LEAF

MOST OF THE SUNLIGHT PASSES THROUGH THE UPPER EPIDERMIS (SKIN), SOME IS USED AND SOME IS REFLECTED

THE WATERPROOF UPPER CUTICLE

GREEN UPPER EPIDERMIS

CHLOROPLASTS MAKE THE PLANT'S FOOD

GREEN, SPONGY TISSUE LETS GASES THROUGH THE LEAF

THE LOWER EPIDERMIS IS PERFORATED BY STOMATA

WATER AND OXYGEN PASS OUT AND CARBON DIOXIDE PASSES IN

BROAD ASH LEAVES CATCH PLENTY OF SUNLIGHT

NARROW CONIFER LEAVES PROTECT THE PLANT FROM COLD AND DROUGHTS

TOUGH, SPINY HOLLY LEAVES PROTECT THE PLANT FROM BEING EATEN BY ANIMALS

Leaf types

There are many different kinds of leaves including narrow, wide, pointed, and feather-like. Each species of plant has its own type of leaf. Some leaf shapes protect the plant from cold or hot, dry climates. Others protect the plant from being eaten. Broad, drooping or pointed leaves are found in rain forests and thin, whip-like leaves in windy areas. Some leaves are even shaped as traps or enable the plant to climb.

FUNGUS DAMAGE

LEAF DAMAGE CAUSED BY
FLEA OR LEAF BEETLES

THE WASTE PRODUCT, OXYGEN,
IS GIVEN OFF THROUGH THE
UNDERSIDE OF THE LEAF

DAMAGE CAUSED BY A
TUNNELLING MOTH
CATERPILLAR

GUARD CELL OF STOMA

THE STOMATA OPENS WHEN
THE GUARD CELLS CONTRACT

THE STOMATA CLOSES WHEN
THE GUARD CELLS EXPAND

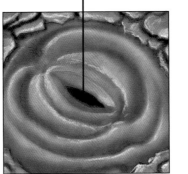

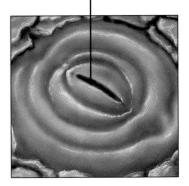

A BUNDLE SHEATH,
SURROUNDING BOTH THE
XYLEM AND PHLOEM,
FORMS A VEIN

Stomata pores
Leaves use water for
photosynthesis and to
help them stay rigid. To
keep the water in they
are waterproof. But
leaves also need to take
in carbon dioxide and
release oxygen. Special

pores under the leaves,
called stomata, control
the movement of these
gases. When open the
guard cells of the
stomata let gases enter
or leave. When closed
they prevent too much
water being lost.

SUGAR AND OTHER FOODS
ARE TRANSPORTED OUT OF
THE LEAF IN PHLOEM VESSELS

WATER AND MINERALS ARE
TRANSPORTED INTO THE LEAF
THROUGH XYLEM TUBES

Roots

ROOTS HAVE two main jobs to do. Firstly they anchor the plant firmly into the ground to stop it from falling over. Secondly they absorb water and mineral nutrients needed by the plant to grow. Some roots also act as a food store. They become fat and swollen with carbohydrates (made from the sugars that the leaves produce during photosynthesis). Special roots have other jobs to do. For example, some plants have roots for climbing, breathing, or propping up the plant.

The single root of a new plant may keep growing to become a thick, main root, or it might be replaced by a mass of thin fibrous roots. Roots usually grow down, away from the light, and towards water in the earth. So most roots grow underground. Some plants have roots that grow in the air, or ones that grow from above ground level before entering the soil.

THE LEAVES AND SHOOTS OF A CARROT GROW FROM THE ROOT TOP

THE SWOLLEN MAIN ROOT OF A CARROT

A SECONDARY ROOT

A CARROT-ROOT FLY

Roots to eat
Carrots have a swollen root full of stored food that we like to eat. Insects, slugs, and wood-lice also like this food. The carrot-root fly uses carrots for food for its growing larvae (young).

Root tips
Roots grow at their tip. Special cells increase in number, causing the root to get longer. A tough cap of cells protects the growing tip as it forces its way through the soil. Tiny hairs grow from cells in the surface of the fine roots and take up water and nutrients from the soil. The water and nutrients pass from cell to cell and then into the xylem tubes that carry them up to the rest of the plant.

WATER AND NUTRIENTS ARE DRAWN UP THROUGH THE TREE'S ROOTS

WATER AND NUTRIENTS TRAVEL THROUGH THE XYLEM TUBES

SUGARS COME DOWN FROM THE TREE'S LEAVES TO FEED THE ROOTS

WATER IS DRAWN IN FROM THE SURROUNDING SOIL PARTICLES

A HARD COVERING PROTECTS THE GROWING TIP OF THE ROOT

ROOT HAIRS ABSORB WATER

Tap root
Many plants have a single large main root. This carrot tap root grows straight down. Smaller secondary roots grow from its sides. These are very fine and absorb water and nutrients. Other plants have many fine-branched roots called fibrous roots.

SURFACE-FEEDING FIBROUS
ROOTS ABSORB NUTRIENTS

Different types of roots
Huge trees in tropical
forests have weak surface
roots which absorb water
and nutrients. Special
flattened buttress roots
are needed to hold the
tree up (1). Plants that are
tall and have a thin stem,
and those that grow in
mud, need special prop
roots to keep them up
(2). Some plants grow on
trees and use clinging
roots to hold on. They
also have long dangling
aerial roots to soak up
moisture from the air (3).
The first root of some
young plants withers
away. It is replaced by
many fibrous roots (4).

ROOTS EXTEND FAR OUT
FROM THE TRUNK IN THEIR
SEARCH FOR WATER

Flowers

FLOWERS come in all shapes, sizes, and colours. They attract insects so that pollination occurs and seeds are produced. Plants like the lily (*right*) have large, single flowers. Others, such as the dandelion, have many tiny flowers packed together into a single flower head. Flowers have central female parts, called carpels. These consist of a stigma, style, and ovary. Each stigma is at the end of a style (stalk) and catches pollen for fertilization. The ovary contains ovules which will become seeds once fertilized. A flower's male parts are the stamens. These consist of an anther held up by a filament. Anthers produce the flower's pollen. Around these are the petals and sepals. Sepals protect a flower when it is in bud. Many flowers have special glands that secrete a sugary fluid called nectar. Nectar provides food energy for insects and is one of the rewards that plants offer in exchange for being pollinated.

WATER SUCKED UP FROM THE ROOTS FORCES THE FLOWER TO OPEN

THE TEPALS (SEPALS) PROTECT THE GROWING FLOWER

A LILY'S SEPALS LOOK LIKE PETALS AND ARE OFTEN CALLED TEPALS

WITHIN THE TIPS OF SPECIAL BRANCHES THE COMPLICATED FLOWER FORMS FROM A BUD

① ② ③ ④

Flower types
Flowers come in many shapes and colours. Some are designed to attract certain insects. Poppies (1) have brightly coloured single flowers that attract bees and some flies. Many orchids (2) mimic, or copy, particular female insects, even down to their scent. The male insects try to mate with the flower and in doing so pollinate them. Dandelions (3) have large flowers made up of hundreds of tiny flowers called florets. The huge tubular flowers of the foxglove (4) attract bumble bees.

Ovules

Inside the heart of the flower lies the next generation of plants. Here, within the female ovary, ovules develop which eventually become seeds. Each ovule consists of an egg cell, supporting tissue, and a protective coat. After fertilization the ovule swells and becomes a seed.

A CROSS-SECTION OF AN OVULE SHOWS THE EGG CELL AFTER FERTILIZATION

THE EGG-CELL WILL GROW INTO A SEED AFTER JOINING WITH A MALE CELL FROM A POLLEN GRAIN

PETALS SHOW OFF THE FLOWER AND MAKE IT ATTRACTIVE TO INSECTS

THE OVARY HOLDS THE DEVELOPING OVULES

THE STYLE SUPPORTS THE STIGMA

POLLEN LIES INSIDE THE ANTHER

A SUGARY SECRETION CALLED NECTAR IS PRODUCED TO ATTRACT INSECTS

LONG FILAMENTS SUPPORT THE ANTHERS

POLLEN GRAIN WITH WALL SURROUNDING MALE CELLS

Pollen

The anthers produce pollen grains, which will land on a visiting insect. The insect may carry them off to another lily. There, the grains may land on the stigma and fertilization will occur.

THE STIGMA RECEIVES POLLEN GRAINS WHICH GROW DOWN TO THE OVULES TO FERTILIZE THE EGG CELLS

SPECIAL MARKINGS ON THE LILY FLOWER ATTRACT INSECTS

THE ANTHER AND FILAMENT TOGETHER FORM THE STAMEN WHICH SCATTERS THE POLLEN ONTO VISITING INSECTS

INSECTS LIKE BEES CARRY POLLEN FROM FLOWER TO FLOWER, AND SO POLLINATE THEM

Pollination

FOR FERTILIZATION to occur and a seed to grow, pollen must pass from a male part of a flower (anther) to a female part (stigma). The way in which the pollen moves is called pollination. Some flowers use their own pollen. Others use pollen from the flowers of other plants of the same species. Plants use many methods to carry pollen between flowers. Grasses and some trees often use the wind. But a more efficient way is to use insects like bees, moths, flies, and beetles. Animals like the honey possum, some bats, birds and even slugs, also pollinate flowers.

After pollen has been passed on to the female stigma of a flower, the pollen develops a tube that grows down the style to an ovule. The male cell in the pollen fuses with the female egg cell in the ovule. The fertilized ovule then develops into a seed.

A STYLE CONNECTS THE FEMALE PARTS OF THE FLOWER – THE STIGMA AND OVULES

THE NECTARY PRODUCES SWEET NECTAR TO ATTRACT INSECTS

THE MALE ANTHERS PRODUCE MASSES OF POLLEN GRAINS

AN ANTHER DEPOSITS STICKY POLLEN ONTO THE INSECT'S BODY

POLLEN BRUSHED FROM AN INSECT'S BODY STICKS TO THE STIGMA

MALE POLLEN CELLS TRAVEL DOWN A POLLEN TUBE TO THE OVULE

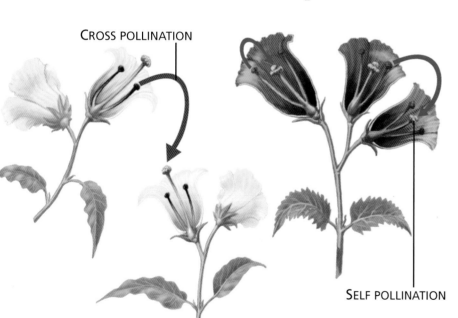

CROSS POLLINATION

SELF POLLINATION

Types of pollination
Plants are self-pollinated when they use their own pollen to fertilize their ovules. Flowers fertilized by pollen from other plants are said to be cross-pollinated. Cross pollination is often better for a plant. It ensures that their offspring have a mix of characters from both parents. Having a mix of characters gives a better chance of survival than just having characters from a single parent.

Insect pollination
Insects attracted to flowers pick up sticky pollen on their bodies. Some flowers, like these roses, just dust the insect all over with pollen, others dab pollen on certain parts of the insect's body. Flowers are specially designed to make sure that the insect picks up pollen from the anthers, and deposits pollen from other flowers right onto the stigma. Such plants often depend upon a particular type of insect for pollination. Bees pollinate flowers as they travel from flower to flower collecting pollen to eat.

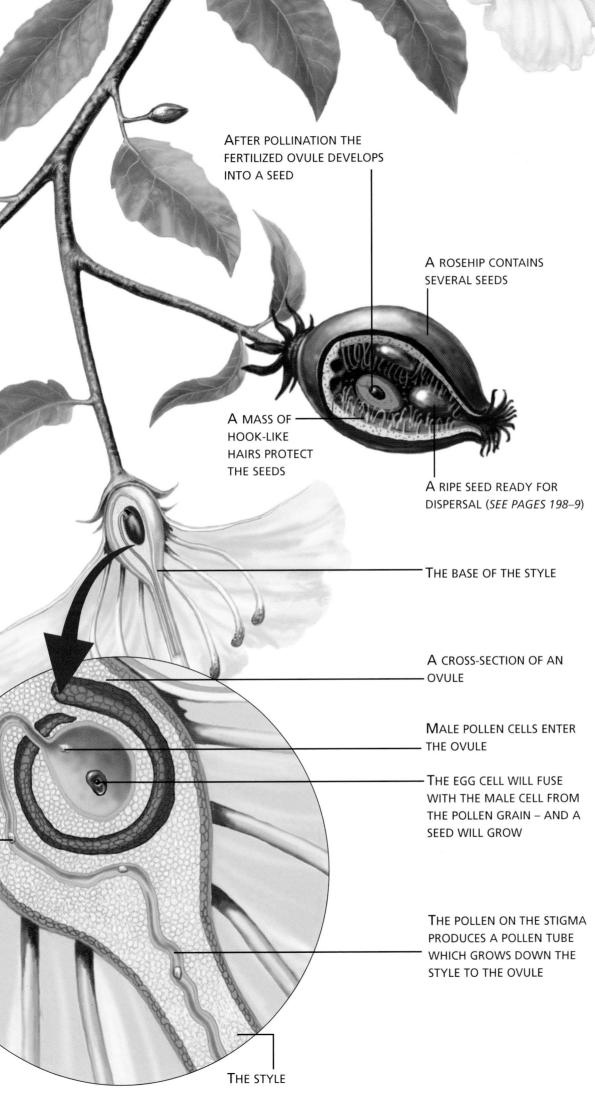

AFTER POLLINATION THE FERTILIZED OVULE DEVELOPS INTO A SEED

A ROSEHIP CONTAINS SEVERAL SEEDS

A MASS OF HOOK-LIKE HAIRS PROTECT THE SEEDS

A RIPE SEED READY FOR DISPERSAL (SEE PAGES 198–9)

THE BASE OF THE STYLE

A CROSS-SECTION OF AN OVULE

MALE POLLEN CELLS ENTER THE OVULE

THE EGG CELL WILL FUSE WITH THE MALE CELL FROM THE POLLEN GRAIN – AND A SEED WILL GROW

THE POLLEN ON THE STIGMA PRODUCES A POLLEN TUBE WHICH GROWS DOWN THE STYLE TO THE OVULE

THE STYLE

Wind pollination
The male and female parts of wind-pollinated plants ripen at different times so that self-pollination does not occur. The flowers have feather-like stigmas to catch the pollen grains.

Bird pollination
Humming birds reach into flowers with their long beaks for nectar. Anthers dust pollen on the bird's head. On visits to other flowers the pollen is transferred to the stigma.

Mammal pollination
Some plants secrete masses of nectar to attract mammals like this honey possum. Pollen smothers the animal's furry head as it eagerly laps up the nectar with its long tongue.

Seeds

SEEDS GROW into the next generation of plants. A seed develops when a plant's ovule has been fertilized (*see pages 196–7*). The seed then grows into an embryo, which is made up of seed leaves (cotyledons), a stem, and a root tip. Some seeds contain a store of food for the young plant to use as it begins to grow. Others store and surround themselves with food attractive to animals. The protective coating around a seed may be smooth, soft, or hard, and it may have 'wings', hairs, spines, or hooks.

Some plants live for only a year and drop their seeds around them. Others live much longer and need to spread their seeds so that the new seedlings will not grow in the soil around them, and so will not take the goodness from the soil that they themselves need. The seeds are spread, or dispersed, in many different ways.

Spreading seeds
Wind, water, and animals help disperse seeds. Some seeds are specially designed to be carried by the wind. Seeds with hooks or spikes are carried away when they become attached to animal fur. Seeds inside fruits are eaten by animals, or birds like the macaw (*above*), who pass them unharmed to the ground through their droppings.

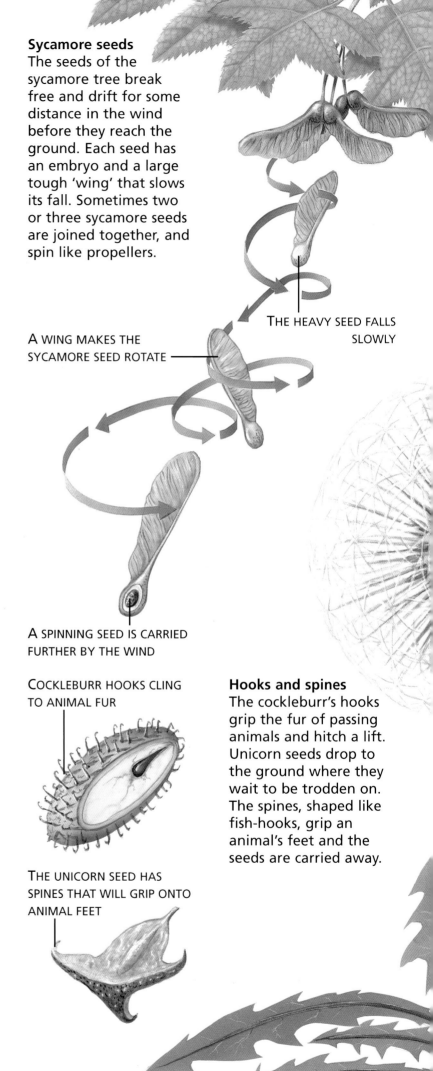

Sycamore seeds
The seeds of the sycamore tree break free and drift for some distance in the wind before they reach the ground. Each seed has an embryo and a large tough 'wing' that slows its fall. Sometimes two or three sycamore seeds are joined together, and spin like propellers.

THE HEAVY SEED FALLS SLOWLY

A WING MAKES THE SYCAMORE SEED ROTATE

A SPINNING SEED IS CARRIED FURTHER BY THE WIND

COCKLEBURR HOOKS CLING TO ANIMAL FUR

THE UNICORN SEED HAS SPINES THAT WILL GRIP ONTO ANIMAL FEET

Hooks and spines
The cockleburr's hooks grip the fur of passing animals and hitch a lift. Unicorn seeds drop to the ground where they wait to be trodden on. The spines, shaped like fish-hooks, grip an animal's feet and the seeds are carried away.

Dandelion seeds

A dandelion flower changes into a cluster of dry one-seeded fruits, called a dandelion clock. On top of each fruit is a ring of white hairs, called the pappus. After fertilization the pappus is pushed to the top of a very thin stalk. This forms the 'parachute' that lets the fruit travel many miles through the air.

THE FRUIT DANGLES ON THE END OF A LONG STALK

PRESSURE SQUIRTS THE CUCUMBER'S SEEDS OUT

THE FEATHERY HAIRS FLOAT WELL IN THE BREEZE

A POPPY'S CAPSULE IS DIVIDED INTO SECTIONS

THE DANDELION CLOCK IS ON A TALL STALK AND CATCHES THE WIND

SEEDS ESCAPE THROUGH HOLES AROUND THE TOP

THE SEEDS ARE SHAKEN OUT OF THE HOLES

THE TINY POPPY SEEDS ARE SCATTERED BY THE WIND

The squirting cucumber

Squirting cucumbers are explosive soft fruits (*above*). Inside the fruit hundreds of small flat seeds are stuck in a slimy mass, and surrounded by cells that are under high pressure. When ripe, the fruit is easily knocked off the plant. Its fall causes the high-pressure cells to expand, squirting the seeds out.

Poppy seeds

The ovaries of a poppy flower form a large fruit called a capsule. This dries out leaving the tiny seeds loose inside. Tiny holes then open around its top, letting the seeds sprinkle out like salt from a salt-cellar.

Apples

The petals, stamens, and five ovaries of the apple flower are fixed to a piece of tissue called the receptacle. When the seeds are fertilized this swells and surrounds them, forming a thick, fleshy fruit.

Hazel nuts

Each nut is a dry fruit containing a seed (the kernel), with a hard, protective ovary wall. Some animals store nuts for winter. Sometimes they forget where they have put them and the nuts germinate and grow.

Blackberries

Each blackberry is made of fruitlets called drupels. The thick ovary wall surrounding the seed is sweet and full of sugar. The seeds, protected by tough outer coats, are eaten by animals and dispersed in their droppings.

New Growth

I N THE RIGHT conditions, seeds begin to grow into new plants in a process called germination. In autumn, bean seeds (*below*) drop from the shrivelled pods of adult plants. Some become buried, while others are eaten or taken away by animals. In spring, the sun warms the soil, and the embryo plant inside the seed comes to life. The seed absorbs water and begins to swell up. Then the embryo starts to grow using food stored in the seed's special fleshy leaves. In a few days, out pops the first root, which grows down, and the first shoot, which grows up.

Seeds are not the only source of new growth. Like seeds, spores also grow into new plants (*see page 202*). Stems, shoots, and roots form new plants too, but in a different way (*above*).

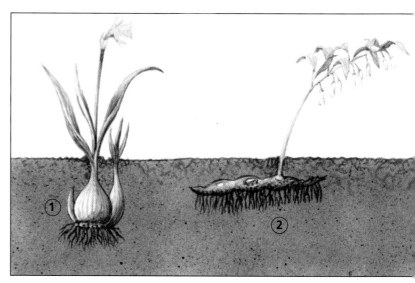

Growth without seeds
Daffodil bulbs are short swollen underground shoots (1). Each has a short stem at its centre, surrounded by fleshy scales that contain food for new plant growth. In spring, buds grow from the bulb and produce roots, flowers, and leaves.

Underground stems, like those of Solomon's seal, grow near the soil surface (2). These are called rhizomes. New leaves, buds, and roots grow from them, spreading new plants across the surrounding area. Hidden and protected underground,

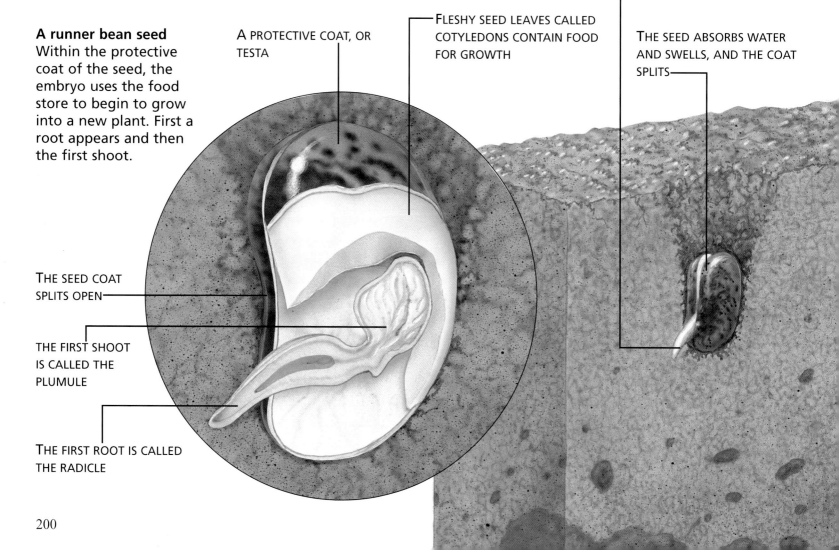

A runner bean seed
Within the protective coat of the seed, the embryo uses the food store to begin to grow into a new plant. First a root appears and then the first shoot.

A PROTECTIVE COAT, OR TESTA

FLESHY SEED LEAVES CALLED COTYLEDONS CONTAIN FOOD FOR GROWTH

THE RADICLE EMERGES AS THE EMBRYO GROWS

THE SEED ABSORBS WATER AND SWELLS, AND THE COAT SPLITS

THE SEED COAT SPLITS OPEN

THE FIRST SHOOT IS CALLED THE PLUMULE

THE FIRST ROOT IS CALLED THE RADICLE

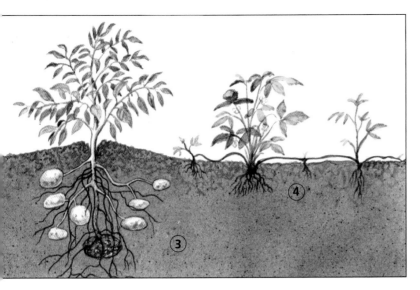

they help the plants to survive in the winter. Thin underground stems grow from near the lower leaves of potato plants (3). These branch and swell into tubers which store food and grow into new potato plants the following year.

Strawberry plants produce special shoots called runners near the soil surface (4). Buds grow at intervals along them. Where the buds touch the soil, roots grow, and a new plant forms.

THE TOP SHOOT WITH NEW LEAVES COILS AROUND A SUPPORTING CANE

A SHIELD BUG SUCKS SAP FROM A LEAF

THE SHRIVELLED REMAINS OF THE SEED LEAVES

THE FIRST REAL LEAVES OPEN AND THE PLANT STARTS TO GROW FASTER

THE PLUMULE BREAKS OUT OF THE SEED COAT AND HEADS UPWARDS, AWAY FROM THE DOWNWARD FORCE OF GRAVITY

THE RADICLE GROWS DOWN, GROWING INTO NEW ROOTS

THE ROOT GROWS AND THE SEED LEAVES WITHER AS THEIR FOOD STORE IS USED

201

Spores

SOME PLANTS, such as mosses, ferns, and conifers, produce spores instead of seeds. Spores are like seeds, but much smaller and simpler. For spores to develop on a moss plant, the plant must produce male gametes (sperm) and female gametes (eggs). Eggs fertilized by the sperm grow while still fixed to the moss plant. At this stage the spores, which grow into other moss plants, are produced. Mosses have simple leaves and a stem, but no roots. They have no vessels to transport water and so are unable to grow taller than 20 centimetres.

Ferns are more complicated, with roots, leaves (fronds), and stems containing vessels that carry water throughout the plant. Spores grow on the underside of the fronds. They fall to the ground and develop into tiny green plants which produce eggs or sperm. The fertilized eggs grow into new fern plants.

Ferns

Like mosses, ferns produce spores and male and female gametes (sperm and eggs). But unlike mosses, the spores and gametes are produced on separate plants called gametophytes.

Ferns like the delicate lady fern (*below*) must live in a damp or wet place because its sperm have to swim to find the eggs.

ON THE UNDERSIDE OF THE FROND SPORES GROW IN TINY CASES CALLED SPORANGIA

Mosses

While still fixed to the plant, a moss plant's fertilized eggs produce capsules in which spores are formed. When the spores are ready, the capsules' lids fall off. As the capsules dry, special teeth bend back, letting the spores escape. Tiny hairs inside the capsules dry too, twist and turn, and force the spores out. Gusts of wind help carry them away. On damp ground they grow into new moss plants.

A FERN'S FROND UNCOILS AS IT GROWS

SPECIAL TEETH BEND OUT TO RELEASE THE THE SPORES

YOUNG FRONDS ARE COILED UP

SPORANGIA OFTEN GROW IN GROUPS

A fern's spores
Spores grow in cases, called sporangia, on the underside of the fronds. Sporangia occur in groups, protected beneath a fold of tissue. When ripe, the spores are flicked out as the walls of the sporangia dry. The spores drift on the wind and germinate (begin to grow) after landing on damp ground.

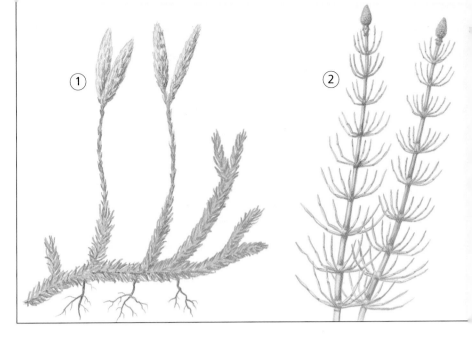

A CROSS-SECTION OF A FROND AND SPORANGIUM

SPORES FORM IN THE SPORANGIUM

SPORES ARE BLOWN AWAY BY THE WIND

Ferns' relatives
Hundreds of millions of years ago clubmosses grew tall and tree-like. Their remains became coal. Today, clubmosses are small plants with roots and a stem densely covered in tiny leaves (1). Clubmosses were the first plants to produce their reproductive parts in cones.

Growing alongside the ancient clubmosses were huge forests of giant horsetails. Today, they do not grow as tall (2 metres at most). Their ridged stems have long thin leaves arranged in rings (2). Both club-mosses and horsetails live in damp places.

A SPORE GERMINATES AND GROWS INTO A TINY FERN PLANT CALLED A GAMETOPHYTE

THE TINY PLANT PRODUCES EITHER MALE SPERM OR FEMALE EGGS

A FEMALE PLANT GROWS EGGS IN A SPECIAL CUP

A MALE PLANT PRODUCES SPERM

SPERM SWIM IN MOISTURE TO FIND AN EGG

THE SPERM JOINS WITH AN EGG

A FERN'S UNDERGROUND STEM CAN ALSO GROW INTO NEW FERN PLANTS

A FERTILIZED EGG GROWS INTO A NEW SPORE-PRODUCING FERN

A YOUNG FERN'S ROOTS GROW DOWN AND ITS TINY STEM AND LEAVES GROW UP

Trees

TREES ARE the largest land plants, growing to over 40 metres in height. Trees can grow this tall because they are made of wood. The wood makes them very strong, but also flexible so that they bend rather than break in the wind. An outer skin of thick dead cells, called the bark, and a layer of dead, spongy cells, called cork, protect the tree. Beneath these are storage tissue and bundles of vessels (tubes), called the phloem, which carry food throughout the plant. Next to the phloem is the cambium – a very thin layer of cells. This is the growing layer of the tree which produces phloem on its outside and live sapwood on its inside. The sapwood contains fibres of strong, thicker cells, and long xylem vessels which carry water up the tree. As the tree grows, the inner sapwood dies and is changed into strong heartwood. In dry or cold weather, growth is slower. This results in a series of annual growth rings.

BUDS OPEN IN SPRING

THE TREE GROWS IN SUMMER

LEAVES FALL IN AUTUMN

THE TREE RESTS IN WINTER

Bark beetles

The bark beetle burrows into the wood behind the bark. Females chew a main tunnel with side galleries in which they lay their eggs. The larvae eat the live tissue and fungi that grow beneath the bark.

AN ASH BARK BEETLE

BARK BEETLE GALLERIES FORM DISTINCTIVE PATTERNS

Deciduous trees

The changing seasons throughout the year affect the growth of a deciduous tree. Winter is a time to rest, with no leaves and little or no growth. In spring the buds open, producing leaves and flowers. During spring and summer the leaves make food for the growing tree. The flowers provide seeds and fruit.

LARGE VESSELS GROW IN THE SPRING AND SUMMER WHEN THE WEATHER IS WARM AND FOOD IS MORE PLENTIFUL

GROWTH RINGS VARY ACCORDING TO CONDITIONS – NARROW RINGS INDICATE SLOW GROWTH DURING PARTICULARLY DRY YEARS

In autumn nutrients and chlorophyll (the green colouring) in the leaves are removed and stored for the following year. The leaves are then sealed off from their water supply causing them to shrivel, die, and fall.

THE XYLEM VESSELS OF THE SAPWOOD CARRY WATER AND SALTS UP THE TREE

THE DEAD HEARTWOOD FORMS THE INNER WOOD AND IS SPECIALLY HARDENED FOR STRENGTH

Food paths
Tiny root hairs absorb water as well as minerals from the soil. Sugars and other foods made by the leaves are carried to the rest of the tree inside the phloem. As water evaporates through the leaves it is drawn up from the roots and carried throughout the tree in the xylem vessels.

WATER IS USED TO MAKE FOOD (PHOTOSYNTHESIS) AND TO TRANSPORT IT AROUND THE TREE

WATER AND NUTRIENTS TRAVEL UP THE TREE; SUGARS AND FOOD TRAVEL DOWN

THE ROOTS ABSORB WATER AND MINERAL NUTRIENTS FROM THE SOIL AND RECEIVE FOODS FROM THE LEAVES

THE PROTECTIVE BARK IS FORMED FROM DEAD CELLS

THE INNER BARK IS SOFT AND SPONGY AND FORMS CORK

A LAYER OF PHLOEM VESSELS AND STORAGE TISSUES GROW OUT FROM THE CAMBIUM

LARGE SUMMER AND SMALL AUTUMN VESSELS TOGETHER MAKE A GROWTH RING

THE THIN CAMBIUM IS THE GROWING LAYER OF THE TREE

LARGE XYLEM VESSEL OF EARLY (SPRING) WOOD

Wood structure
Wood is formed from a mass of vessels that carry water and nutrients up the tree. These are supported by strong, fine fibres. Vessels produced in the spring and summer are much larger than those in the autumn. Between the vessels food storage cells form strands, called rays, at right angles to the growth rings.

FOOD IS STORED IN SPECIAL STRANDS THAT LIE ACROSS THE GROWTH RINGS IN THE SAPWOOD

LICHENS (PLANTS WHICH ARE PART FUNGI AND PART ALGAE) GROW ON THE BARK

SMALL VESSEL OF LATE (AUTUMN) WOOD

LARGE BANDS OF STORAGE TISSUE

Conifers

UNLIKE DECIDUOUS trees, conifers do not produce flowers. Instead of flowers, they have cones. Male cones make pollen which is then carried by the wind to female cones. The pollen fertilizes the female cone's ovules, which develop into seeds.

Many conifers grow in places that are too cold or dry for other trees. Conifer seeds are very tough so they can withstand the intense winter cold. The trees themselves have needle-like leaves which greatly reduces water-loss. This is especially important in winter, when the soil is frozen and water is unavailable. They also have resins and oils in their wood which seal any injuries and protect the tree against the cold.

In the regions where conifers grow, the summers are short so the trees grow very fast. Huge forests of conifers occur across northern Europe, Asia, and Canada.

Corsican pine
Unlike many pines, the Corsican pine originally grew in warm, dry areas (in Corsica and southern Italy). It is now very common everywhere – in parks, gardens, and in large forests on poor, sandy soils. It grows to over 40 metres and has greenish-grey leaves.

SLOPING BRANCHES ENABLE SNOW TO FALL OFF EASILY

BRANCHES ARE LONGER LOWER DOWN THE TRUNK – FOR STABILITY AND SO THAT THEY CAN GATHER SUNLIGHT

FAST-GROWING, STRAIGHT TRUNK

Pine needles
Because they live in dry places conifers need special leaves. Plants usually lose water through stomata on the surface of their leaves. The leaves of conifers are long and narrow, so less water can escape. To protect the stomata the leaves are rolled with the stomata tucked in the fold. The leaves are also covered in a thick, waxy waterproof 'skin'.

CHANNEL FOR TRANSPORTING RESIN (A STICKY, OILY FLUID)

STOMA PROTECTED IN A SUNKEN PIT

TOUGH, WAXY 'SKIN'

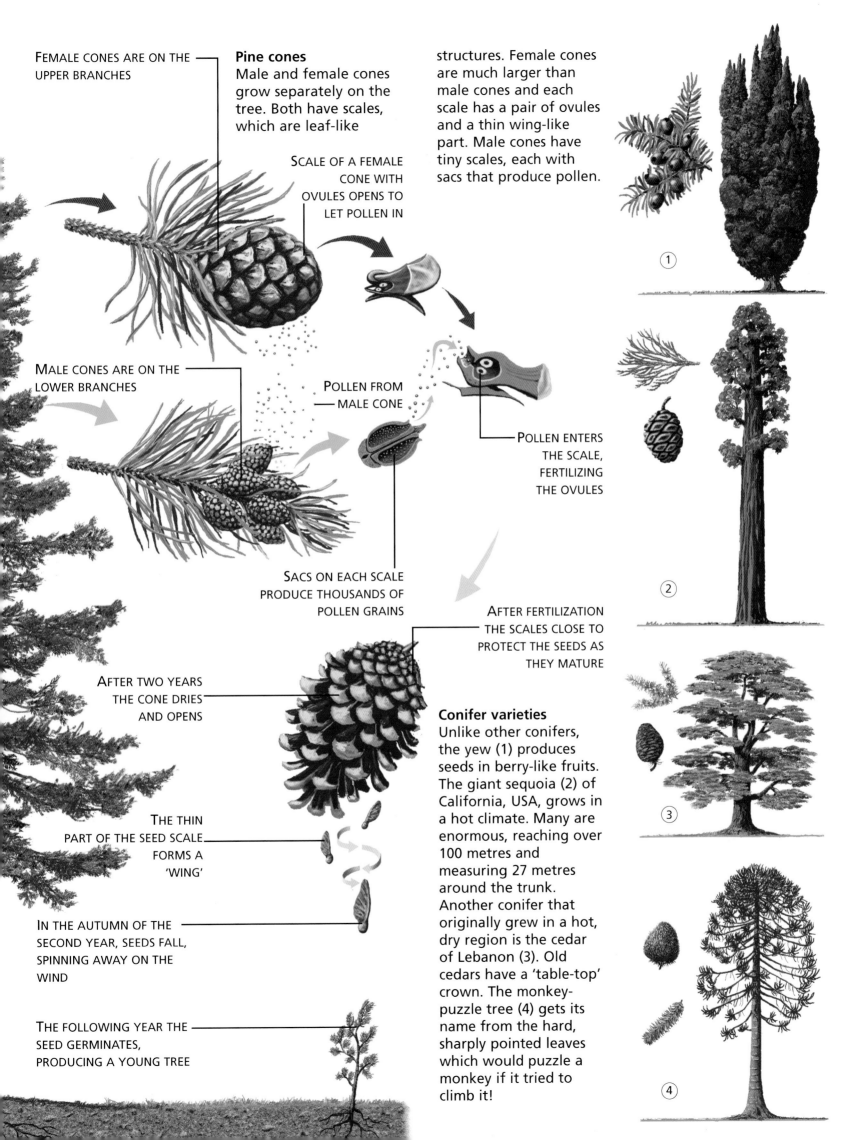

FEMALE CONES ARE ON THE UPPER BRANCHES

Pine cones
Male and female cones grow separately on the tree. Both have scales, which are leaf-like

structures. Female cones are much larger than male cones and each scale has a pair of ovules and a thin wing-like part. Male cones have tiny scales, each with sacs that produce pollen.

SCALE OF A FEMALE CONE WITH OVULES OPENS TO LET POLLEN IN

MALE CONES ARE ON THE LOWER BRANCHES

POLLEN FROM MALE CONE

POLLEN ENTERS THE SCALE, FERTILIZING THE OVULES

SACS ON EACH SCALE PRODUCE THOUSANDS OF POLLEN GRAINS

AFTER FERTILIZATION THE SCALES CLOSE TO PROTECT THE SEEDS AS THEY MATURE

AFTER TWO YEARS THE CONE DRIES AND OPENS

Conifer varieties
Unlike other conifers, the yew (1) produces seeds in berry-like fruits. The giant sequoia (2) of California, USA, grows in a hot climate. Many are enormous, reaching over 100 metres and measuring 27 metres around the trunk. Another conifer that originally grew in a hot, dry region is the cedar of Lebanon (3). Old cedars have a 'table-top' crown. The monkey-puzzle tree (4) gets its name from the hard, sharply pointed leaves which would puzzle a monkey if it tried to climb it!

THE THIN PART OF THE SEED SCALE FORMS A 'WING'

IN THE AUTUMN OF THE SECOND YEAR, SEEDS FALL, SPINNING AWAY ON THE WIND

THE FOLLOWING YEAR THE SEED GERMINATES, PRODUCING A YOUNG TREE

①

②

③

④

Desert Plants

PLANTS THAT live in deserts have to put up with extremely dry conditions and often great changes in temperature. However, a wide variety of plants live here, each using different ways to survive in the hostile climate. Many are succulent. This means they hold the water that reaches them, either in their leaves, their stems, or their roots. Some avoid water-loss by having no leaves at all, or by having waterproof or thin leaves which can easily be shed in a drought. The stomata are often hidden deep in pits. The leaves may even reflect the sun's heat or prevent damage from frost at night. Their flowers may be quite large, relying not so much on insects but on birds and bats to pollinate them. Tough coats protect their seeds during long periods of drought. When rain falls or floods rise they quickly germinate and grow.

THE WHITE PETALS ATTRACT BIRDS FOR POLLINATION

Flowering cactus
The flowers of some cacti, like this saguaro, open during the day, but many cacti flowers open at night. They are often large and extremely beautiful. They attract large moths, bats and birds, which pollinate them.

SIDE SHOOT WITH FLOWER BUDS

Plant types
The dense rosette of succulent agave leaves (1) have special tissues for storing water. Fibres from the leaves are sometimes used to make string. The masses of spines covering the bushy opuntia (2) protect it against grazing animals and reflect the sun's heat. Echinocerus (3) is well-adapted to the desert and has no leaves. Its ridged stem can expand to store water.

The common prickly pear cactus (4) forms dense prickly scrub. This American cactus has been introduced into other parts of the world and has grown so well it has become a plague.

SAND PILES UP ON THE WINDWARD SIDE

ROOTS GATHER RARE AND VALUABLE WATER FROM RAIN AND DEW

THE ELF OWL MAKES ITS
NEST IN HOLES IN THE
LIVING CACTUS

IN THE HOLE, CHICKS ARE
PROTECTED FROM THE
HEAT OF THE SUN

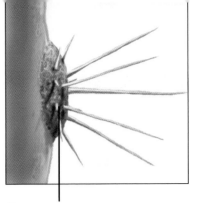

TUFTS OF SPINES PROTECT
THE PLANT FROM GRAZING
ANIMALS AND REFLECT THE
SUN'S HEAT AWAY

CACTUS SKIN HAS A THICK
WAXY LAYER FOR
WATERPROOFING

HARD, WOODY TISSUE
CARRIES WATER THROUGH-
OUT THE PLANT

LONG FIBROUS ROOTS SEEK
OUT NUTRIENTS JUST
BENEATH THE SOIL SURFACE

SOFT STEM TISSUE
CARRIES SUGARY FOODS

STOMATA

A THICK LAYER OF LARGE
CELLS STORES WATER

A THICK MASS
OF FIBROUS ROOTS
ANCHORS THE PLANT

Inside cacti
In cacti the stomata,
which all plants need for
the exchange of carbon
dioxide and oxygen, are
sunk deep inside pits to
reduce water-loss. Large
cells form a thick, soft
layer for storing water.
Soft tissues deep within
the stem carry water and
nutrients throughout
the plant.

Wetland Plants

THERE ARE many kinds of wetlands, including salty coastal waters, muddy swamps and marshes, freshwater lakeshores and ponds, and fast-flowing rivers. They provide many different habitats where plants can live, from water-logged soils to sunlit surface waters.

A pond that gets plenty of sunshine (*right*) can provide all that a plant needs, including nutrients and support. However, living in water has its problems. Oxygen and carbon dioxide may be in short supply, so some plants have special air-carrying tissue. Light may not reach the bottom of a pond, so many plants must float near the surface. The water and its surface provide support for plants. Some water plants have leaves and flowers that rest on the surface, while their flimsy stems are supported by the water below.

Water lilies
The anchoring roots of water lilies form food-storing tubers. Other water plants have roots that dangle in the water, absorbing nutrients. Water lily flowers attract insects during the day, and then close at night, trapping them. During the night the insects pollinate the ovules. In the morning the flowers open again, releasing their guests.

REEDS AND OTHER MARSH PLANTS GROW IN THE WATER-LOGGED SOIL

PLANTS LIKE BULRUSHES HAVE SPECIAL STEMS TO TAKE OXYGEN DOWN TO THEIR SUBMERGED ROOTS

WATER LILY FLOWERS AND LEAVES REST ON THE SURFACE OF THE WATER

Algae
Surrounded by nutrients, many microscopic plants, called algae, grow freely in the water or attach themselves to other plants or rocks. Many algae are made of single cells or groups of cells. Spirogyra, also known as blanket weed (*right*), forms dense tangled mats, providing homes to many other tiny algae and animals.

SPIROGYRA (VIEWED THROUGH A MICROSCOPE)

BARE SURFACES, LIKE ROCKS, BECOME COVERED IN ALGAE

THE ROOTS OF SOME WATER PLANTS HOLD THEM FIRMLY IN THE MUD

THE TINY FLOWERS ON A BULRUSH ARE PACKED INTO THESE SAUSAGE SHAPES

TALL PLANTS GROWING ON THE EDGE OF THE POND HAVE STRONG ANCHOR ROOTS

Ribbon-weed
The tropical ribbon-weed (*below right*) uses the water for pollination. Male flower buds develop and are released (1). They float to the surface, open, and sail across to a female flower (2). The female flower opens on the surface to reveal its stigma (3). Once fertilized by a male bud, the female stalk spirals down (4), pulling the fertilized ovule to the bottom, where the seeds are released.

HORSETAILS HAVE HOLLOW STEMS THAT EXTEND VERY DEEP INTO THE SOIL

DUCKWEEDS HAVE NO STEM – THEY ARE THE SMALLEST FLOWERING PLANTS

THE WATER SOLDIER RESTS ON THE BOTTOM UNTIL LATE SPRING, THEN RISES TO THE SURFACE AND FLOWERS

Ocean Plants

FLOWERING sea grasses and simple non-flowering algae live in the oceans. Most ocean plants are tiny algae called phytoplankton, which live near the surface. Many larger species of algae (seaweeds) live in cool, shallow coastal waters and on seashores. Like all plants, algae need sunlight for photosynthesis, so cannot live deeper than 175 metres where sunlight does not reach.

Seaweeds do not have vascular tissue (xylem and phloem), or proper leaves, roots, or stems. The larger ones grow as delicate tufts, flat sheets, and thick fronds. Some are over a hundred metres long. They reproduce by growing spores which join in the open sea to form new plants. Seaweeds are classified according to their colour. Brown and most green seaweeds need direct sunlight, so live in shallow water. Many red seaweeds and a few greens need only a little light and are found in deeper waters.

Phytoplankton
Microscopic phytoplankton live in the top few metres of cooler seas. They can be very abundant (a mouthful of seawater may contain 30 million)! Phytoplankton are very important as they produce much of the oxygen we breathe. They also provide food for tiny animals and form the beginning of the marine food chain.

TOUGH FRONDS CAN WITHSTAND THE BATTERING OF THE SURF

AIR-FILLED BLADDER

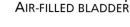

THE FRONDS ARE UNCOVERED WHEN THE TIDE GOES OUT

THE TOUGH FRONDS WITHSTAND DRYING OUT BECAUSE THEY CONTAIN SPECIAL SLIME THAT PROTECTS THEIR CELLS

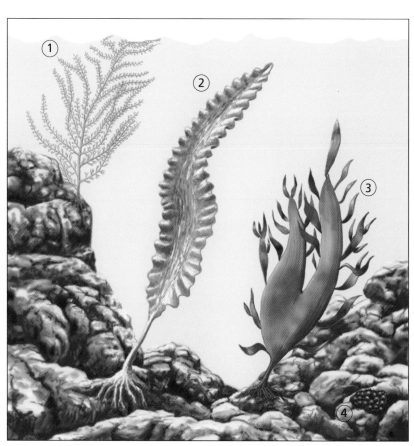

Types of seaweed
Sea sorrel (1) is a green seaweed that lives on rocks in shallow pools. It has a disc-like holdfast and feathery branched stem. Sugar kelp (2) is a large brown seaweed, so-called because it is sweet and edible. The greatest variety of seaweeds are red. Calliblepharis (3) has a leafy frond. It is an annual plant (lives for a year), unlike sugar kelp which is a perennial (lives for several years). Not all seaweeds are leafy, strap-like, or feathery. The brown seaweed, ralfsia, forms irregular lumps on exposed rocks (4).

Life around a seaweed
The seaweed itself, especially its holdfast, provides a safe home for many animals. Some, such as crabs, leave their safe retreat to feed in the open. Others, such as various limpets, eat the seaweed.

SUNLIGHT PENETRATES
THE SEA DOWN TO ABOUT
175 METRES

Reproduction
The seaweed on the left
is called bladder wrack.
It has eggs and sperm
which are produced
inside special cavities
called conceptacles.
These are located at the
tips of the fronds. They
release the sperm and
eggs into the sea where
they fuse and settle on
rocks to grow into new
seaweed plants.

BLADDERS KEEP FRONDS
AFLOAT SO THAT THEY
CAN REACH AS MUCH
LIGHT AS POSSIBLE

RIPENING FEMALE EGG

MALE SPERM
ARE RELEASED

JELLY-LIKE INTERIOR

CONCEPTACLES PRODUCE
EGGS AND SPERM

Agar jelly
A jelly called agar is
extracted from the jelly
plant (right). This is used
in the drug industry for
growing bacteria. It is
also added to many
foods, such as canned
food and ice-cream as a
gelling agent. Dentists
also use it to take
impressions
of teeth.

THE STRONG STIPE (STEM) IS
FLEXIBLE

SEAWEED HAS A ROOT-LIKE
HOLDFAST WHICH FIRMLY
ANCHORS THE PLANT TO A
ROCK

LIMPET

SPONGE

CRAB

Carnivores

THERE ARE about 550 species of plants from all over the world that are carnivorous, which means meat-eating. They live in places where there is little food in the soil, so they need extra food. They attract, trap, and digest insects, spiders, small animals such as lizards, and even small mammals. The way they trap these creatures varies. Some, like the sundew plant, have sticky hairs to hold their prey, while the Venus flytrap uses its leaves as spring-loaded 'jaws'. The pitcher plant (*right*) lures its victims into a slippery jug filled with a liquid that drowns them and helps the plant to digest them. All carnivorous plants use enzymes (chemicals) to dissolve their victims, and have special cells that absorb the food, which is then transported around the plant to help it grow.

THE SPECIAL LEAVES OF A PITCHER PLANT SPROUT FROM THE STEM AND ARE LEAF-LIKE FOR PART OF THEIR LENGTH

PERISTOMES (TEETH-LIKE STRUCTURES) COATED IN SLIPPERY WAX POINT DOWNWARD

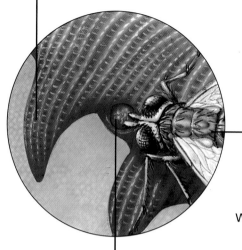

INSECT SLIPS AND FALLS WHILE TRYING TO REACH NECTAR

THE NECTAR GLAND MAKES A SWEET LIQUID TO ATTRACT INSECTS

A STRONG SPRINGY TENDRIL SUPPORTS THE PITCHER

Slippery edge
Wax makes the edge of the pitcher very slippery (*above*). Insects lured by the nectar cannot grip the surface. They slip, fall, and drown in the liquid.

THE SPIRAL GIVES THE PLANT MORE HOLD ON NEIGHBOURING PLANTS

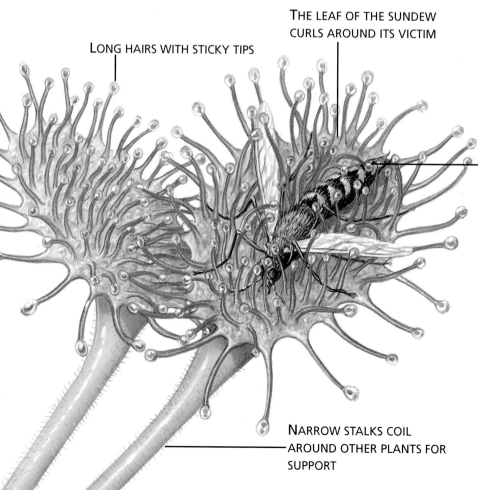

LONG HAIRS WITH STICKY TIPS

THE LEAF OF THE SUNDEW CURLS AROUND ITS VICTIM

THE INSECT IS STUCK, TRAPPED BY STICKY HAIRS

Sundew
Long hairs tipped with a sweet and sticky substance cover the leaves of the sundew. An insect may be attracted to the sweetness and settle to feed, or it may land on the leaves to rest. It soon gets stuck to the hairs, and as it struggles it gets more stuck. The plant's enzymes (digestive juices) then dissolve the insect into a liquid, which the plant absorbs.

FLUID IS DRAWN UP INTO THE PLANT

NUTRIENT FLUID IS TAKEN UP IN LEAF TUBES

NARROW STALKS COIL AROUND OTHER PLANTS FOR SUPPORT

TRIGGER BRISTLES CLOSE THE
TRAP IF TOUCHED BY
AN INSECT

NECTAR GLANDS
ATTRACT INSECT

A FLY LANDS ON THE PAD

THE LID CREATES A SHADOW
WHICH HELPS LURE INSECTS
IN AND KEEPS TROPICAL
RAINS OUT

A FLY IS ATTRACTED TO
THE NECTAR

THE FLY TOUCHES
TRIGGER HAIRS

ONCE TRIGGER
HAIRS ARE TOUCHED,
THE TRAP STARTS TO
CLOSE

THE RIBBED RIM
PROVIDES A LANDING
PLATFORM FOR INSECTS

THE INNER SURFACE OF
THE PITCHER IS WAXY
AND VERY SLIPPERY

THE TRAP CLOSES – THERE IS
NO ESCAPE FOR THE INSECT
AS SPINES ALONG THE
TRAP'S EDGE FORM A CAGE

THE FLY IS SLOWLY DIGESTED
IN THE TRAP

ONCE AN INSECT FALLS INTO
THE POND IT CANNOT GET OUT

Venus flytrap
When an insect lands on
the lobes of the Venus
flytrap's leaf, it touches
fine trigger hairs that
cause the trap to shut.
As the insect struggles,
the trap tightens. The
plant secretes water and
digestive enzymes into
the trap, drowning and
dissolving the insect.

GLANDS PRODUCE DIGESTIVE
ENZYMES

ENZYMES SECRETED INTO THE
POND DISSOLVE THE INSECTS
SO THE FOOD IS IN A FORM
THAT THE PLANT CAN DIGEST

REMAINS OF INSECTS

Parasitic Plants

SOME FLOWERING plants lack chlorophyll and so cannot make their own food. Plants like cytinus (see *right*) and the giant flowering rafflesia are called parasites and rely on other plants, their hosts, for their food. Half-parasites, such as mistletoe, contain chlorophyll which makes food for the plants, but as they live away from the soil they depend on their hosts for water and minerals.

Most parasitic plants cling to their host and invade its tissues using suckers, called haustoria. These root-like organs connect with the host's vascular tissue, through which the host's nutrients are flowing. The parasite taps onto and takes the nutrients, like a vampire sucking blood. Some parasites, such as rafflesia, are almost hidden inside the host, only emerging to flower. Others, such as mistletoe, grow mainly on the outside of their host.

How it feeds
The parasite cytinus detects chemicals on the surface of a shrub, which show that it is a suitable host. It grows a patch of tissue over the host's root. From this patch, root-like haustoria burrow in. Strands of xylem and phloem in the haustoria make a connection from the vascular tissue of the parasite to that of the host.

CYTINUS HAS NO CHLOROPHYLL AND SO CANNOT PHOTOSYNTHESIZE FOOD

IN THE SUMMER A TIGHT MASS OF FLOWERS GROWS

BRACTS SURROUND AND PROTECT THE DELICATE FLOWERS

BRACTS ARE LEAF-LIKE STRUCTURES

THE PARASITE INVADES THE ROOT OF THE HOST

ROOT OF THE HOST PLANT

HAUSTORIA GROW INTO THE ROOT OF THE HOST AND DRAW UP THE HOST'S NUTRIENTS

VASCULAR TISSUE FROM THE PARASITE JOINS THE HOST'S XYLEM AND PHLOEM

THE BRIGHT, COLOURFUL FLOWERS ATTRACT INSECTS FOR POLLINATION

THE PARASITE GROWS A PATCH OF TISSUE AROUND THE ROOT OF THE HOST

THE HOST'S ROOT

WHEN NOT IN FLOWER CYTINUS IS ONLY VISIBLE AS A LUMP OF TISSUE ON THE HOST'S ROOT

PHLOEM AND XYLEM FORM THE VASCULAR TISSUE OF THE HOST

HAUSTORIA PENETRATE INTO THE HOST'S XYLEM

Mistletoe

Unlike other parasites, the evergreen leaves of the mistletoe produce food for the plant. But its haustoria join the host's xylem in order to get water and minerals, taken from the soil by the host's roots.

Balanophores

Parasites called balanophores have strange flowers. These parasites infect the roots of tropical trees. The seeds settle on the roots and grow large tubers. These penetrate the host's roots.

Rafflesia

This parasite grows almost entirely in its host's roots. Its flowers, the biggest in the world (up to 1.5 metres across), burst from the roots. They smell awful but rodents like to eat the berries. Its seeds are carried to new hosts in the rodent's droppings.

Fungi

FUNGI ARE not classed as plants. Although some look like plants, they are quite different. Unlike most plants they do not contain chlorophyll and cannot make their own food. Instead, fungi feed on dead and living animal and plant material. The honey fungus (*see right*) feeds on the wood of both living and dead trees.

The main part of a fungus is called the mycelium. It is made up of a mass of delicate, thread-like tubes called hyphae. The reproductive parts of fungi are called fruiting bodies. A great variety of fruiting bodies are produced by different types of fungus, from tiny balls on stalks to large mushrooms that people like to eat.

Spores

To reproduce, fungi use spores. Many larger fungi produce their spores on the surface of plates called gills. These dangle beneath the cap and are arranged like the spokes of a wheel. Special club-shaped cells on the surface of the gills, the basidia, produce spores on the ends of tiny fingers. A single basidium usually produces four spores, but sometimes two or eight.

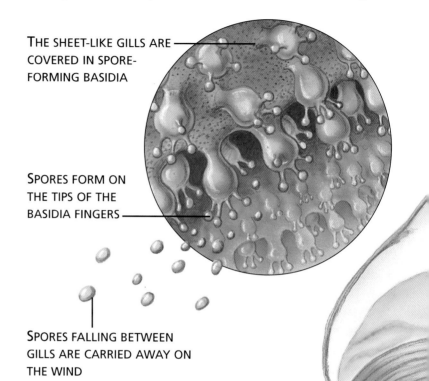

THE SHEET-LIKE GILLS ARE COVERED IN SPORE-FORMING BASIDIA

SPORES FORM ON THE TIPS OF THE BASIDIA FINGERS

SPORES FALLING BETWEEN GILLS ARE CARRIED AWAY ON THE WIND

THE WIND OR FALLING RAINDROPS FORCE THE SPORES OUT

THE SPORES ARE CARRIED INTO THE AIR

MASSES OF SPORES FORM IN THE THICK WHITE FLESH OF THE FRUITING BODY

THE OUTER SKIN OF THE STIPE (STALK)

THE FLESHY STIPE IS MADE OF MYCELIUM

AS THE MUSHROOM AGES THE GILLS DARKEN

The giant puff-ball

The fruiting body of the giant puff-ball (*left*) is a thick fleshy white mass where special cells produce spores. Slowly the cells die and the white flesh dries up. The spores are left behind inside the now dry, papery shell. The touch of a raindrop or breeze forces the tiny spores out.

THE CAP, OR UMBRELLA, FLATTENS AND MAY CURL AT THE EDGES

A YOUNG MUSHROOM DEVELOPS AS A 'BUTTON' OF DENSE MYCELIUM

THE DENSE MYCELIUM FORMS A ROOT-LIKE MASS

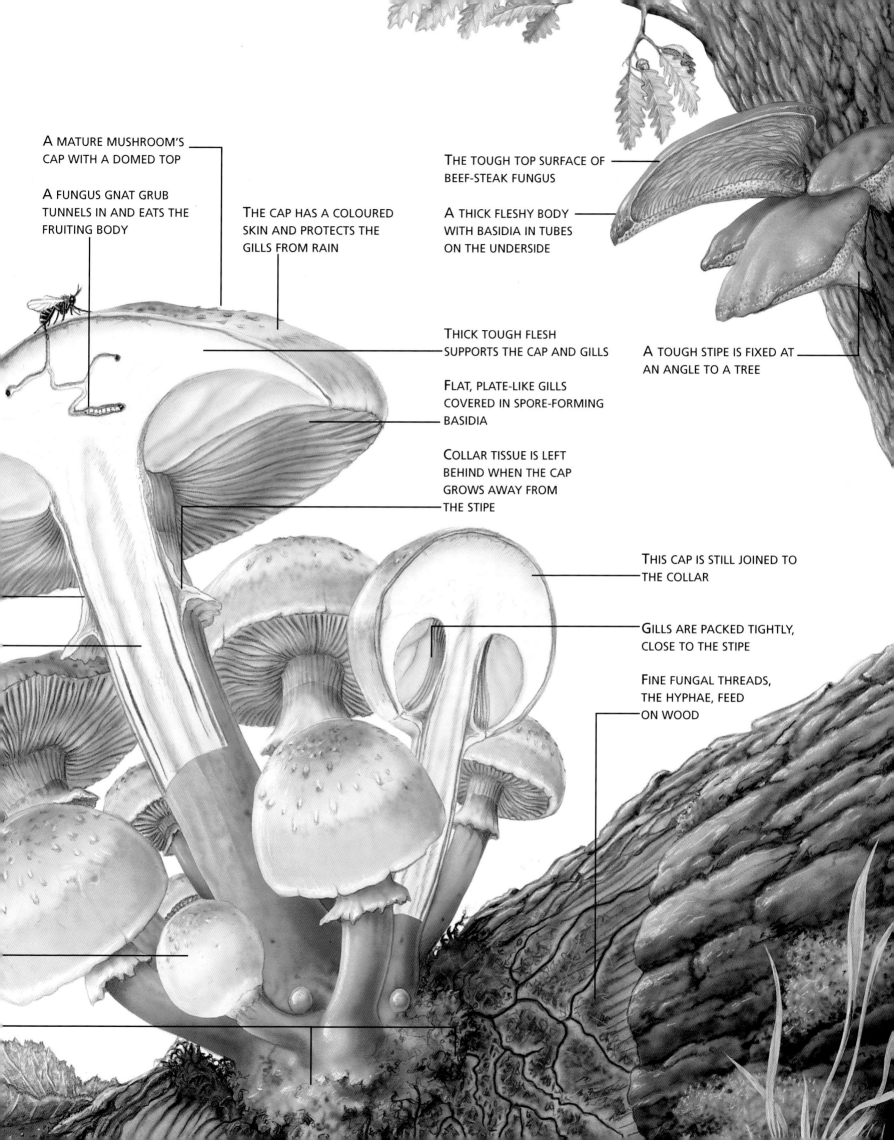

A MATURE MUSHROOM'S CAP WITH A DOMED TOP

A FUNGUS GNAT GRUB TUNNELS IN AND EATS THE FRUITING BODY

THE CAP HAS A COLOURED SKIN AND PROTECTS THE GILLS FROM RAIN

THE TOUGH TOP SURFACE OF BEEF-STEAK FUNGUS

A THICK FLESHY BODY WITH BASIDIA IN TUBES ON THE UNDERSIDE

THICK TOUGH FLESH SUPPORTS THE CAP AND GILLS

A TOUGH STIPE IS FIXED AT AN ANGLE TO A TREE

FLAT, PLATE-LIKE GILLS COVERED IN SPORE-FORMING BASIDIA

COLLAR TISSUE IS LEFT BEHIND WHEN THE CAP GROWS AWAY FROM THE STIPE

THIS CAP IS STILL JOINED TO THE COLLAR

GILLS ARE PACKED TIGHTLY, CLOSE TO THE STIPE

FINE FUNGAL THREADS, THE HYPHAE, FEED ON WOOD

Rainforest

TROPICAL rainforest provides perfect growing conditions for plants. As many as 700 different kinds of tree grow in a single area. Most grow over 50 metres tall. The animal life is as rich as the plant life, and the two depend upon each other.

The rainforest is divided into layers. From the air it looks like a green ocean. This is the canopy, the top layer, where the trees expose their crowns to the sun. Most of the rainforest animals are found in this crowded layer. Beneath the canopy, young trees form an understorey layer. If a tree falls, light breaks through the canopy, and young understorey trees quickly grow to fill the space. Vines and creepers also climb to reach the light. Orchids, ferns, and bromeliad plants grow on branches. In the lowest layer of the forest there is almost no sunlight and few plants can grow.

THE CANOPY IS THE BRIGHTEST, WARMEST, AND WETTEST LAYER

VERY TALL TREES EMERGE ABOVE THE CANOPY

THE SOIL IS THIN AND FULL OF FINE TREE ROOTS, WHICH QUICKLY ABSORB THE NUTRIENTS

Bromeliads
Bromeliads are epiphytes – plants that grow on others without harming them. They rely on trees to lift them from the darkness of the forest floor. Bromeliads' cup-like leaves trap water which would otherwise run down to the ground.

FROGS AND INSECTS LIVE IN THE WATER IN BROMELIADS

Ant plants
Ant plants have a swollen stem that provides ants with a safe home to live in. The ants help the plant in return by defending it against attack from other insects. Also, the ants' droppings give the plant extra nutrients for growth.

THE ANT PLANT'S HOST TREE

NEST IN SWOLLEN STEM

Rainforest life
The tall trees of the canopy provide timber for building and furniture. When a tree falls it tears an opening in the canopy, letting light flood in. Seedlings and young trees quickly grow to fill the gap.

In one hectare of forest 1500 species of plant can be found. Lianas climb up to the canopy to produce their own crowns. Birds, mammals, and insects pollinate the trees. The trees' branches and trunks are covered in ferns and mosses. Medicines, coffee, rubber, and chocolate, come from rainforest plants.

EMERGENT TREES ARE 100 METRES TALL – ALMOST TWICE AS HIGH AS THE CANOPY BELOW

MANY BIRDS, SUCH AS THIS TOUCAN, EAT FRUITS THAT GROW IN THE TREES

SPIDER MONKEYS FEED IN THE TREE-TOPS, SPREADING SEEDS FAR AROUND

LIANAS CLIMB TO REACH THE LIGHT

MOST OF THE LEAVES ARE SPECIALLY SHAPED SO THAT THEY CATCH RAINWATER AND POUR IT OFF AT THEIR TIPS

RAFFLESIA IS A PARASITE THAT LIVES ON LIANA ROOTS AND HAS THE LARGEST OF ALL FLOWERS

FUNGI HELP DEAD WOOD AND LEAVES TO ROT

FALLEN LEAVES QUICKLY ROT AWAY TO FORM A THIN SOIL

BROMELIAD LEAVES CATCH AND HOLD WATER – DEAD INSECTS DECAY IN THE WATER PROVIDING NUTRIENTS FOR THE PLANT

STRANGLER FIGS ARE CARRIED UP TO THE LIGHT BY GROWING TREES, WHICH THE STRANGLER FIGS SURROUND AND EVENTUALLY KILL

THE CANOPY

THE UNDERSTOREY LIES BENEATH THE CANOPY

STRONG, WIDE BUTTRESS ROOTS SUPPORT THE HUGE TREE

Forest Growth

FORESTS ARE communities of trees and other plants. Many different kinds of forest grow, depending on the types of plants, the climate, terrain, and soil, and the influence of humans and other animals. Forests develop over tens, or even millions, of years – they are at the end of a long succession (sequence of changes) in which different plants take over. On bare soil, 'opportunist' plants soon appear. They are well-adapted to exploiting new ground. Over time, other species replace them. This plant succession usually leads to forests, like the beech forest shown here. Forests are called climax communities because they are at the end of a succession.

Plant defences
Plants are a source of food for many animals. To defend themselves from herbivores (plant-eaters), many plants use poisons, a tough skin, spines, or thorns. Nettles use fine, needle-sharp hairs. These pierce the animals' skin and break, releasing a tiny amount of painful, stinging acid. Large animals that would otherwise eat nettles soon learn to leave them alone.

NEEDLE-SHARP NETTLE HAIRS

1) Bare ground
Bare or cleared chalky ground is soon invaded by quick-growing annual plants. Other species then arrive.

OTHER PLANTS INVADE, AND REPLACE THE 'OPPORTUNISTS'

THE NEW CARPET OF PLANTS INCLUDES THYME, CLOVER, MILKWORT, AND GRASSES

RABBITS GRAZE, KEEPING THE CHALK GRASSLAND PLANTS SMALL

A DENSE SCRUB OF DOGWOOD, ROSE, AND HAWTHORN BUSHES DEVELOPS

BARE CHALKY SOIL – READY FOR PIONEER PLANTS TO COLONIZE THE LAND

RAGWORT, COLTSFOOT, AND MOSSES ARE OPPORTUNISTS INVADING THE BARE GROUND

2) Chalk grassland
Grazing by rabbits and sheep, and also cutting by humans, helps to develop a rich carpet of growth. Many of the plants are specially adapted to living on the chalky soil.

3) Scrub
Where there is little or no grazing, woody plant species invade. Bushes form a dense scrub which creates too much shade for delicate grassland plants to grow.

THE CROWNS OF THE BEECH
TREES REACH UPWARDS FOR
SUNLIGHT

A BEECH FOREST FINALLY
DEVELOPS AT THE END OF A
LONG SUCCESSION

4) Ash wood
Ash trees form
their own wood-
land. Sheltered
beneath the
canopy of ash
trees, beech seeds
can germinate
and grow. The
ash trees act as a
nursery for these
slower growing
trees.

ASH TREES HAVE
SPACED OUT LEAVES
SO SUNLIGHT CAN
REACH THE GROUND
AND NEW PLANTS
CAN GROW

5) Beech forest
The leaves of the
beech trees shade the
soil below. Little else
grows here except for
special plants like dog's
mercury. Where there is
enough light, brambles
and nettles flourish.

DOG'S
MERCURY

④

⑤

YOUNG BEECH BEGIN TO
GROW WITH THE HELP OF THE
ASH TREES

FEW PLANTS GROW IN THE
SHADE OF THE BEECH TREES

BRAMBLES AND NETTLES
HAVE STINGS AND SPIKES TO
STOP THEM BEING EATEN

DEAD PLANT AND ANIMAL
MATERIAL SLOWLY CHANGES
INTO NUTRIENT-RICH SOIL –
TREES USE THE NUTRIENTS
FOR GROWTH

223

Mountain Zones

THE HIGHER you climb up a mountain, the colder the climate gets. Prevailing winds affect the climate too, making it wetter on one side of the mountain than the other. The wind and rain, and changes in temperature with height, create different vegetation zones on a mountain. In central Africa the lowland plains at the foot of a mountain are dominated by savanna grassland and acacia woodlands. Between 1500 and 2400 metres, moist, high rainforest flourishes. Above this, mountain bamboo is the dominant vegetation. Higher still, sub-alpine moorland extends up to about 4000 metres. Beyond this lies the Afro-alpine zone, where the days are warm and the nights are cold. From 4800 metres to the bleak summit, there is little or no vegetation except for scattered lichens.

Mountain rainfall
Moisture-rich winds are forced up the mountain side. This causes the moisture to condense as clouds, which form mists. When there is too much moisture in the air, it falls as rain, sleet, or snow. This effects the pattern of the vegetation zones.

Bamboo belt
Between 2400 and 3000 metres, mountain bamboo forms a dense vegetation up to 15 metres in height. These giant grasses grow from rhizomes. They grow so densely that sunlight is unable to get through to the ground.

BAMBOO HAS FAST GROWING WOODY STEMS

Afro-alpine zone
Above 4000 metres plants have to protect themselves against the frost that forms at night and melts during the day. White hairs keep ice off the plant's skin and absorb the sun's warmth. Some plants grow close to the ground for shelter. The hyrax, a small, hoofed mammal, lives amongst the rocks.

TREE-DAISY LEAVES HAVE SILVERY HAIRS TO REDUCE HEAT LOSS

IN THE AFRO-ALPINE ZONE MANY PLANTS HUG THE GROUND FOR WARMTH

ABOVE THE BAMBOO ZONE, LARGE SHRUB-LIKE HEATHERS GROW IN THE MOORLAND ZONE

Savanna
The hot, dry lowlands are covered in savanna grasslands. Only drought-resistant grasses and trees grow here. In the rainy season there is lots of growth, providing food for many animals.

In the dry season, hot winds dry the vegetation so much that fires are common (caused by lightning and people). But after a fire, acacia trees soon sprout, and grasses emerge again from underground.

THE TREE CANOPY OF THE HIGH RAINFOREST

ACACIA WOODLAND MERGES WITH RAINFOREST AS RAINFALL INCREASES WITH HEIGHT

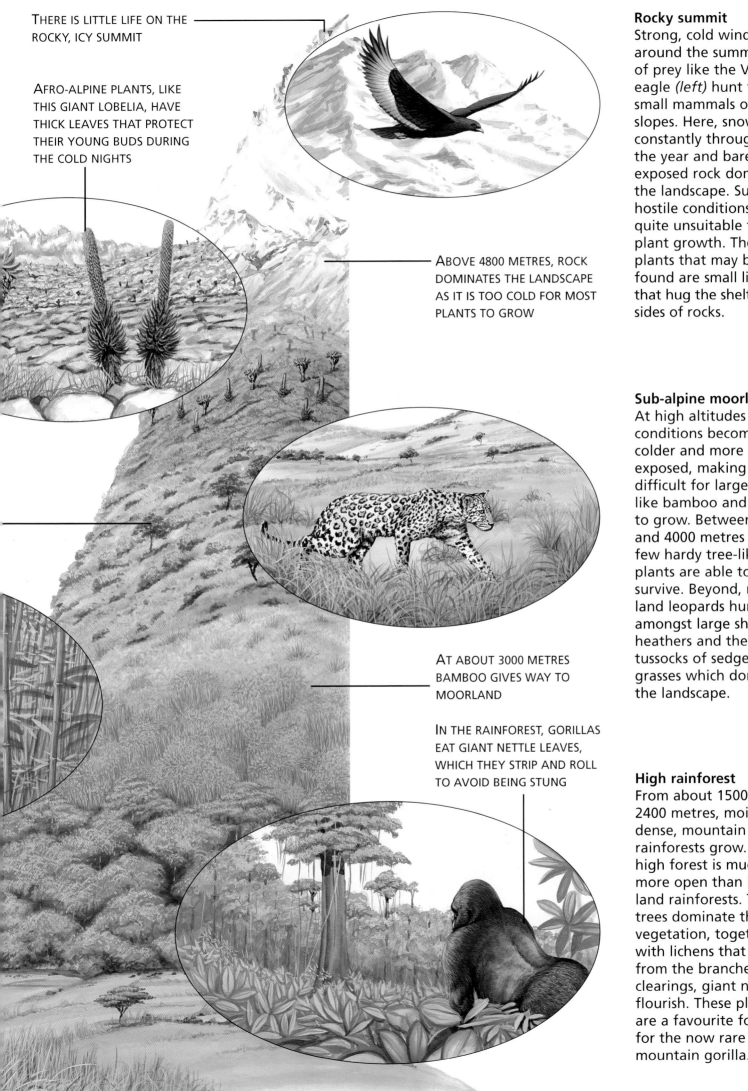

THERE IS LITTLE LIFE ON THE ROCKY, ICY SUMMIT

AFRO-ALPINE PLANTS, LIKE THIS GIANT LOBELIA, HAVE THICK LEAVES THAT PROTECT THEIR YOUNG BUDS DURING THE COLD NIGHTS

ABOVE 4800 METRES, ROCK DOMINATES THE LANDSCAPE AS IT IS TOO COLD FOR MOST PLANTS TO GROW

AT ABOUT 3000 METRES BAMBOO GIVES WAY TO MOORLAND

IN THE RAINFOREST, GORILLAS EAT GIANT NETTLE LEAVES, WHICH THEY STRIP AND ROLL TO AVOID BEING STUNG

Rocky summit
Strong, cold winds blow around the summit. Birds of prey like the Verraux eagle *(left)* hunt for small mammals on the slopes. Here, snow falls constantly throughout the year and bare, exposed rock dominates the landscape. Such hostile conditions are quite unsuitable for plant growth. The only plants that may be found are small lichens that hug the sheltered sides of rocks.

Sub-alpine moorland
At high altitudes conditions become colder and more exposed, making it more difficult for large plants like bamboo and trees to grow. Between 3000 and 4000 metres only a few hardy tree-like plants are able to survive. Beyond, moorland leopards hunt amongst large shrub-like heathers and the tussocks of sedges and grasses which dominate the landscape.

High rainforest
From about 1500 to 2400 metres, moist, dense, mountain rainforests grow. This high forest is much more open than lowland rainforests. Tall trees dominate the vegetation, together with lichens that dangle from the branches. In clearings, giant nettles flourish. These plants are a favourite food for the now rare mountain gorilla.

DISCOVERING
PREHISTORY

Robert Muir Wood

DISCOVERING PREHISTORY CONTENTS

What is Prehistory?

HOW OLD is the Earth? Have the continents moved? How are mountains formed? How do we know about the dinosaurs? Where did people come from? Such questions can only be answered by exploring prehistory.

Prehistory means before history – that is, before our earliest written records, which go back about 4,000 years. Prehistory covers a much longer period – the billions of years of deep time. To explore prehistory we need all the skills of a detective, searching for clues preserved in the Earth.

IN THE TERTIARY PERIOD, MAMMALS GREW TO BECOME THE LARGEST ANIMALS ON BOTH LAND AND SEA

THE FIRST BIRDS, SUCH AS *ARCHAEOPTERYX*, EVOLVED FROM THE REPTILES

THIS EARLY MAMMAL EVOLVED INTO THE HORSE

WE LIVE AT THE END OF THE QUATERNARY PERIOD

WOOLLY MAMMOTHS LIVED IN THE QUATERNARY ICE AGES

PEOPLE EVOLVED AT THE END OF THE TERTIARY PERIOD, ABOUT 3 MILLION YEARS AGO

REPTILES EVOLVED FROM
GIANT AMPHIBIANS, SUCH
AS *ERYOPS*, WHICH HAD TO
RETURN TO THE WATER
TO LAY THEIR EGGS

FIVE HUNDRED MILLION
YEARS AGO THE SEAS WERE
FILLED WITH TRILOBITES

THE EARTH WAS FORMED
ABOUT 4,500 MILLION
YEARS AGO

ALL EARLY LIFE WAS TINY
AND SINGLE-CELLED, LIKE THIS
BLUE-GREEN ALGAE

IN THE PERMIAN PERIOD,
GIANT REPTILES LIVED IN
FORESTS

MAMMALS APPEARED IN THE
TRIASSIC PERIOD

MOST DINOSAURS LIVED IN
THE CRETACEOUS, JURASSIC
AND TRIASSIC PERIODS

WHALES ARE MAMMALS
THAT EVOLVED FROM LAND
ANIMALS NO LARGER THAN
A BEAR

Key to prehistory
(mya = millions of years ago)

Today	
Quaternary	1.5 mya
Tertiary	65 mya
Cretaceous	135 mya
Jurassic	205 mya
Triassic	250 mya
Permian	290 mya

Carboniferous	355 mya
Devonian	410 mya
Silurian	440 mya
Ordovician	510 mya
Cambrian	570 mya
Precambrian	4,600 mya

Evolution

Deep time has been divided into periods, each covering many millions of years. As we travel back in time, the types of animals and plants alive on Earth change. Many that once lived on the Earth died out and disappeared for ever – they became extinct.

There are many reasons why a type of plant or animal becomes extinct. Perhaps it was unable to adapt to changes in the environment or climate. Perhaps another animal or plant appeared that was more successful. Plants and animals that do survive adapt to the changes over many generations and millions of years. The way in which animals or plants adapt, or change, is called evolution.

231

Digging Up the Past

O UNCOVER the past we have to dig down into the Earth. Sometimes rivers have done much of the work, by cutting gorges into the land. In Arizona, USA, the Colorado River has cut a gorge down through more than a kilometre of rock. This gorge, called the Grand Canyon, shows a spectacular section of the prehistoric past. Walking to the bottom of the Canyon, you can almost walk back in time: the layers of rock around you, and the fossils found within them, get older the further down you go.

SEDIMENTS FORMED OVER THE PAST 250 MILLION YEARS HAVE BEEN WORN AWAY

A SIMPLE RULE OF SEDIMENTS: YOUNGER LAYERS ARE FOUND ON TOP OF OLDER ONES

KAIBAB LIMESTONE (250 MILLION YEARS OLD)

COCONINO SANDSTONE (290 MILLION YEARS OLD)

HERMIT SHALE (350 MILLION YEARS OLD)

FOSSILS OF FISH SCALES ARE FOUND IN THIS LAYER, WHICH IS 390 MILLION YEARS OLD

BRIGHT ANGEL SHALE (530 MILLION YEARS OLD)

THE ROCKS HERE ARE MUCH OLDER AND HAVE TILTED DURING THE FORMATION OF MOUNTAINS

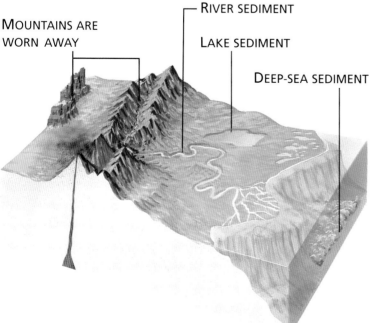

MOUNTAINS ARE WORN AWAY

RIVER SEDIMENT

LAKE SEDIMENT

DEEP-SEA SEDIMENT

How the layers formed
Mountains are continually worn away. Fragments of the mountain are carried off by ice, water and wind, finally settling on lowland, or beneath the water of a lake or sea. These deposits are called sediments. Over millions of years layers of sediment pile up and harden, forming sedimentary rocks.

THESE ROCKS FORMED 1,700 MILLION YEARS AGO, WHEN THE ONLY LIFE ON EARTH WAS TINY SINGLE-CELLED ORGANISMS

THE RIVER CUTS DOWN
THROUGH THE CANYON
ROCKS

① ② ③ ④

Fossils in layers

The age of a layer of sediments is known from the fossils found within it (*see pages 234–5*). Fossils are the remains of living things preserved in rock. As a result of evolution, life has changed through time. Fossils show us the different life forms that have lived during each period of prehistory. Here, some of the layers that contain fossils are shown enlarged.

Kaibab limestone (1)

Near the top of the Grand Canyon is a layer of Kaibab limestone and sandstone. This was deposited in a shallow sea 250 million years ago and is filled with the fossil shells of sea-living creatures such as ammonites.

Coconino sandstone (2)

The Coconino sandstone sediment was laid down on land about 290 million years ago. It contains footprints of primitive reptiles and amphibians, which lived before the dinosaurs.

Hermit shale (3)

Below the sandstone is Hermit shale. Laid down around 350 million years ago in shallow pools, these mudstones contain raindrop prints, and fossils of insects and ferns.

Bright Angel shale (4)

This shale was deposited when there were no plants or animals on land. Fossils include trilobites (ancient sea creatures), shells and creatures' burrow marks, of 530 million years ago.

233

How Fossils Form

FOSSILS have taught us most of what we know about prehistoric plants and animals. They are the traces of past life preserved in rock. Most are formed from the hard parts of animals and plants, but fossils can also record marks such as an animal's footprint left in sand. In order for something to become fossilized it must be buried in sediments quickly before it starts to decay away. As new layers of sediments are deposited on top, the lower layers become squashed, or compressed, into rock. In this way the animal or plant fragment in the lower layers becomes fossilized.

ONLY WHEN AN ANIMAL IS SUDDENLY COVERED IN SEDIMENT, PERHAPS IN A VOLCANIC ERUPTION, WILL ITS BONES STAY TOGETHER

DELICATE PLANT MATERIAL ONLY STAYS IN ONE PIECE IF IT IS COVERED WITH MUD OR STAGNANT WATER

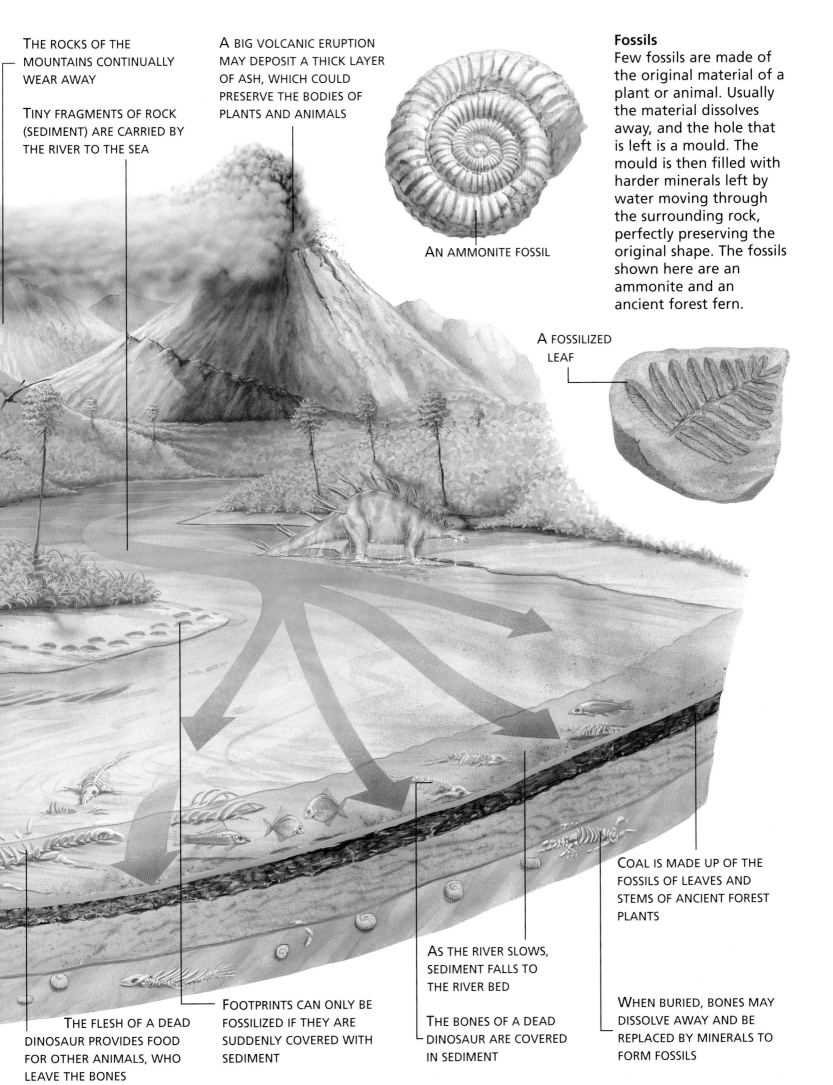

THE ROCKS OF THE MOUNTAINS CONTINUALLY WEAR AWAY

TINY FRAGMENTS OF ROCK (SEDIMENT) ARE CARRIED BY THE RIVER TO THE SEA

A BIG VOLCANIC ERUPTION MAY DEPOSIT A THICK LAYER OF ASH, WHICH COULD PRESERVE THE BODIES OF PLANTS AND ANIMALS

AN AMMONITE FOSSIL

Fossils
Few fossils are made of the original material of a plant or animal. Usually the material dissolves away, and the hole that is left is a mould. The mould is then filled with harder minerals left by water moving through the surrounding rock, perfectly preserving the original shape. The fossils shown here are an ammonite and an ancient forest fern.

A FOSSILIZED LEAF

THE FLESH OF A DEAD DINOSAUR PROVIDES FOOD FOR OTHER ANIMALS, WHO LEAVE THE BONES

FOOTPRINTS CAN ONLY BE FOSSILIZED IF THEY ARE SUDDENLY COVERED WITH SEDIMENT

AS THE RIVER SLOWS, SEDIMENT FALLS TO THE RIVER BED

THE BONES OF A DEAD DINOSAUR ARE COVERED IN SEDIMENT

COAL IS MADE UP OF THE FOSSILS OF LEAVES AND STEMS OF ANCIENT FOREST PLANTS

WHEN BURIED, BONES MAY DISSOLVE AWAY AND BE REPLACED BY MINERALS TO FORM FOSSILS

Comparing Evidence

Correlation between excavation sites
These two excavation sites are 1,500 kilometres apart – one in Denmark (*left*), the other in Greece (*right*). Sediments, brought by rivers and the

NO SINGLE place on Earth can give us a complete record of prehistory. Parts of the record are found scattered in different areas of the world. To link these fragments together we have to find materials that were formed in different places but at the same time. This process is called correlation. We can also date layers in the soil by correlating objects made by people. For example, we know that bronze was not used by people until about 5,000 years ago. So wherever a bronze item is found, we know the soil it was found in is not more than 5,000 years old.

AN ARCHAEOLOGIST EXPLORES THE PREHISTORY OF HUMAN BEINGS

SOME SOFT DRINK CONTAINERS ARE SO UNIVERSAL WE COULD CORRELATE THEM ACROSS THE WORLD

Tools and treasures
One form of correlation uses the objects made by early peoples. The first tools and arrowheads, made from flint and other stone (1), were made to a similar design for tens of thousands of years. The first carved figures date from more than 20,000 years ago (2). By 10,000 BC people started to bake pottery jars and cups. They travelled thousands of kilometres and exchanged their new ideas with other peoples. The discovery of how to make bronze, around 3000 BC, led to new ornaments being made (3). And with the discovery of iron-smelting around 1000 BC, new, more effective weapons were possible (4). So, when we find an iron weapon we know it must date from after 1000 BC.

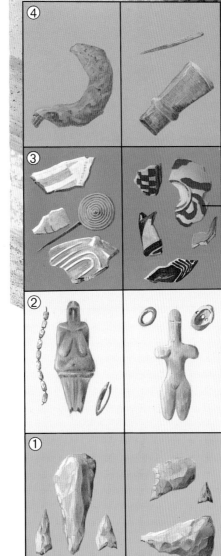

FRAGMENTS OF IRON TOOLS AND WEAPONS, 2,500 YEARS OLD, WERE FOUND IN THIS LAYER AT BOTH SITES

THE DISCOVERY OF BRONZE OBJECTS MEANS THE LAYER IS NOT MORE THAN 5,000 YEARS OLD

NOT ALL OBJECTS ARE THE SAME EVERYWHERE – THE DESIGNS ON POTTERY, FOR EXAMPLE, VARIED FROM REGION TO REGION

wind, were laid down at both sites over the past few thousand years. A number of objects and fossils have been found that allow the different layers of sediment to be correlated and dated.

OUR RAPIDLY CHANGING TECHNOLOGY WILL MAKE IT EASIER FOR FUTURE ARCHAEOLOGISTS TO DATE THE OBJECTS WE THROW AWAY

A GEOLOGIST EXPLORES THE PREHISTORY OF LIFE AND OF THE EARTH

AMMONITES

TRILOBITES

Fossil correlation
Fossils of animals that lived in shallow seas are very useful for correlation. Sea animals tended to evolve quickly so that one particular type was unique to a particular time. Evolving ammonites were common in the Jurassic period, whereas evolving trilobites were common in the Cambrian period. Their fossils have been discovered all round the world, enabling world-wide correlation.

POTTERY FIGURES WERE FOUND AT BOTH SITES IN ROCK LAYERS OF THE SAME AGE

THIS LAYER WAS DEPOSITED BY DUST STORMS DURING THE LAST ICE AGE 20,000 YEARS AGO

IN THIS LAYER, PRIMITIVE STONE TOOLS WERE FOUND

FINDING SIMILAR TOOLS AT BOTH SITES CAN SUGGEST THE LAYERS ARE OF A SIMILAR AGE

Continuous Cores

SOME parts of nature hold secrets of their age within them. In the same way that we can follow the evolution of the Earth by digging into it, we can study the passing of time by looking at the layers in the wood of a tree or the ice of an ice-sheet. Taking out a core from a tree or an ice-sheet allows us to count the years back into the past. Such cores record changes in the pattern of the weather, some of which can be correlated around the globe.

Tree cores

Trees do most of their growing in the summer. If a tree trunk is cut across its width, you can see a pattern of rings: wider bands of spring early-wood, separated by narrow, darker bands of autumn and winter late-wood. Changes in climate alter the widths of the rings from year to year. By studying the ring patterns and matching them against older tree cores, we can learn how the climate has changed over thousands of years.

USING A NARROW CORER, IT IS POSSIBLE TO OBTAIN A CONTINUOUS SECTION THROUGH A LIVING TREE WITHOUT DAMAGING IT

A CORE TAKEN FROM THE CENTRE OF A LIVING TREE

WOOD FROM A PREHISTORIC BOAT (1,500 YEARS OLD)

WOOD FROM A CHURCH DOOR (900 YEARS OLD)

WOOD FROM THE BEAMS OF A HOUSE (500 YEARS OLD)

156 AD

RING PATTERNS CAN BE COMPARED AND MATCHED (CORRELATED)

385 AD

BY SWITCHING TO OLDER AND OLDER PIECES OF TIMBER, TREE RINGS HAVE BEEN COUNTED BACK THOUSANDS OF YEARS

942 AD

BY COUNTING THE RINGS WE LEARN THE TREE'S AGE

1415 AD

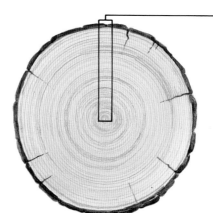

THICK RINGS REVEAL LONG, WARM, WET SUMMERS

238

Ice core

In winter, high on a mountain ice-sheet, there are fresh falls of snow. In summer the crust of the snow melts, and then freezes once again before new snow falls. Bands of ice and snow are left and can be seen thousands of years later in the ice-sheet core. Ice-sheet cores from Greenland, over 3,000 metres deep, record more than 200,000 years of history. The cores show how the seasons and the chemistry and temperature of the air have changed year by year.

Deep-sea cores

In the deep sea, sediment forms from a slow rain of tiny dead sea plants and animals. During the Ice Ages, when ice-caps covered the northern parts of Europe and America, the temperature of the sea surface dropped. This caused the changes in the types of organisms and sediments now seen in deep-sea cores. These cores reveal the world's changing climate. People once thought there had been only two or three Ice Ages. Deep-sea cores show that in fact there have been Ice Ages almost every hundred thousand years for the past two million years!

THE DRILL-CORE REACHES THROUGH SIX KILOMETRES OF WATER TO THE OCEAN FLOOR

UNDER THE MICROSCOPE: PARTICLES OF VOLCANIC ASH SHOW THERE WAS A VOLCANIC ERUPTION

A LAYER OF VOLCANIC ASH

BY STUDYING FOSSILIZED SEA-LIFE WE CAN DISCOVER PAST DIFFERENCES IN OCEAN TEMPERATURE

THIN LAYERS OF VOLCANIC ASH MAY CORRELATE WITH SIMILAR LAYERS IN THE ICE CORES

Counting Radio-isotopes

THE YEARS of deep time can be charted in rocks. Rocks contain radio-isotopes – atoms that are unstable and fall apart (decay) at a constant rate. A large number of these radio-isotope atoms slowly change from parent atoms to daughter atoms. The age of a rock can be found by measuring how many of the parent atoms have decayed into daughter atoms. For some radio-isotopes millions of years will pass before they have all become daughter atoms.

The radio-isotope of the element potassium is useful for dating prehistory because it is found in many ancient rocks. The parent atom potassium decays into the daughter atom argon. By counting the radio-isotopes we can find the age of ancient rocks that are sometimes billions of years old. Radio-isotope dating provides a calendar of prehistory, helping us to reconstruct the past.

Volcanic rocks (1)
Volcanic rocks, or lava, often contain potassium-rich minerals. By counting the radio-isotopes we can date when the volcano erupted. This could help us date the fossils of dinosaurs that died in the red-hot lava.

① DATING THIS ROCK SHOWS THE VOLCANO ERUPTED 250 MILLION YEARS AGO

ONLY ONE POTASSIUM ATOM HAS BECOME AN ARGON ATOM

METEORITE CRATER

LAVA (MOLTEN ROCK FROM THE VOLCANO) RUNS ACROSS THE LAND

FOSSILS SHOW THAT THE DINOSAUR *DIMETRODON* DIED IN THE ERUPTION

TRILOBITE FOSSILS

A LAYER OF SEDIMENTARY ROCK

LAVA COOLS AND SOLIDIFIES OVER DINOSAUR REMAINS

ROCKS FROM THIS PREHISTORIC SCENE COULD BE FOUND TODAY, AND DATED

Meteorites (2)

It takes 11,000 million years for half of the total potassium atoms in a rock to become argon atoms. In this meteorite many of the potassium atoms have decayed into argon. The rock is very old, and was formed at the same time as the Earth. Meteorites are large rocks hurtling in space around the Sun. The largest ones leave giant craters when they hit the Earth. The remains of many giant craters have been found and can be dated.

PARENT POTASSIUM ATOMS ── DAUGHTER ARGON ATOMS

②

LAVA FORMS A LAYER OF VOLCANIC ROCK

THIS METEORITE FORMED AT THE SAME TIME AS THE EARTH, 4,500 MILLION YEARS AGO

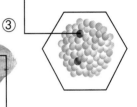

ISOTOPES IN POTASSIUM-RICH MINERALS IN THIS SEDIMENT SHOW AN AGE OF 500 MILLION YEARS

③

THIS TRILOBITE FOSSIL IS ALSO 500 MILLION YEARS OLD

Sedimentary rocks (3)

Some sedimentary rocks contain minerals rich in potassium, making potassium-argon dating possible.

The older the rock, the greater the number of daughter (argon) atoms. When the rock's age has been calculated, the age of fossils found within it will also be known.

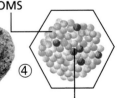

POTASSIUM ATOMS

④

ARGON ATOM

THIS METAMORPHIC ROCK DATES FROM 3,000 MILLION YEARS AGO

A LAYER OF METAMORPHIC ROCK

Metamorphic rocks (4)

Metamorphic rocks have been heated deep underground. As they were heated argon may have escaped because, unlike potassium, argon is a gas. The escape of the daughter argon atoms may make the rock seem younger than it really is when the radio-isotopes are counted. As the metamorphic rock cools, argon atoms become trapped, and radio-isotope dating is accurate again.

241

Radiocarbon Dating

RADIOCARBON (or carbon 14) dating gives archaeologists an accurate age of any formerly living material. While radio-isotope dating can be used for measuring rocks that have been around since the origin of the Earth, radiocarbon dating can only be used for dating material from the past 40,000 years.

Carbon 14 is a radioactive form of the element carbon that is continually being created at the top of the atmosphere. Carbon is taken up by plants. Animals (including humans) take in carbon 14 when they eat plants and when they breathe. When the plant or animal dies, carbon 14 is no longer taken in. But the carbon 14 left in the dead material gradually decays. By measuring the amount left in the material, archaeologists can tell how long it is since the organism died.

PLANTS ABSORB CARBON 14 IN CARBON DIOXIDE

Prehistoric farmers
This scene of prehistoric farmers shows how carbon 14 is taken in by the living plants and people of the time. If we found any dead remains from this prehistoric scene today, we would be able to date it using radiocarbon dating.

THE RADIOCARBON DATE OF THIS BOAT WOULD SHOW WHEN THE TREE DIED

REMAINS OF ALL THE LIVING OBJECTS IN THIS SCENE COULD BE RADIOCARBON DATED

CLOTH WOVEN FROM PLANTS, SUCH AS FLAX, CAN BE DATED

BY DATING THE REMAINS PRESERVED IN A BOG WE CAN RECONSTRUCT A SCENE LIKE THIS FROM 2,500 YEARS AGO

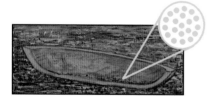

2,500 YEARS AGO

2,000 YEARS AGO

Carbon 14
When a tree is cut down, it dies and stops taking in more carbon 14 from the atmosphere. The tree might be made into a boat but the carbon 14 in the wood would continue to decay. After 5,730 years half the carbon 14 will have gone. After 11,460 years only a quarter will be left. Pictured left is a boat that was made by prehistoric farmers. Buried in the soil it gradually decayed. Radiocarbon dating of a piece of the boat today might show it as being 2,500 years old, with more than a quarter of the carbon 14 gone.

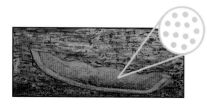

TODAY

242

CARBON 14 IS MADE WHEN COSMIC RAYS ZAP NITROGEN ATOMS IN THE UPPER ATMOSPHERE

THE REMAINS OF THE PEOPLE WHO ATE THE PLANTS COULD BE RADIOCARBON DATED

MANY REMAINS LEFT BY THIS PREHISTORIC SETTLEMENT OF EARLY FARMERS COULD BE CARBON DATED

COSMIC RAYS COME FROM STARS, DEEP IN SPACE

NITROGEN ATOMS (BLUE) ARE CONVERTED TO CARBON 14 ATOMS (GREEN)

ALL PLANTS OBTAIN THEIR CARBON 14 FROM THE ATMOSPHERE

CARBON 14 BREAKS DOWN AND IS RETURNED TO THE ATMOSPHERE

AS SOON AS THE TREE OR PLANT IS CUT DOWN, CARBON 14 IS NO LONGER TAKEN IN

THE DATING OF OBJECTS WOVEN FROM PLANTS WILL SHOW WHEN THE PLANTS DIED

Dinosaur Excavation

IMPORTANT fossil finds require very careful digging or excavation. The first discovery may be the chance sighting of a fossil sticking out of a cliff or the glimpse of a bone as the foundations of a new building are being dug. This *Iguanodon* skeleton is unusually complete. The animal died and was preserved all in one place. Finds like this are very rare and demand the most careful excavation to ensure that nothing is broken and nothing is missed. To help rebuild the skeleton accurately, scientists have to record the location of every tiny fragment of bone.

THE SITE IS EXCAVATED LAYER BY LAYER – A PICKAXE IS USED TO BREAK UP THE TOP LAYER OF ROCK

THE TOP LAYERS OF ROCK ARE REMOVED FIRST

THE EXACT LOCATION OF ALL THE BONES IS ACCURATELY RECORDED, USING A GRID

A GROOVE IS CUT ROUND THE BONE WITH A HAMMER AND CHISEL

SIEVES CATCH SMALL FRAGMENTS OF THE SKELETON

FRAGILE BONES ARE CLEANED WITH A PAINTBRUSH

THE SKULL OF THE *IGUANODON* IS ALREADY BEING FREED

BONES ARE WRAPPED IN STRIPS DIPPED IN PLASTER OF PARIS

In the laboratory

The jawbone is the strongest part of a skull and may be the only piece to survive. The amount the teeth are worn down can reveal the animal's age when it died, and the kind of food it ate.

The jawbone arrives in the laboratory in its protective covering. This is removed and any stone left on it is dissolved in weak acid.

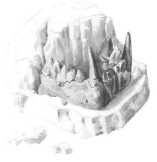

Detailed cleaning is carried out using various tiny instruments, like a dentist's drill or a small chisel. The cleaned bone fragments are then carefully examined to see how they fitted together. The teeth can be put back into the jawbone and glued into place. Any missing pieces of bone or teeth are replaced with plaster. At this stage scientists can start to build up a picture of what the dinosaur was like.

EVERY FIND IS LISTED

THE PROTECTED BONES CAN BE GENTLY LIFTED AND PACKED IN CRATES

CRATES ARE WHEELED TO A LORRY, AND TAKEN TO THE LABORATORY

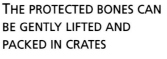

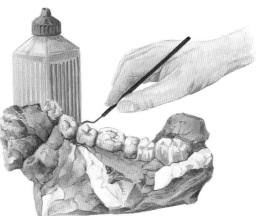

Dinosaur Reconstruction

WHAT did dinosaurs look like? The bones are impressive enough, but to flesh out the bones it is necessary to rebuild the whole dinosaur with muscles and skin. The first stage, putting a dinosaur skeleton together, is like solving a jigsaw puzzle. Some of the pieces may be missing and others badly broken. However, there are so many similarities between dinosaurs and animals living today, it is possible to find the right places for almost all the bones simply by comparing their shapes to those of today's animals. Once the skeleton has been formed, the muscles can be added, and then the skin.

THE MUSCLES HAD TO BE LARGE ENOUGH TO ALLOW *TRICERATOPS* TO CHARGE ITS ATTACKERS

THE MUSCLES OF DINOSAURS WERE SIMILAR IN SHAPE TO THOSE OF BIRDS AND CROCODILES

What is the skin like?
Fossilized fragments of dinosaur skin are sometimes found. The fragment above shows a pattern similar to that of a lizard's, but on a larger scale. The skin had to be very tough to withstand being dragged through spiny trees or bushes. Skin-colour does not show on the fossil.

TRICERATOPS WAS PROBABLY GREY, LIKE THE MODERN ANIMAL THAT SHARES A SIMILAR LIFESTYLE – THE RHINOCEROS

THE PATTERN OF MUSCLES CAN BE RECONSTRUCTED BY WORKING OUT HOW THE LIMBS MOVED

THE OVERALL SHAPE OF THE SKELETON SHOWS THAT IT WALKED ON ITS TOES

Where were the muscles attached?

There are often markings on the bones where large muscles were attached. From these muscle-scar markings, it is possible to begin to reconstruct the muscles of the legs and body.

HORNS WERE USED AS
WEAPONS AGAINST ATTACK

MISSING PARTS OF THE FOSSIL
ARE FILLED IN WITH PLASTER

PLASTER

Missing bones

Many bones in a body are the same as other bones; one rib is very similar to another rib. If a bone is missing, either a copy can be made or it can be reconstructed from those that do exist. Cast in plaster, these newly made bones can be used to complete the skeleton.

Assembling the skeleton

First the whole skeleton is laid out on the floor (1).

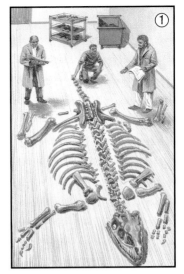

Starting with the spine, the vertebrae (back-bones) are wired together. The spine is then hauled into the air. The leg bones are put together and then attached to the spine (2).

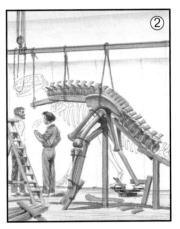

For dramatic displays, skeletons are assembled into life-like poses, such as a fighting scene, with their necks bent and jaws open (3). A metal frame is used to support the skeleton.

How the Dinosaurs Lived

WHAT were the dinosaurs like? Did they walk or run? How did they fight? What kind of noises did they make? Will we ever know how they lived? Just like any other animal, every part of a dinosaur's body helped it to survive. So every part of a dinosaur that we find tells us something about how it lived.

Several of the most amazing dinosaurs lived alongside each other. *Parasaurolophos* was a duck-billed dinosaur that lived in forests. The *Ankylosaur* was an armoured dinosaur that lived in open grassland. Both were attacked by the fearsome *Tyrannosaurus*. A few million years later these and all the other dinosaurs on Earth were dead.

Dinosaur nest

We know some dinosaurs had nesting colonies, where they laid their eggs together. The remains of some of these colonies have been found in fossilized form. These *Maiasaurus* nests were made of mounds of sand. Beside one nest there were fossils of 15 newly-hatched dinosaur babies.

A dinosaur's meal

We even know what a dinosaur last had to eat before it died. This *Compsognathus* had just eaten a lizard. The lizard's skeleton was fossilized in the dinosaur's ribcage.

THE FOSSIL OF A LIZARD'S SKELETON

PERHAPS THE CREST WAS USED TO MAKE TRUMPETING NOISES TO ATTRACT OTHER *PARASAUROLOPHUS*

TUBES FOR AIR RAN THROUGH ITS CREST

THESE TEETH WERE SHAPED FOR GRINDING VEGETATION

A duck-billed dinosaur

This plant-eating *Parasaurolophos* is called a duck-billed dinosaur because of the crest on its head. The one-metre long crest was partly a colourful ornament to show off to other dinosaurs. But it also contained air tubes which may have given the animal an acute sense of smell.

AN EXTRA JOINT ALLOWED ITS JAWS TO OPEN EXTRA WIDE AND BITE THE BODIES OF THE LARGEST DINOSAURS

A meat-eater
The most frightening of the meat-eating dinosaurs, *Tyranno-saurus*, was designed for fighting. It grew up to 14 metres long, and its massive jaws were filled with dagger-like teeth, used for ripping flesh.

TYRANNOSAURUS WAS SO HEAVY IT COULD NEVER HAVE RUN VERY FAST

AS A FIGHTING ANIMAL, *TYRANNOSAURUS* HAD VERY STRONG MUSCLES AND SKIN

THESE BONES HAD TO BE ENORMOUS FOR THE ATTACHMENT OF MASSIVE LEG MUSCLES

TYRANNOSAURUS HAD TINY, WEAK ARMS AND HANDS WITH ONLY TWO FINGERS

IT MAY HAVE USED ITS ARMS, WHICH COULD NOT REACH ITS MOUTH, TO STEADY ITS BODY AS IT STOOD UP

TYRANNOSAURUS RAN ON ITS TWO MASSIVE BACK LEGS

An armour-plated dinosaur
Ankylosaurs were plant-eaters that grew about six metres long and weighed up to two tonnes. Their backs were covered with a bony armour, and their skulls were protected with bony plates and large horns. Even their eyelids were bony.

ANKYLOSAURS HAD SOFT BELLIES BUT THEIR BACKS WERE PROTECTED WITH BONY ARMOUR-PLATING

STRONG TAIL-BONES ENDED IN A MASSIVE BONE CLUB

BONES PROTECTED THE *ANKYLOSAUR*'S EYES

THE LIMBS AND MUSCLES OF *ANKYLOSAURS* SUGGEST THEY WERE VERY POWERFUL, BUT SLOW-MOVING

How the Dinosaurs Died

DINOSAURS ruled the Earth for 150 million years. Then, quite suddenly, 65 million years ago, all the dinosaurs died. They were not, however, the only animals to become extinct at this time. Many animals living in the sea also disappeared along with many varieties of tiny sea-dwelling plants. The remains of these plants and animals settled on the sea and river beds. Over millions of years these remains formed layers of sedimentary rock. It is this rock which helps us understand why the dinosaurs disappeared. The main cause appears to have been an asteroid that collided with the Earth, causing massive damage. But sediments in the rock suggest other causes, too, such as volcanic activity and climate change.

AN ASTEROID IS A MOUNTAIN-SIZED BOULDER FROM OUTER SPACE

A DUST CLOUD MAY HAVE FILLED THE SKY

THE GIANT CRATER FORMED BY SUCH AN ASTEROID HAS BEEN FOUND BENEATH THE COAST OF MEXICO

PERHAPS THE EARTH BECAME POISONED BY CLOUDS OF VOLCANIC GAS AND DUST

A DARK LAYER FORMED WHEN SEA-LIFE HAD ALMOST DISAPPEARED

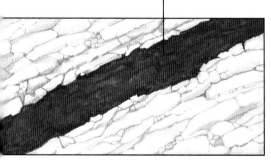

Death in the sea
Climate also changed at this time. A drop in temperature, as a result of thick smoke and dust in the air, would explain why so many animals died. In many parts of the world, amidst thick layers of chalk (formed from the remains of sea-life) a dark layer of clay records where life almost ended.

A LAYER RICH IN CHARCOAL

Forest fires
Tiny particles of burnt wood, or charcoal, have been found in sediments laid down at the time the dinosaurs died. This charcoal must have come from huge forest fires, perhaps covering millions of square kilometres. Many of the dinosaurs may have perished in the fires and smoke.

IN WESTERN INDIA THERE WERE ENORMOUS VOLCANIC ERUPTIONS AT THE TIME THE DINOSAURS DIED

BROKEN QUARTZ

An asteroid
Quartz is a mineral found in many rocks. When scientists examined ancient rock formed at the same time that the dinosaurs died they found that the quartz crystals were filled with breakages. Such damage could only have been caused by a massive explosion, as of a giant asteroid colliding with the Earth. The impact would have caused a huge dust cloud. This would have cut out the sunlight for months, causing temperatures to drop. Frosts would have killed forests, and many animals would have died.

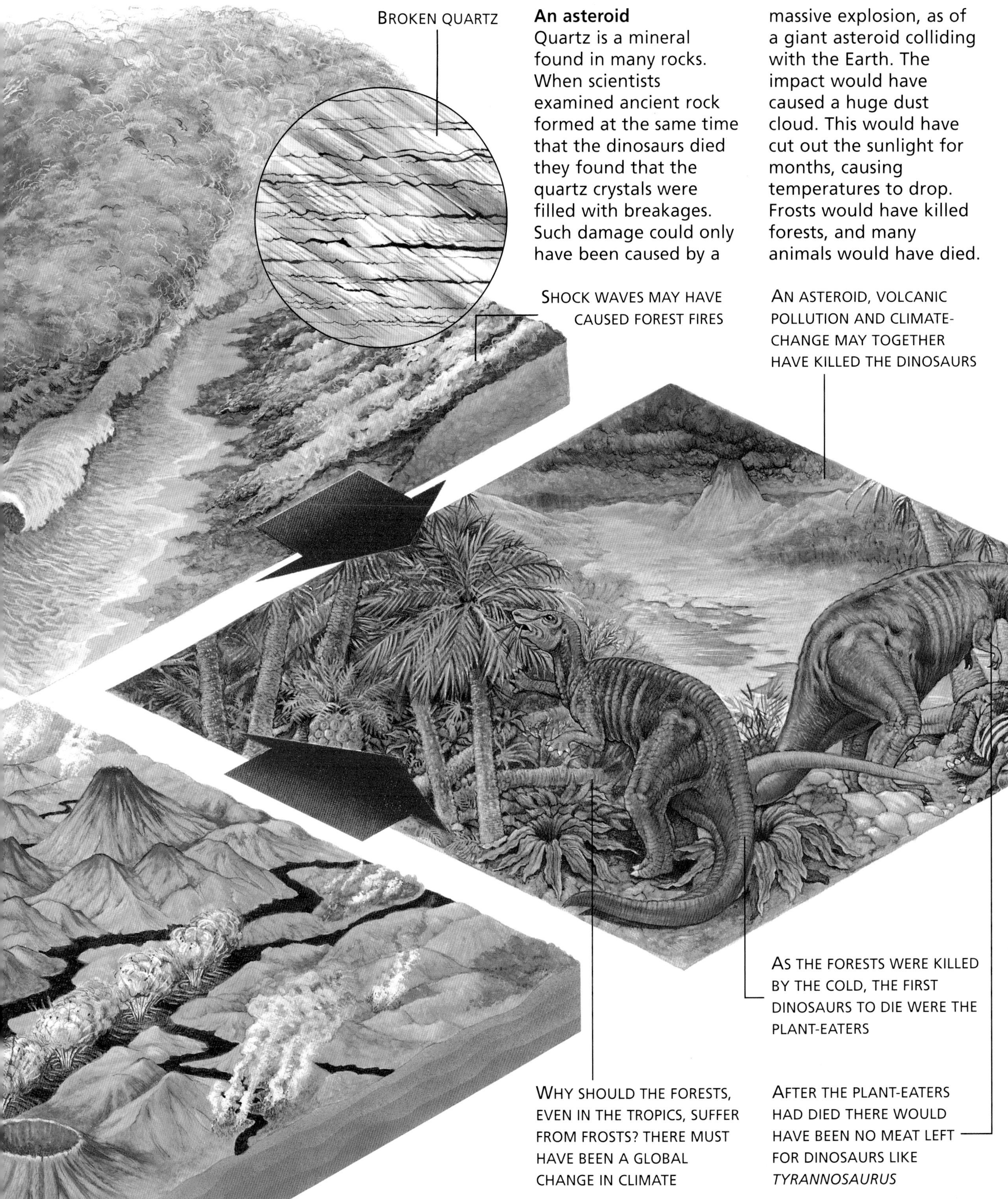

SHOCK WAVES MAY HAVE CAUSED FOREST FIRES

AN ASTEROID, VOLCANIC POLLUTION AND CLIMATE-CHANGE MAY TOGETHER HAVE KILLED THE DINOSAURS

AS THE FORESTS WERE KILLED BY THE COLD, THE FIRST DINOSAURS TO DIE WERE THE PLANT-EATERS

WHY SHOULD THE FORESTS, EVEN IN THE TROPICS, SUFFER FROM FROSTS? THERE MUST HAVE BEEN A GLOBAL CHANGE IN CLIMATE

AFTER THE PLANT-EATERS HAD DIED THERE WOULD HAVE BEEN NO MEAT LEFT FOR DINOSAURS LIKE *TYRANNOSAURUS*

251

Ancient Climates

CLIMATE is the weather observed over many years: how hot, cold, wet and dry it is. Climate affects the type of landscape, plants and animals that are found in a region. Over millions of years the climate of the world has changed. Sometimes there have been great ice-sheets over parts of the Earth. Sometimes deserts have covered whole continents, and then lush rain forest has grown on these same lands. Great forests have sunk to become barren salt lakes, and these in turn have been flooded as the rain returned. The continents have also moved across the globe, passing from one climate region to another.

When sediments are laid down they contain 'climate fossils' – evidence we can use to reconstruct the type of weather and landscapes that existed at that place millions of years ago.

DIFFERENT TYPES OF SEDIMENT ARE EVIDENCE OF DIFFERENT CLIMATES

REMEMBER: THE TOP SEDIMENTS ARE THE YOUNGEST; THE BOTTOM SEDIMENTS ARE THE OLDEST

LIMESTONE SEDIMENTS FORM IN SHALLOW SEAS

FOSSILS OF SEA-LIFE

DRY LAKES IN DESERTS LEAVE LAYERS OF SALTY SEDIMENT

FOSSILIZED RAIN FORESTS BECOME THICK LAYERS OF COAL (SEE PAGES 254–5)

TILTED SANDY LAYERS SHOW THERE WERE ONCE SAND DUNES

AS GLACIERS MELTED THEY LEFT THICK PILES OF MUD AND BOULDERS

ICE-AGE RIVERS DROPPED THICK SEDIMENTS IN THE SUMMER, BUT LITTLE IN THE WINTER, WHEN THEY FROZE

EVEN AFTER THE ICE MELTED, EVIDENCE OF THE ICE AGE WAS LEFT BEHIND

200 MILLION YEARS AGO SOME OF THE DESERTS IN NORTH AMERICA AND EUROPE WERE FLOODED BY SHALLOW SEAS

250 MILLION YEARS AGO DESERTS AND DRY SALT LAKES COVERED PARTS OF NORTH AMERICA AND EUROPE

300 MILLION YEARS AGO MUCH OF NORTH AMERICA AND EUROPE WAS TROPICAL RAIN FOREST

400 MILLION YEARS AGO MUCH OF NORTHERN EUROPE AND NORTH AMERICA WAS A DESERT

AROUND 600 MILLION YEARS AGO THERE WAS A GREAT ICE AGE ON EARTH

MOVING ICE-SHEETS CARVED THE LANDSCAPE (*SEE PAGES 256–7*)

Climate zones

▨	Desert (hot and dry)
▨	Equatorial (hot and wet)

① ② ③ ④

Climate zones

The continents are always moving around the globe (*see pages 258–9*). During prehistory these giant land masses moved into different climate zones. Around 400 million years ago, after an Ice Age had passed, much of North America and Europe were in a desert belt (1). The continents then moved north and about 300 million years ago were deeper into the hot, wet equatorial zone where rain forests would grow (2). By about 250 million years ago they were partly in another desert belt (3). Around the time of the dinosaurs (250 million years ago) North America and Europe had moved further north into a wetter zone, and some of the deserts were flooded by shallow seas (4).

253

Carboniferous Forests

THE FIRST primitive plants moved out of the water onto the land about 420 million years ago. The first tropical rain forests formed about 70 million years later, and in another 50 million years the forests covered enormous areas of lowland. In the forests the plants grew into giant, tree-like forms, reaching higher and higher above each other, seeking the sun. Below the tree-tops the crowded forests were dark and damp. These forests were much like today's rain forests, although many of the trees looked very different and there were no birds or monkeys. Instead, in the air and on the forest floor, there were giant insects. There were also large, fish-eating amphibians living in the swamps. We know what lived in these rain forests because a great many fossils were left behind in the rock we call coal.

Evidence from coal

The first rain forests appeared in the Carboniferous period. When the trees in the early forests died they sank into a swamp (1). Here, where the land was slowly sinking, rotting leaves and logs gradually formed a damp soil called peat (2). As the layer of peat became covered by more sediment, the water in it was squeezed out. Over millions of years more and more water was squeezed out until it became coal. All that we know about the first rain forests has come from studying pieces of coal, the material that is dug from coal mines and burned in power stations (3).

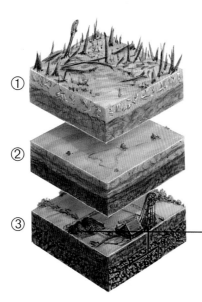

GIANT CLUBMOSSES GREW IN THE SWAMPS

GIANT TREE FERNS

A LAYER OF ROTTING PLANT AND ANIMAL REMAINS

A LAYER OF PEAT, WHICH SLOWLY TURNED INTO COAL OVER MILLIONS OF YEARS

THE COAL THAT WE BURN IN FIRES IS THE REMAINS OF 300-MILLION-YEAR-OLD RAIN FORESTS!

GIANT MILLIPEDES, UP TO TWO METRES LONG, CRAWLED ACROSS THE FOREST FLOOR

GIANT DRAGONFLIES, WITH
WINGSPANS OF UP TO 70
CENTIMETRES, FLEW
THROUGH THE AIR

FOSSIL TREE-TRUNKS SHOW
THAT THE TREES REACHED
HEIGHTS OF 30 METRES

THIS GIANT CLUBMOSS IS
CALLED A *LYCOPTERIS*

Fossils from the forest
Coal comes from dead
plants. Well-preserved
fossils of leaves, stems
and trunks are often
found in coal, although
they are always highly
compressed (squashed).
The rings of this fossilized
tree-trunk have been
compressed.

The bark of the tree
lycopteris, a giant
clubmoss, had over-
lapping scales. Fern-
leaf fossils are often
found in coal.

Most of the insects alive
300 million years ago
would look familiar
today, although many
were much larger than
we would expect.

Fossils of the *Eryops*
show that it was the
largest of the early land-
living amphibians.

THE LARGE AMPHIBIAN
ERYOPS LIVED IN THE RAIN
FOREST – DINOSAURS HAD
YET TO APPEAR ON EARTH

EOGYRINUS WAS ANOTHER
FISH-EATING AMPHIBIAN – IT
LIVED IN THE SWAMP, LIKE
AN ALLIGATOR

THE JAW OF *ERYOPS* OPENED
DOWNWARDS, WHICH
WOULD HAVE BEEN IDEAL
FOR CATCHING FISH

Ice Age

THE plains of northern Europe and northern North America are filled with strange mounds and ridges. The soils contain stones and boulders, some of which have been carried there across hundreds of kilometres. The mountains of northern Europe and Canada are rounded and smoothed, as if worn down and polished by a sculptor. In the high mountains of California and the Alps, however, there are sharp mountain peaks, and in the mountain valleys there are lakes. All these features have been formed by moving ice. For a long period up until 12,000 years ago, these regions were covered by thick ice-sheets. By comparing land today with how it looked in the past, we can see how the ice-sheets changed the landscape.

AS THE GLACIER CARVED THE MOUNTAINS, IT LEFT SPIKY 'ALPINE' PEAKS

THE ICE FLOWED DOWNHILL LIKE A GREAT TONGUE OF STICKY LIQUID

THE LARGEST CONTINENTAL ICE-SHEETS MAY HAVE BEEN 3000 METRES THICK

UNDER THE HUGE WEIGHT OF MOVING ICE, THE LANDSCAPE WAS CARVED AND SCULPTED

THE GLACIER CARRIED SHARP BOULDERS IN THE ICE, WHICH SCRATCHED DEEP GROOVES IN ROCK SURFACES

ROCKS AND DEBRIS WERE DEPOSITED BY THE ICE-SHEETS, FORMING HILLS CALLED DRUMLINS

HUGE BOULDERS WERE CARRIED BY THE ICE AND DROPPED HUNDREDS OF KILOMETRES AWAY

Drumlins
Where the ice-sheets flowed over and around hard rocks, debris carried by the ice was dropped. The piles of debris rose higher and higher until rounded hills, called drumlins, were formed.

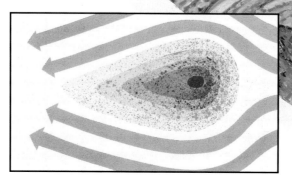

HOLLOWS CARVED BY THE GLACIER FILLED WITH WATER WHEN THE ICE MELTED

LONG AFTER THE ICE MELTED THE LANDSCAPE OF THE ICE-SHEET REMAINS LITTLE CHANGED

The last Ice Age

Around 18,000 years ago ice-sheets covered almost all of Canada, stretching down into the north-eastern part of the United States. In Europe the ice-sheets stretched across most of Britain. Ice-sheets also existed in many mountain ranges. Today, ice-sheets are only found in Greenland and Antarctica.

ALL OVER THE REGION ONCE COVERED BY THE ICE THERE ARE MORAINES: SANDY SOILS FILLED WITH STONES AND BOULDERS

ROADS OR RAILWAYS SOMETIMES FOLLOW ANCIENT MORAINE RIDGES

Ice Age animals

The animals that lived on the plains next to the ice-sheets included the mammoth, an extinct relative of the elephant, with a woolly coat. The tusks and bones of mammoths are sometimes found in marshland far away from the ice-sheets of today.

257

Drifting Continents

S INCE the Earth first formed, its continents have been moving across the globe. Volcanic eruptions and earthquakes are visible signs that the continents crash into and slide past one another. Yet the continents' movements are very slow – just a few centimetres each year. Rocks hold many clues as to the speed and direction of the continents' movements over the past hundreds of millions of years. They can tell us about the different climates the land has experienced, as the continents have moved towards or away from the equator (*see pages 252-3*). The best clues come from evidence of the Earth's magnetism that is trapped in rocks.

The Earth's magnetism
The Earth's magnetic field is generated by the movement of hot liquid metal in the centre of the Earth. The lines of magnetic force curl through the Earth, causing the needle of a compass to point north.

LINES OF MAGNETIC FORCE

NORTH

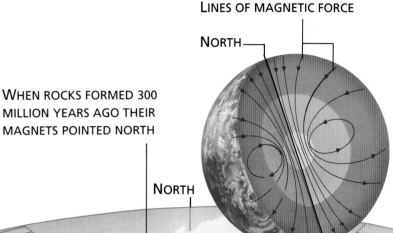

WHEN ROCKS FORMED 300 MILLION YEARS AGO THEIR MAGNETS POINTED NORTH

NORTH

200 MILLION YEARS AGO TODAY'S CONTINENTS WERE JOINED INTO ONE SUPERCONTINENT, CALLED PANGAEA

ECHIDNA

GLOSSOPTERIS
PLATYPUS

SOUTH

THE GREEN AREA SHOWS WHERE *GLOSSOPTERIS* GREW ACROSS PANGAEA

AROUND 250 MILLION YEARS AGO PANGAEA STARTED TO BREAK APART

Plants and animals
The fern *glossopteris* once grew widely on the supercontinent Pangaea. Fossils of the fern are now found in all the lands that made up the supercontinent. The primitive animals echidna and platypus live in Australia, but animals very like them live far away on the continent of South America. They drifted apart on the moving continents, having once lived on the same single supercontinent.

Magnets in rock

When the hot liquid rock that lies deep in the Earth seeps up onto the Earth's surface through a volcano, it cools and hardens. This causes its iron-rich crystals to solidify and become magnetized. These tiny magnets all point in the direction of the Earth's magnetic field – north. The magnets are all set, 'frozen' in time, pointing in the same direction. If the continents then move, carrying the rocks with them, the 'frozen' magnets may no longer point north. By measuring the direction in which the ancient rock magnets now point, it is possible to know where the rock was when it formed. By looking at many rock magnets, scientists can work out where an entire continent used to be.

65 MILLION YEARS AGO THE SUPERCONTINENT HAD BROKEN UP

NORTH

BY MEASURING THE 'FROZEN' MAGNETS (BLACK ARROWS) AGAINST THE DIRECTION OF NORTH (RED ARROWS) WE CAN TRACE THE MOVING CONTINENTS

THE OCEAN FLOOR SPREADS WIDER AS TWO CONTINENTS DRIFT APART

THIS GREEN AREA SHOWS WHERE *GLOSSOPTERIS* FOSSILS WERE CARRIED

Spreading oceans

At the centre of the Atlantic Ocean floor lies a ridge where two continents are drifting apart. As they separate, hot liquid rock oozes out and solidifies to fill the gap left in the ocean floor. The growing ocean floor records the Earth's magnetic field. It shows that about twice every million years, the Earth's magnetic field switches direction, so compasses would point south, not north!

259

Changing Sea-levels

WHERE the sea meets the land there is usually a beach. The breaking waves build banks of sand and shingle, and cut into the land to carve cliffs and rocky platforms. Where a river meets the sea, as the flow of the river slows, sediment carried by the current is dropped and a delta eventually forms. Beaches, cliffs and deltas are features of the sea-level. Over thousands of years the sea-level changes. On these pages we look at past sea-levels in western Europe, and discover the evidence they leave behind, such as ancient beaches, cliffs and deltas.

DURING THE LAST ICE AGE ICE-SHEETS COVERED THE LAND

120,000 YEARS AGO A RIVER DELTA FORMED – LEAVING SEDIMENTS WE STILL FIND TODAY

THREE MILLION YEARS AGO THE SEA REACHED THESE MOUNTAINS

Climate change
Variations in sea-level are a result of climate change. Three million years ago the sea-level was high because the Earth was warmer and there were no ice-sheets. Sediments laid down at that time, in seas such as the North Sea, are filled with fossils of corals and other warm-water life. A million years later these seas were covered in ice!

FOSSILS SHOW THAT THE SEA WAS WARM ENOUGH FOR CORAL REEFS TO GROW

THREE MILLION YEARS AGO SEA-LEVELS WERE 40 METRES HIGHER THAN TODAY

260

Flooded forests

After the last Ice Age ended 12,000 years ago, the sea rose rapidly. On many coasts there are drowned forests below the level of today's sea. Sometimes fallen fossil tree-trunks record great wind storms that came with the floods. In the sea, fishermen have also found tools and bones from ancient flooded settlements.

THESE MOUNTAINS USED TO BE SEA-CLIFFS – THEY WERE LEFT BEHIND AS THE SEA-LEVEL FELL

EVIDENCE OF AN ANCIENT DELTA WHERE A RIVER ONCE FLOWED INTO THE SEA

TODAY'S SEA-LEVEL CONTINUES TO RISE ABOUT 1 MILLIMETRE A YEAR

THESE PLATFORMS WERE BEACHES WHEN THE SEA-LEVEL WAS HIGHER

AS THE ICE MELTED, THE SEA-LEVEL ROSE, FLOODING ANCIENT SETTLEMENTS AND FORESTS

HUGE AREAS OF SHALLOW SEA BECAME DRY LAND

120,000 YEARS AGO THE SEA-LEVEL WAS 5 METRES HIGHER THAN IT IS TODAY

ONLY 18,000 YEARS AGO THE SEA-LEVEL WAS 130 METRES LOWER THAN TODAY

Flooded villages

Bones and flint remains show that 120,000 years ago prehistoric people camped on the seashores, making flint tools and collecting shellfish.

WATER FROZE AND BECAME TRAPPED IN ICE-SHEETS

261

Mountain Building

MOUNTAINS rise, are worn down, and eventually disappear. Across the world there are mountains at different stages of this cycle. The highest are formed where continents collide. The Himalayas, rising to more than eight kilometres, are forming where the Indian land mass is crashing into the rest of Asia. Some mountains are volcanoes, forming where molten rock, or magma, from deep in the Earth pours out at its surface. Others are made from deep-sea sediments that were deposited by rivers and have since been thrust high into the sky. While some mountains are rising, many are slowly being worn away. By studying rocks from mountains at these different stages, geologists are able to build a model of the life cycle of an ancient mountain range.

SNOW, ICE, WIND AND RAIN ATTACK THE ROCK, WEARING IT DOWN

MANY MOUNTAINS DATE FROM FAR INTO PREHISTORY – TENS TO HUNDREDS OF MILLIONS OF YEARS AGO

THE ROCKS AT THE HEART OF ANCIENT MOUNTAINS WERE ONCE 10–20 KILOMETRES UNDERGROUND

MOST MOUNTAINS BEGIN LIFE AS SEDIMENTS ON THE OCEAN FLOOR

OCEAN SEDIMENTS BECOME LAYERS OF ROCK DEEP UNDERGROUND

WHERE CONTINENTS COLLIDE, LAYERS OF ROCK ARE SQUEEZED AND PUSHED UP

WHERE TWO CONTINENTS SEPARATE, A RIDGE APPEARS ON THE OCEAN FLOOR

MAGMA POURS OUT ONTO THE OCEAN FLOOR TO FILL THE WIDENING GAP IN THE OCEAN FLOOR

SQUASHED, FOLDED ROCKS RISE UP OUT OF THE OCEAN TO FORM MOUNTAINS

WHERE CONTINENTS COLLIDE, ONE CONTINENT MAY BE PUSHED DOWN BENEATH THE EARTH'S SURFACE

Mountain remains
Folded rock layers that form mountains are eventually worn down. By looking at the shapes and angles of the remaining rock layers we can see where the mountains used to be.

Sea shells
Fossil shells have been found on the highest mountain of all, Mount Everest. These show that the rocks on the mountain range were formed about 200 million years ago on the floor of a shallow sea.

VOLCANOES BUILD MOUNTAINS OUT OF MAGMA FROM UNDER THE EARTH

IF THE PIPE WHICH THE MAGMA TRAVELS UP IS BLOCKED, THE VOLCANO MAY EXPLODE (ERUPT)

MOUNTAIN ROCKS REVEAL THE HISTORY OF THE LAND BEFORE THE MOUNTAINS EXISTED

EVENTUALLY AN OLD MOUNTAIN RANGE WILL BE WORN AWAY

A NEW OCEAN MAY COVER THE LAND, DEEP-SEA SEDIMENTS WILL BE DEPOSITED AND MOUNTAIN BUILDING WILL BEGIN AGAIN

263

Early Peoples

A T THE same time that northern Europe was covered in ice-sheets, there were forests in the river valleys of south-western France. Beneath soils of wind-driven dust and river sediment, archaeologists have found traces of the people who lived in this region between 15,000 and 10,000 BC. These Magdalenian people were hunters, living on the large herds of animals that moved through the valleys. Food was plentiful and the people had time to create new tools and even make ornamental objects. The Magdalenian people have left many clues as to how they lived. By excavating the region, we have been able to build up a picture of their lives.

Wall paintings
The people of this region painted pictures of the animals they hunted, such as this bison, along the walls of caves. Forms of natural mineral dye, such as red ochre, were used as paint.

THE HEARTH OF A FIRE LEAVES A PATCH OF BURNT BONES, SCORCHED STONES AND CHARCOAL FRAGMENTS

EXCAVATED REMAINS HAVE BEEN ASSEMBLED ON BOARDS AND LABELLED

MAMMOTH AND ANTLER BONE WERE CARVED INTO TOOLS

FLINT ARROWS AND SPEAR-HEADS WERE FITTED ONTO WOODEN STICKS, WHICH HAVE SINCE ROTTED AWAY

PIECES OF A SHELL AND BEAR-TOOTH NECKLACE HAVE BEEN FOUND AND GATHERED TOGETHER

NEEDLES MADE FROM IVORY (MAMMOTH TUSKS) WERE USED FOR SEWING SKINS TO MAKE CLOTHES

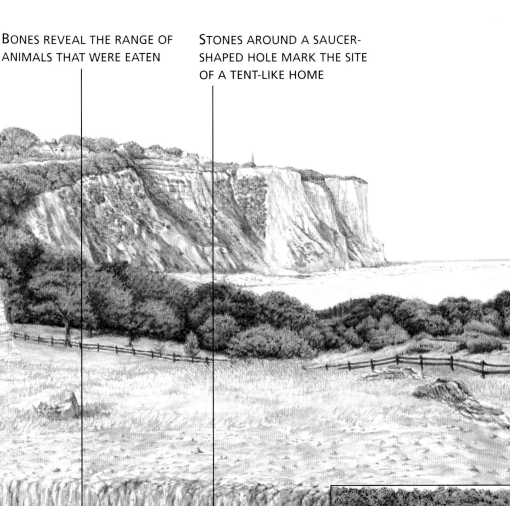

BONES REVEAL THE RANGE OF ANIMALS THAT WERE EATEN

STONES AROUND A SAUCER-SHAPED HOLE MARK THE SITE OF A TENT-LIKE HOME

Clues to a lifestyle

Fossils from the site of the Magdalenian people show they hunted herds of bison and reindeer, and also fished. Their food was cooked over a fire. They probably lived in communities and exchanged goods with other members of their tribe. From their carvings we can tell that they communicated with other tribes across the whole of central Europe. Objects found at their burial places seem to show they believed the dead would live again in this, or another, world. The Magdalenians were among the first humans to make art objects. Items such as carved animals may have been more than ornaments, having magical importance.

THIS BISON WAS CARVED OUT OF A REINDEER ANTLER

THIS SITTING BEAR WAS CARVED OUT OF SOFT STONE

THIS HUNTER WAS BURIED IN A SPECIAL CEREMONY, SURROUNDED BY WEAPONS AND TOOLS

RADIOCARBON DATING OF THE BONES SHOWS THAT THIS MAN AND THE ANIMALS ARE FROM THE SAME PERIOD

Skins for warmth

The Magdalenian people lived only a few hundred kilometres south of the ice-sheet, so it was not very warm. Animal skins were used for clothing, as well as for lining their tent-like homes.

Reconstructing Faces

MISSING PARTS OF THE FOSSIL
ARE FILLED WITH PLASTER

WHAT were the first human beings like? The only remains that archaeologists have found are fragments of fossil bones and skulls. Bones of early humans known as *Australopithecus Afarensis* have been found in sediments laid down in eastern Africa. We can tell the age of these bones from the volcanic ash sediments in which they are found. The sediment layers were dated using the potassium-argon radio-isotope technique (*see pages 240-1*), and found to be more than three million years old. Fossils of the legs of a female *Australopithecus* show that these ancient humans walked upright. Fully grown, a female was around 150 centimetres tall.

After piecing together fragments of the skull we can also tell what the face of this prehistoric human looked like. On these pages we see the processes involved in reconstructing the face.

THE SKULL PIECES ARE
GLUED TOGETHER

THE MUSCLES OF THE FACE
ARE BUILT UP ON THE SKULL
USING CLAY

1) The clay model

Fossil skulls are rarely complete. Fragile bones such as those of the nose tend to splinter and are lost. So the first job is to repair the skull. Pieces are glued together and missing sections filled with plaster.

By looking at the skull, and at the muscles on faces of modern human beings, scientists can work out where the muscles would have been. The face muscles are formed on the skull using clay. Careful measurements of the skull are also taken to decide how big the nose and eyes should be.

For the skin on the *Australopithecus*, a simple layer of clay, 2–3 millimetres deep, is added. This final layer is shaped and sculpted with wrinkles and lines to make it more realistic.

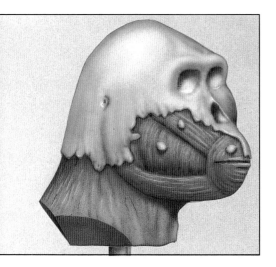

WHEN THE CLAY SKIN LAYER
IS ADDED, BLOBS OF CLAY
ARE USED TO KEEP THE
LAYER EVEN

THE CLAY MODEL WILL BE
USED TO MAKE A MOULD

2) The plastic copy

When the clay model is complete, rubber is poured over it to make a mould. When the mould is ready, plastic is poured into it and left to set. The rubber mould is then peeled off leaving a rigid plastic copy of the clay model. The clay model, containing the precious bone, can be returned to the museum. The plastic copy is passed over to the artist.

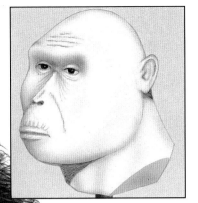

EARS, LIKE THE NOSE, HAVE TO BE SCULPTED INTO SHAPES BASED ON APES' AND HUMAN EARS

GLASS EYES OF THE CORRECT SIZE ARE INSERTED INTO THE EYE SOCKETS

THE SKIN IS RECREATED IN A COLOUR TYPICAL OF THIS HOT REGION OF AFRICA

THE HARD PLASTIC MODEL IS PAINTED

A LASER BEAM SCANS THE SKULL

HUMAN HAIR IS USED TO MAKE SURE IT LOOKS REALISTIC

3) The completed face

The model is brought to life with paint, glass eyes and hair. The amount of hair on the *Autralopithecus* can only be guessed at, although the hair on modern humans and living apes can be used as a guide. The amount of hair added changes the appearance greatly.

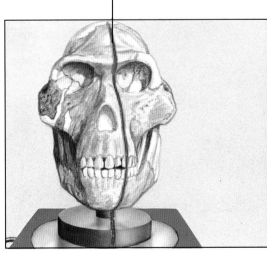

Computer faces

Computers are also used to reconstruct faces. The skull is scanned by a laser so that its exact shape can be seen on a computer screen. Muscles and skin are added onto the image electronically. Different skin tones and hair length or colour can be tested, too

Early Beliefs

MUCH of what we know about prehistoric peoples comes from the many monuments they left behind. Some of these were built as burial chambers; others were used for ceremonial purposes. Among the most mysterious monuments is Stonehenge: 162 blocks of stone, built on a plateau in southern England. Most of our discoveries about the monument and the people who built it have come from excavations at the site. We know that some of the stones were quarried hundreds of kilometres away, and that it probably took hundreds of men to haul just one of them. The immense effort involved suggests the people had very strong reasons for building Stonehenge.

Why was Stonehenge built?

The sun aligns with certain stones at the mid-summer and mid-winter solstice (the longest and shortest days of the year). The sun also aligns with stones at the equinoxes (days of equal day and night). So it is possible that Stonehenge was used as an astronomical calendar, showing when to plant crops or observe festivals.

Stonehenge

The picture below shows three stages in the life of Stonehenge: its building (*below*), its completion (*centre*) and the ruins left today (*right*).When complete, Stonehenge comprised a ring of upright stones with a continuous roof of lintels (stones laid flat). There was an inner horseshoe-shaped ring of five pairs of separate uprights, each pair with its own curved lintel. Inside both rings stood smaller stones (bluestones). The monument was in the middle of a round bank surrounded by a ditch, and a broad avenue led to the site.

THE LINTELS WERE PERHAPS LIFTED ON PLATFORMS

PERHAPS A POLE WAS USED TO LIFT THE STONES

WHEN COMPLETE, STONEHENGE PROBABLY LOOKED LIKE THIS

STONEHENGE WAS BUILT AT DIFFERENT STAGES IN PREHISTORY

THE OLDEST RADIOCARBON DATE MEASURED AT THE SITE SHOWS THAT THE BANK AND DITCH WERE CUT AROUND 3200–3000 BC

THE STONES WERE CARVED TO FIT TIGHTLY AGAINST EACH OTHER

THE GIANT INNER STONES WEIGH UP TO 45 TONNES EACH

SOME OF THE STONES ARE STILL STANDING TODAY

Burial mounds
In the region around Stonehenge there are many burial mounds, know as barrows. They were built at the same time as the great stone circle. To explore barrows a series of trenches are dug. The barrow shown here has a passageway and several burial chambers where human bones were found.

THE OUTER CIRCLE WAS BUILT AROUND 2100 BC USING STONES QUARRIED ABOUT 30 KILOMETRES AWAY

THE BLUESTONES WERE BROUGHT OVER 210 KILOMETRES FROM SOUTH WALES IN AROUND 1550 BC

EVERY YEAR THOUSANDS OF PEOPLE COME TO SEE THE RUINS OF STONEHENGE

DISCOVERING THE
UNIVERSE

Stuart Clark

DISCOVERING THE
UNIVERSE
CONTENTS

Big Bang

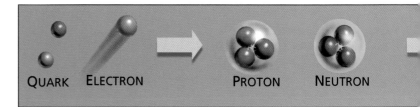

ASTRONOMERS believe that the Universe began about 15 billion years ago with an event known as the Big Bang. At the Big Bang the Universe began as the smallest of points and then suddenly began to expand. In about the same amount of time as it will take you to read this page, the Universe developed and all the matter (material) within it was created. Enough matter to become everything we see today in space was created in the first few minutes. Even the particles that make up this book were formed in the first few seconds after the Big Bang.

To start with everything was crammed into a tiny space, so the Universe was very dense. At this point atoms, the building blocks of matter, began to form. As time went by and the Universe expanded more it became less dense. Today, space is mostly empty with dense parts (the planets, stars, and galaxies) only dotted around here and there.

Formation of matter
A millionth of a second after the Big Bang simple particles called quarks and electrons appeared. Quarks then joined together to form neutrons and protons. A single proton is known as a hydrogen nucleus. Later, neutrons and protons joined together to make helium nuclei. Finally, electrons began to orbit these nuclei and turn them into atoms.

THE FIRST STARS FORMED BUT PLANETS LIKE THE EARTH COULD NOT YET FORM AROUND THEM

GALAXIES BECOME ELLIPTICAL IF THEY SUFFER A COLLISION WITH ANOTHER LARGE GALAXY

AFTER 300,000 YEARS, THE TEMPERATURE WAS LOW ENOUGH FOR ATOMS TO FORM

The first seconds
At first the Universe was a frenzy of activity. Matter existed only in simple particles, called quarks. These quarks were not yet stable and kept turning into energy. The energy then turned back into quarks.

THE TEMPERATURE DROPPED AND THE QUARKS FORMED NEUTRONS AND PROTONS

SPACE SUDDENLY INFLATED (EXPANDED) TO MANY TIMES THE SIZE IT HAD BEEN AND QUARKS BECAME STABLE

AFTER A FEW MINUTES ONE QUARTER OF THE MATTER WAS TURNED INTO HELIUM

AFTER ONE BILLION YEARS, GALAXIES WERE BEGINNING TO FORM – THEY STARTED AS HUGE COLLAPSING CLOUDS OF GAS

HYDROGEN
NUCLEUS

HELIUM
NUCLEUS

HYDROGEN
ATOM

HELIUM
ATOM

PLANETS LIKE THE
EARTH HAD FORMED
AROUND STARS

OUR SOLAR SYSTEM IS FOUND
IN THE MILKY WAY GALAXY

THE UNIVERSE IS NOW ABOUT
15 BILLION YEARS OLD AND
CONTINUES TO EXPAND

TEN BILLION YEARS AFTER
THE BIG BANG, THE SUN AND
THE PLANETS IN OUR SOLAR
SYSTEM FORMED

Birth of a solar system

Solar systems like ours
formed when gas clouds
in galaxies collapsed. First
a gas cloud began to
shrink and a star began
to form at its centre (1).
As the cloud collapsed
more, gases gathered in a
disc around the star (2).

The gases in this disc
collided and stuck
together, gradually
turning into dust grains.
The dust grains continued
to grow in this way until,
after tens of thousands
of years, planets were
formed and a solar
system was born (3).

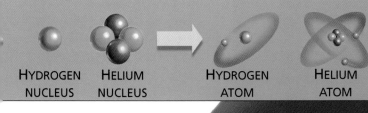

①

②

③

The Universe

THE UNIVERSE is so large that astronomers measure most distances in light-years. One light-year is the distance light travels in a year (9.5 thousand billion kilometres). A ray of light travels at 300,000 kilometres a second – faster than anything else in the Universe.

There are many different types of object found in the Universe. Some are very large and others are tiny. The largest things in the Universe are gigantic filaments, which are made of superclusters. These contain clusters (groups) of galaxies. Galaxies are the homes of stars. A spiral galaxy, like our Milky Way, is about 100,000 light-years across. Some galaxies are still forming stars today but others stopped millions of years ago. Planets are found orbiting (moving round) the stars. The smallest solid objects in the Universe are the tiny particles of dust that lie between the planets.

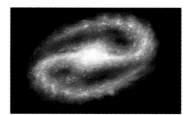

Types of galaxies
Galaxies can be split into three types: elliptical galaxies (*top left*); spiral galaxies with curved arms of stars (*middle*); and barred-spiral galaxies which have a bar of stars between their arms and their centres (*bottom*).

THE NEAREST SPIRAL GALAXY TO OURS IS CALLED ANDROMEDA

THE OBSERVABLE UNIVERSE IS A SPHERE WITH A DIAMETER OF 30 BILLION LIGHT-YEARS

THE MILKY WAY IS PART OF A SMALL CLUSTER OF GALAXIES KNOWN AS THE LOCAL GROUP. THE MILKY WAY IS SURROUNDED BY SMALLER SATELLITE GALAXIES

SUPERCLUSTERS OF GALAXIES CAN BE HUNDREDS OF MILLIONS OF LIGHT-YEARS LONG. THEY CONTAIN MANY CLUSTERS OF GALAXIES

INDIVIDUAL CLUSTERS OF GALAXIES CAN CONTAIN SEVERAL THOUSANDS OF GALAXIES

GIGANTIC FILAMENTS ARE MADE UP OF SUPERCLUSTERS

THERE ARE MANY LARGE, EMPTY VOIDS IN THE UNIVERSE TODAY

STARS ORBIT THE CENTRE OF THE MILKY WAY

THE SUN IS LOCATED IN THE SPIRAL ARMS OF THE MILKY WAY GALAXY

PLANETS FURTHER FROM THE SUN, TAKE LONGER TO ORBIT

THE EARTH IS THE THIRD PLANET FROM THE SUN

PLANETS ORBIT THE SUN IN ELLIPTICAL ORBITS, AS IF FOLLOWING THE OUTER EDGE OF A SQUASHED CIRCLE

OUR GALAXY CONTAINS HUNDREDS OF BILLIONS OF STARS

THE SOLAR SYSTEM CONTAINS THE SUN AND NINE PLANETS

THE EARTH TAKES 365 DAYS TO ORBIT THE SUN

THE MOON TAKES 28 DAYS TO ORBIT THE EARTH

AS THE UNIVERSE GETS BIGGER, THE TIME IT TAKES TO DOUBLE IN SIZE INCREASES

IMAGINE SPACE IS A BALLOON AND THE GALAXIES ARE PAINTED ON THE OUTSIDE. WHEN PARTLY BLOWN UP, THE GALAXIES ARE CLOSE TOGETHER

THE GALAXIES ON THE IMAGINARY BALLOON ARE FURTHER APART AS THE BALLOON IS BLOWN-UP MORE

GALAXIES USED TO BE CLOSER TOGETHER

GALAXIES ARE NOW FURTHER APART

The expanding Universe

In the 1920s astronomers Edwin Hubble and Milton Humason showed that the Universe was expanding. They were studying galaxies and noticed that the light from them was being stretched. This stretching affects the colours of light from galaxies and so became known as redshift.

The further away the galaxy, the greater its redshift. This stretching of their light is caused by the expansion of space. The further away the galaxy is, the more space there is between us and it that can expand. Astronomers now use redshift to measure the distances of galaxies.

The Solar System

W E LIVE ON Earth. The Earth belongs to a family of nine planets which orbit the Sun. Both the planets and the Sun formed about 4.6 billion years ago and are known as the Solar System. The four inner planets – Mercury, Venus, Earth, and Mars – are all similar. They are rocky worlds, but only Earth has an atmosphere (the gas surrounding a planet) which humans can breathe. Beyond Mars is the asteroid belt. This contains millions and millions of rocks which also orbit the Sun. Still further away are four large planets: Jupiter, Saturn, Uranus, and Neptune. These are gas giants with very thick atmospheres and no solid surfaces. Jupiter is the largest planet. Beyond the gas giants is Pluto. This is the smallest of the planets and the coldest, because it is so far from the Sun. Astronomers have found evidence that other planets exist around stars in our Galaxy.

The Galaxy

The Sun is one of billions of stars which make up the Galaxy. Also known as the Milky Way, the Galaxy has a flat, spiral shape. The Sun is not at its centre. In fact, it is in one of the spiral arms, closer to the Galaxy's edge than its centre. Its location is shown by the red dots below. The Sun orbits the centre of the Galaxy once every 220,000,000 years. Our Galaxy is one of billions in the Universe.

Orbits

The planets are held in the Solar System by the gravity generated from the Sun. The Sun contains so much matter that its force of gravity is very large. It causes the planets to move in orbits around it. The patterns of these orbits are similar to circles.

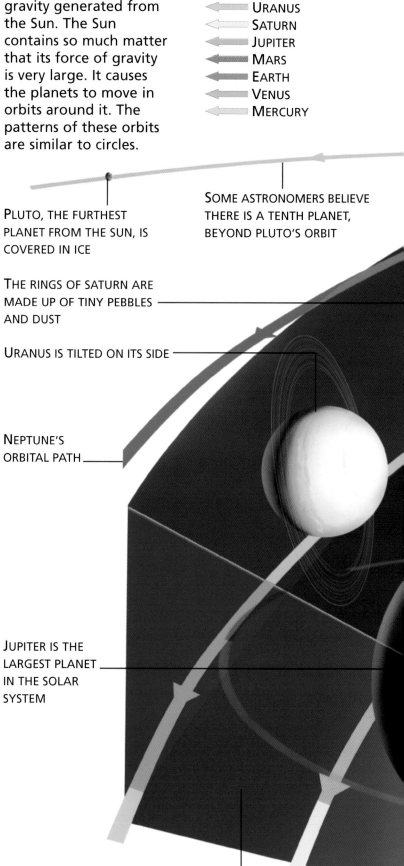

PLUTO
NEPTUNE
URANUS
SATURN
JUPITER
MARS
EARTH
VENUS
MERCURY

PLUTO, THE FURTHEST PLANET FROM THE SUN, IS COVERED IN ICE

SOME ASTRONOMERS BELIEVE THERE IS A TENTH PLANET, BEYOND PLUTO'S ORBIT

THE RINGS OF SATURN ARE MADE UP OF TINY PEBBLES AND DUST

URANUS IS TILTED ON ITS SIDE

NEPTUNE'S ORBITAL PATH

JUPITER IS THE LARGEST PLANET IN THE SOLAR SYSTEM

THE OUTER SOLAR SYSTEM

ASTEROIDS WERE DISCOVERED BY ASTRONOMERS LOOKING FOR A PLANET BETWEEN MARS AND JUPITER

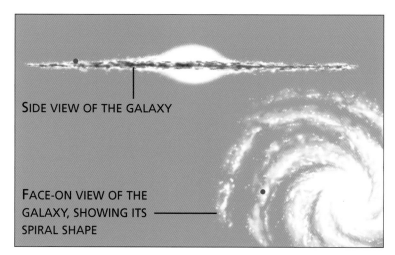

SIDE VIEW OF THE GALAXY

FACE-ON VIEW OF THE GALAXY, SHOWING ITS SPIRAL SHAPE

EVERY FEW HUNDRED YEARS NEPTUNE IS THE FURTHEST PLANET, BECAUSE ITS ORBIT CROSSES PLUTO'S

SATURN HAS YELLOW CLOUDS, AND LARGE WHITE STORMS SOMETIMES APPEAR IN ITS ATMOSPHERE

ALL GAS GIANTS HAVE RINGS

SATURN'S ORBIT AROUND THE SUN

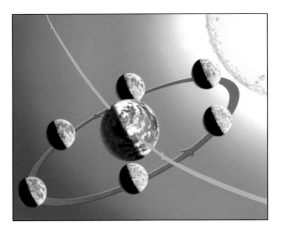

The Moon's phases
The Moon orbits the Earth and reflects the light from the Sun. When it is in front of the Earth we see a new Moon. When it is behind the Earth we see a full Moon.

THE EARTH IS PART OF THE INNER SOLAR SYSTEM

THE SUN

The Planets

ALL NINE planets of the Solar System orbit the Sun but each one is unique. Many have moons in orbit around them. The four 'gas giants' – Uranus, Jupiter, Neptune, and Saturn – have rings as well.

The matter inside a planet or moon is found in layers. The densest material is at the centre and is usually made up of iron. The outer material consists of rocks. Gas, which is a planet's lightest material, sits above the planet's surface and is known as the atmosphere. This layering of the planets and moons proves that when they formed they were made of molten lava (collisions with other new planets had made their rocks melt). While they were molten, the heavy material could easily sink to the centre and the light material could float to the surface.

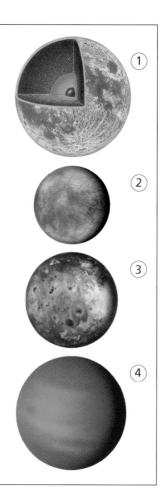

Moons
Earth's Moon is rocky with a small iron core (1). There are many other moons, mostly around the gas giants. Jupiter's moons include Europa (2), which may have an ocean beneath its icy crust and Io (3), which has the most volcanoes in the Solar System. Saturn's largest moon, Titan (4), is always covered in cloud.

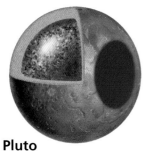

Pluto
The tiniest planet is Pluto (*above*). It is made up of ice surrounding a large core of rock and iron. It is orbited by a moon called Charon, shown here eclipsing the Sun.

PLUTO'S MOON, CHARON, WAS DISCOVERED IN 1978

SOMETIMES THE SUNLIGHT IS BLOCKED BY CHARON, AND A SHADOW IS CAST ON PLUTO

Uranus
This gas giant (*below, right*) has a thick atmosphere of gas over an even thicker region of gas, ice, and rock particles. It may have a rocky core about the size of the Earth at its centre.

Neptune
The planet Neptune (*left*) is about the same size as Uranus. It also has a similar inner structure. The rings of Neptune are patchy. Some areas are rather dense whilst others are sparse.

JUPITER IS CIRCLED BY A THIN, DUSTY RING

NARROW RINGS AROUND URANUS ARE MADE UP OF SMALL DARK DUST PARTICLES

Jupiter
The diameter of Jupiter (*above*) is eleven times that of Earth. Below the surface of Jupiter, a mixture of hydrogen and helium gas is squeezed so much it behaves like a liquid. Below this, the mixture is squeezed even more and acts like a liquid metal. In the very centre of the planet there may be a rock and iron core five times bigger than the Earth.

Mercury

Mercury (*left*) is the closest planet to the Sun. It has a large iron core, covered by a layer of rocky material. On top is the crust, cratered by collisions with smaller objects such as asteroids.

Venus

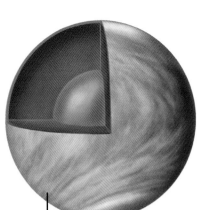

Venus (*left*) is almost the same size as Earth but is very different in other ways. It is permanently covered in clouds of carbon dioxide and its surface is hotter than an oven.

THE CLOUDS AROUND VENUS HIDE A LANDSCAPE OF CLIFFS, VALLEYS, HIGHLANDS, AND LOWLANDS

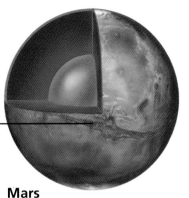

THE MARINER VALLEY IS ABOUT 4,000 KILOMETRES LONG

Mars

The diameter of Mars (*above*) is about half that of Earth. It has a very large rift valley called the Mariner Valley, named after the space probe that discovered it.

JUPITER'S GREAT RED SPOT IS A STORM AS LARGE AS PLANET EARTH

SATURN'S RINGS HAVE GAPS CAUSED BY THE GRAVITY OF ITS MOONS

Saturn

The interior of Saturn is similar to that of Jupiter. One difference between them is that inside Saturn it is possible for helium gas to become a liquid. It then falls as rain into the central region of the planet.

281

Planet Earth

EARTH is the planet on which we live. It formed with the Sun and other planets 4.6 billion years ago. Originally, Earth was a sphere of lava (molten rock). Heavy chemicals such as iron sank into the planet, while lighter ones floated to the top. Water and the atmospheric gases that allow us to live and breathe were brought to the planet by colliding balls of ice known as comets.

Earth has a core of iron surrounded by a large region of molten rocks, called the mantle. Heat travelling through the outer mantle causes the molten rocks to move in large oval pathways. The rocky crust of the Earth is broken into large pieces called plates. These float on the mantle. Where they collide, earthquakes occur and volcanoes erupt.

The Earth's core
The Earth's core contains one third of our planet's mass. Geologists have monitored the way in which sounds travel through the Earth and discovered that the core is divided into two regions. The outer core is made up of liquid iron. The inner core is solid iron.

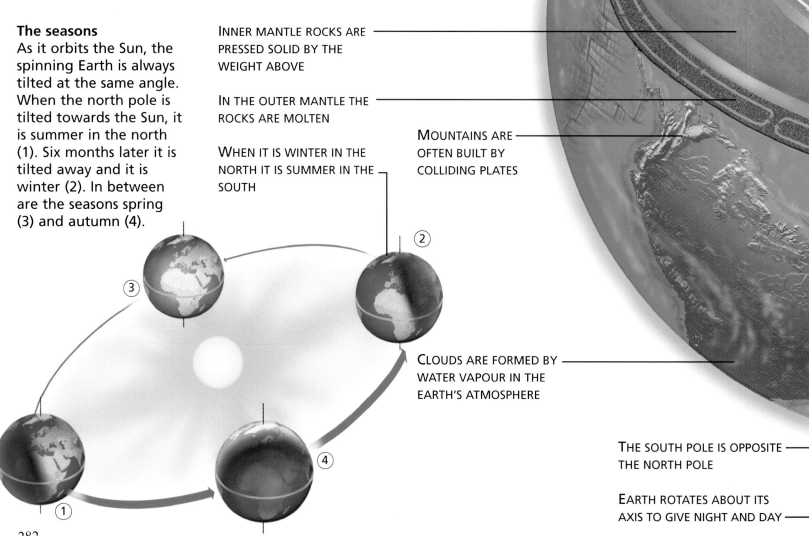

HEAT FROM INSIDE THE EARTH MAKES THE OUTER MANTLE'S MOLTEN ROCK CONVECT (MOVE IN CIRCULAR PATTERNS)

THE THIN CRUST IS MADE UP OF PIECES (PLATES) OF SOLIDIFIED ROCK. OCEAN PLATES FORM THE OCEAN FLOOR; CONTINENTAL PLATES FORM THE LAND

CONVECTION IN THE OUTER CORE CAUSES EARTH TO GENERATE A MAGNETIC FIELD

WHERE OCEAN PLATES COLLIDE, ONE IS FORCED DOWN INTO THE MANTLE

The seasons
As it orbits the Sun, the spinning Earth is always tilted at the same angle. When the north pole is tilted towards the Sun, it is summer in the north (1). Six months later it is tilted away and it is winter (2). In between are the seasons spring (3) and autumn (4).

INNER MANTLE ROCKS ARE PRESSED SOLID BY THE WEIGHT ABOVE

IN THE OUTER MANTLE THE ROCKS ARE MOLTEN

WHEN IT IS WINTER IN THE NORTH IT IS SUMMER IN THE SOUTH

MOUNTAINS ARE OFTEN BUILT BY COLLIDING PLATES

CLOUDS ARE FORMED BY WATER VAPOUR IN THE EARTH'S ATMOSPHERE

THE SOUTH POLE IS OPPOSITE THE NORTH POLE

EARTH ROTATES ABOUT ITS AXIS TO GIVE NIGHT AND DAY

THE EARTH ROTATES ONCE
EVERY 23.93 HOURS

THE THERMOSPHERE SUFFERS
LARGE CHANGES IN
TEMPERATURE

MOST CLOUDS FORM IN THE
TROPOSPHERE WHICH IS
THE LOWEST LAYER
OF THE ATMOSPHERE

THE NORTH POLE

NOT ALL LIGHT REACHES THE
SURFACE OF THE EARTH, A
SMALL PERCENTAGE IS
REFLECTED BACK INTO SPACE

THE TEMPERATURE OF THE
ATMOSPHERE DROPS TO −75°C
IN THE MESOSPHERE

THE STRATOSPHERE
CONTAINS THE OZONE
LAYER WHICH BLOCKS OUT
HARMFUL SOLAR RADIATION

CONTINENTAL SHELVES
ARE GREAT SLOPES
OF ROCK JOINING
OCEAN PLATES TO
CONTINENTAL PLATES

The atmosphere

The atmosphere of the
Earth is the blanket of
gases surrounding the
planet. It insulates the
planet, keeping it warm.
It also blocks out most of
the Sun's harmful
radiation such as
ultraviolet light. Most
importantly, it allows us
to breathe.

The celestial sphere

From the Earth it looks
as if the stars are
painted onto a huge
sphere surrounding the
planet. This is called the
celestial sphere.
Throughout the year the
night-time side of the
Earth faces various
directions in space and
so different stars on the
sphere are seen.

THE STARS APPEAR
TO MOVE ACROSS
THE NIGHT SKY
BECAUSE THE EARTH
IS ROTATING

THE CELESTIAL EQUATOR
DIVIDES NORTH FROM
SOUTH ON THE SKY

A FAULT LINE APPEARS AT
PLATE EDGES

THE MID-ATLANTIC TRENCH IS
A VERY LONG FAULT LINE
RUNNING DOWN THE MIDDLE
OF THE ATLANTIC OCEAN
FLOOR

THE EARTH'S
ROTATION ALSO
MAKES THE SUN
APPEAR TO FOLLOW A
PATH ACROSS THE SKY

283

Rocket Power

THE CONCEPT of the rocket can be traced back to the Ancient Greeks of the 4th century BC. In the 13th century AD, the Chinese built rockets made of gunpowder and bamboo tubes. They attached these to arrows and launched them. In peaceful times rockets were used as fireworks but during wars they were used as weapons.

The principle behind the way a rocket works is that every action creates an equal and opposite reaction. This was stated as a law of nature by Sir Isaac Newton in 1687. If an explosion produces gas and that gas can be directed out of a tube, the gas leaving the tube will cause the tube itself to move in the opposite direction.

Rockets blast off from launch pads and take objects, such as communications satellites, into space. In the future, space planes will use rocket engines to take off like aeroplanes from runways and fly so high they reach outer space.

THE LARGEST ROCKET EVER BUILT WAS SATURN V, WHICH WENT TO THE MOON; IT WAS OVER 110 METRES HIGH

THE SATELLITES THAT ARE TAKEN INTO ORBIT ARE KNOWN AS THE PAYLOAD

THIS SATELLITE IS A TELESCOPE TO BE PLACED IN A LOW EARTH ORBIT

PAYLOADS MUST BE DESIGNED TO FIT INTO THE ROCKET FROM WHICH THEY WILL BE LAUNCHED

Stages

Although early rockets contained single engines, scientists soon realized that rockets should be built in stages. A stage is a part of the rocket that can fall away when it is no longer needed. This reduces the mass of the rocket so that it can be accelerated more easily by the remaining rocket engines.

The best designs are three-stage rockets in which a large first stage lifts it from the ground. When its fuel tanks are empty, it is cast off and the second stage takes over. Finally, a third stage places the rocket into orbit.

THE SPACE SHUTTLE DOES NOT GO AS FAR AS THE MOON SO IT IS SMALLER THAN SATURN V

SATELLITES MAY HAVE SMALL ROCKETS OF THEIR OWN TO PLACE THEM IN THEIR FINAL ORBITS

ARIANE 4 IS A EUROPEAN-BUILT ROCKET, LAUNCHED FROM AFRICA. IT IS 60 METRES HIGH

History of rockets

Early in the 20th century an American called Robert Goddard launched the first modern rocket (1). It flew to a height of 12.5 metres. Rockets have always been used as weapons and in the Second World War the Germans developed the V-2 rocket to launch attacks on London (2). Many countries have developed rockets. Russia built the D-class vehicles to launch their Soyuz missions (3). The Saturn V rocket (4) was developed by America for the Apollo Moon missions and the present day Space Shuttle (5) is the first reusable spacecraft.

ONCE IN SPACE THE FAIRING (CASING AROUND THE PAYLOAD) SPLITS IN TWO AND RELEASES THE SATELLITES

THIS SATELLITE IS A COMMUNICATIONS SATELLITE TO BE PLACED IN A HIGH ORBIT

A LARGE PAYLOAD BAY

Flight path

The Ariane rocket takes off (1) using the first stage and the strap-on boosters. When the boosters are out of fuel they are cast off (2). Shortly afterwards the first stage also runs out of fuel and is dropped (3). The fairing splits (4) in preparation for releasing the satellites. The second stage uses its fuel and is discarded (5). The first satellite is deployed (6) and achieves low Earth orbit (7). The second satellite is boosted to a much higher orbit (8).

THE THIRD-STAGE ROCKET LIFTS THE SATELLITES INTO ORBIT

THE SECOND STAGE ACCELERATES THE ROCKET SO THAT IT TRAVELS TWICE AS FAST

THE FIRST-STAGE FUEL TANK

TO ACHIEVE LIFT OFF, A ROCKET MUST PRODUCE ENOUGH THRUST TO OVERCOME THE FORCE OF GRAVITY

LIQUID HYDROGEN FUEL IS SUPPLIED TO THE ROCKET FROM THE FUEL TANK

A SUPPLY OF OXYGEN HELPS THE FUEL IGNITE

THE FIRST STAGE IS HELPED BY STRAP-ON BOOSTER ROCKETS

THE COMBUSTION CHAMBER LIGHTS THE FUEL AND DIRECTS THE THRUST BEHIND THE ROCKET – THIS MAKES THE ROCKET MOVE UPWARDS

Rocket fuel

Rocket engines ignite fuel to produce thrust. Liquid oxygen mixed with another liquid fuel, such as hydrogen or fluorine, produces more thrust than a single fuel could. In the future, rockets may use three fuels and gain even more energy.

FIRST-STAGE OXYGEN TANK

FIRST-STAGE ROCKET ENGINES

285

Early Missions

T HE RUSSIANS were the first to place a human being in space. The astronaut, Yuri Gagarin, flew in the rocket Vostok 1 on 12 April 1961. His flight lasted just 89 minutes but during that time he made a complete orbit of the Earth and then returned safely.

Vostok 1 had been launched from the former Soviet Union by a rocket designed as a missile to carry explosives. The Russians launched Vostok 2 just a few months later on 6 August 1961. This time the astronaut stayed in space for a whole day.

A year later the Russians launched astronauts in Vostok 3 and 4 with just 24 hours between the launches. Both spacecraft successfully returned to Earth a few days later. In 1963 Vostok 5 and 6 were launched. Vostok 6 carried the first woman into space. She was called Valentina Tereshkova.

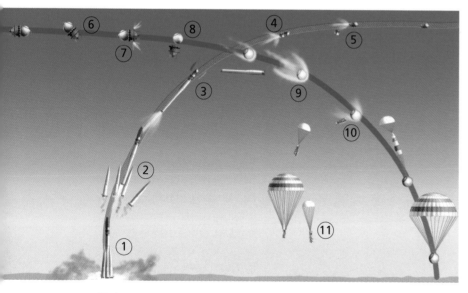

Flight profile
Vostok 1 blasts off (1) and drops the first-stage boosters (2). The nose casing is ejected as the second stage accelerates Vostok's speed (3). The final stage puts it in orbit (4) and then separates (5). After an orbit Vostok turns (6) and fires its retro-rocket (7). The instrument module is discarded (8) and Vostok 1 re-enters the atmosphere (9). The astronaut is ejected (10). Parachutes return the module and astronaut safely to Earth (11).

The instrument module
The instrument module was controlled by the scientists on the ground. It was equipped with rocket engines that could control the spacecraft movement once it was in orbit. Communication antennae were also attached to it. The module was ejected and allowed to burn up during re-entry to Earth.

VOSTOK 1'S INSTRUMENT MODULE

SPECIAL VENTS STOPPED VOSTOK FROM OVERHEATING

THE RETRO-ROCKET WAS USED TO SLOW DOWN THE SPACECRAFT AND MAKE IT RE-ENTER THE EARTH'S ATMOSPHERE

ORBITAL CONTROL INSTRUMENTS WERE FITTED IN THE INSTRUMENT MODULE

THE POD FELL TO EARTH

THE HATCH WAS EJECTED TO ALLOW THE ASTRONAUT TO LEAVE THE FALLING DESCENT MODULE

THE ASTRONAUT WAS EJECTED FOR LANDING

CONTAINERS OF OXYGEN
AND NITROGEN ALLOWED
THE ASTRONAUT TO BREATHE

STRONG TENSION BANDS
HELD THE DESCENT CAPSULE
AND INSTRUMENT MODULE
TOGETHER

Delivery to orbit
Exactly 156 seconds after
lift off, the nose casing
surrounding the Vostok
module fell away. Then,
300 seconds after lift off,
the second stage fell
away and the final stage
of the launch rocket

THE EJECTION SEAT CONTAINED
FOOD, WATER, AND A DINGHY
IN CASE THE ASTRONAUT
EJECTED OVER THE SEA

ignited. Its rocket engine
burned for the next 376
seconds and put the
craft into orbit. There
the spherical capsule
and the conical
instrument module were
released.

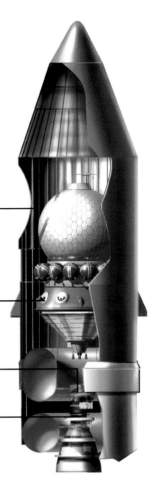

THE NOSE CASING
CONTAINED VOSTOK'S
DESCENT CAPSULE AND
INSTRUMENT MODULE

THE INSTRUMENT MODULE

THE FINAL STAGE OF THE
ROCKET PLACED VOSTOK
INTO ORBIT

FUEL AND OXYGEN IS MIXED
IN THE ROCKET ENGINE

THIS PORTHOLE HAD A
DEVICE FOR SHOWING THE
POSITION OF THE MODULE

THE CONTROL PANEL OF THE
SPACECRAFT SHOWED FLIGHT
DATA TO THE ASTRONAUT

VOSTOK MODULES
CONTAINED TELEVISION AND
STILL CAMERAS TO RECORD
THE FLIGHT

HEAT-RESISTANT
MATERIAL PROTECTED THE
MODULE DURING RE-ENTRY

Astronaut ejection
The Vostok module
landed on solid ground.
Although the module
was slowed by parachutes
the impact might have
hurt the astronaut inside.
So the astronaut was
ejected, and came down
by parachute separately.

ONLY IN AN EMERGENCY
WAS THE ASTRONAUT
ALLOWED TO TOUCH THE
SPACECRAFT CONTROLS

THE RE-ENTRY CAPSULE
MEASURED 2.5 METRES
ACROSS

COMMUNICATION ANTENNAE
ARE FOUND AT THE FRONT
AND REAR

Emergency procedure
All Vostoks were
launched so that they
would re-enter the
Earth's atmosphere
naturally after a period
of ten days. This
prevented the loss of
the astronaut's life
should the retro-rocket
fail to slow the
spacecraft down. In
order to survive for
ten days, the Vostok
capsule was stocked
with enough food and
water. This precaution
was never needed.

Apollo Mission

ONE OF the greatest achievements of the human race has been the space missions of the late 1960s and early 1970s, which placed humans on the Moon. On 20 July 1969, Apollo 11 touched down on the surface of the Moon. Shortly afterwards, astronaut Neil Armstrong became the first human being to walk on a world in the Solar System other than Earth.

There were seven manned missions to the Moon. Each carried three astronauts. One stayed in the command and service module while the other two descended to the Moon's surface in the landing module.

Apollo 13 almost became a disaster when an electrical system short-circuited and caused an explosion, destroying an oxygen tank. The landing on the Moon was abandoned and the astronauts were returned safely to Earth. They used oxygen from the landing module to keep themselves alive.

THE ENGINE USED FOR ORBIT CHANGES

Command and service module
The command and service module was the astronauts' home during the voyages to and from the Moon. The conical section at the front is the command module, where the astronauts sat. It separated from the service module and re-entered the Earth's atmosphere when the mission was complete.

THIS RADAR DISH HELPED THE MODULES TO RECONNECT

A HATCH FOR GETTING IN AND OUT OF THE LANDING MODULE

THE ASCENT-STAGE ROCKET ENGINE

OXYGEN FROM THIS TANK IS MIXED WITH ROCKET FUEL AND FED TO THE MAIN DESCENT ENGINE

A LADDER FOR THE CREW TO CLIMB DOWN ONTO THE MOON

LANDING STRUTS ABSORB THE SHOCK OF LANDING

WHEN LANDING, AS SOON AS THESE SENSORS TOUCHED THE MOON'S SURFACE THE ENGINES WERE TURNED OFF

Arriving at the Moon
When the Apollo spacecraft arrived at the Moon it was made up of the command and service module and landing module joined together. After a retro-rocket was fired, both spacecraft entered lunar orbit. Two astronauts climbed into the lander. The landing module then separated and fired another retro-rocket. This made it drift slowly down to the surface of the Moon to land.

THE VOYAGE BETWEEN THE EARTH AND MOON TOOK ABOUT THREE DAYS

THE COMMAND AND SERVICE MODULE STAYED IN ORBIT

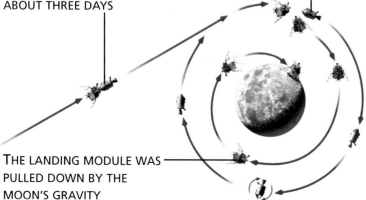

THE LANDING MODULE WAS PULLED DOWN BY THE MOON'S GRAVITY

THRUSTERS (SMALL ROCKETS) ARE USED TO CHANGE THE DIRECTION OF THE MODULE

A DOCKING CLAMP FOR GRABBING THE LANDER WHEN IT ASCENDED FROM THE MOON

THE RETURNING COMMAND MODULE SPLASHED DOWN IN THE OCEAN

ANTENNAE ALLOW THE MODULES TO COMMUNICATE

THE DOCKING HATCH IS AT THE TOP OF THE SPACECRAFT

Back to Earth

When the moon walks were finished, the ascent stage of the landing module lifted off and docked with the command and service module. The astronauts then travelled back to Earth. The lander was left to fall back onto the Moon.

FIRING A ROCKET PUTS THE COMMAND AND SERVICE MODULE IN AN ORBIT BACK TO EARTH

REACTION CONTROL THRUSTERS WERE USED TO KEEP THE LUNAR LANDER UPRIGHT DURING LANDING AND TAKEOFF

A FUEL TANK FOR THE ASCENT

A FUEL TANK FOR THE DESCENT – MORE FUEL WAS NEEDED ON DESCENDING

STORAGE SPACE FOR LUNAR EQUIPMENT

THE OXYGEN TANK FOR THE CREW TO BREATHE

THE MAIN DESCENT ENGINE SLOWED THE LANDER AS IT WENT DOWN

The landing module

The landing module was the small spacecraft that took the astronauts to the surface of the Moon. It was split into two parts. The top part was where the astronauts sat. Underneath was a section used for equipment storage.

When it was time to leave the Moon, only the top part of the lander would take off. This was called the ascent stage. Because the force of gravity is less powerful on the Moon than it is on Earth, only a small rocket was needed to lift off.

On the Moon

AFTER APOLLO 11 touched down on the Moon's surface, the astronauts prepared to go outside. During this first crewed Moon landing the astronauts made one trip outside the lunar lander. Their walk lasted two and a half hours. Then they climbed back aboard and prepared for take-off.

On each of the following Apollo missions the astronauts spent longer and longer on the Moon's surface. By the final Apollo missions (Apollos 16 and 17), the astronauts made several journeys out of the lander and spent over 20 hours working on the Moon's surface. Apollo missions stopped after the Apollo 17 mission in December 1972. In 1998, a space probe called Lunar Prospector discovered ice at the Moon's poles. This can be used in the future to make rocket fuel.

Moon walking

While they were on the surface of the Moon the astronauts performed many tasks. They collected rock samples and also left packages of experiments behind that sent information back to Earth long after the astronauts had left.

THE ROVER'S ANTENNA WAS USED TO COMMUNICATE WITH MISSION CONTROL

STILL PICTURES WERE TAKEN WITH THIS CAMERA PACK

THE PLSS IS STRAPPED ONTO THE SPACESUIT

THE TELEVISION CAMERA FILMED THE LUNAR ROVER'S JOURNEY

THE COMMUNICATION SYSTEM'S ELECTRONICS

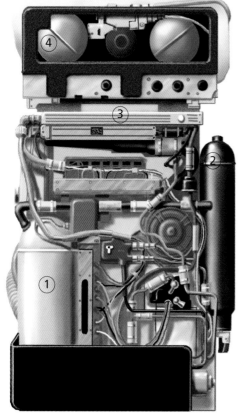

Portable life support system

Because the Moon is so small there is no air on its surface. This means that astronauts have to wear spacesuits to stay alive. The Apollo spacesuit was connected to a backpack called the Portable Life Support System (PLSS). The PLSS pumped oxygen (1) and water (2) to the spacesuit so that the astronaut could breathe and keep their body temperature normal. A radio (3) enabled the astronauts to talk to each other. An emergency oxygen supply (4) was also included.

Surveyor probes
Before humans set foot on the Moon, Surveyor probes were sent there. Cameras on the probes took pictures of the surface – these helped scientists to choose Apollo landing sites.

APOLLO 12 ASTRONAUTS COLLECTED THE CAMERA FROM SURVEYOR 3

ROCK SAMPLES WERE STORED IN THE ROVER

THE LUNAR LANDER WAS THE ASTRONAUTS' HOME

SCOOPS WERE USED TO COLLECT SAMPLES

ASTRONAUTS BROUGHT BACK MANY KILOGRAMS OF LUNAR ROCK

CONTROLS FOR DRIVING THE ROVER

A DISPLAY CONSOLE HELPED ASTRONAUTS TO KNOW WHICH DIRECTION THEY WERE TRAVELLING IN

The lunar rover
Apollos 15, 16, and 17 each took a lunar rover to the Moon. It was folded up and kept in the storage bay of the lunar lander. On the Moon it was unfolded and used by the astronauts to travel much further than they could possibly walk.

THE ROVER WAS MADE OF LIGHTWEIGHT ALUMINIUM

ROVER WHEELS WERE MADE OF LIGHTWEIGHT WIRE MESH

DUST SHIELDS HELP KEEP THE ROVER MOVING

Space Shuttle

THE SPACE Shuttle is the first spacecraft that can be used more than once. In the early days of space exploration, spacecraft were only able to fly on one mission. Most parts of the rocket burned up in the atmosphere or were left in space. The first Space Shuttle, called *Enterprise*, never flew in space but proved that such a large craft could glide successfully down to Earth.

The second Space Shuttle, *Columbia*, was launched in 1981. This was followed by the Space Shuttles *Challenger*, *Discovery*, *Atlantis*, and *Endeavor*. In 1986, the *Challenger* blew up on take-off, tragically killing all seven astronauts on board.

Apart from this dreadful accident the Space Shuttle has been very successful. It is being used to construct the International Space Station (*see pages 296–7*).

THE SHUTTLE WORKS IN LOW EARTH ORBIT, WHICH HAS AN ALTITUDE OF 282 KILOMETRES

THE MANOEUVRING ROCKETS ARE USED FOUR TIMES TO PLACE THE SHUTTLE IN ORBIT

BOTH SCIENTIFIC AND COMMUNICATIONS SATELLITES HAVE BEEN LAUNCHED BY THE SPACE SHUTTLE

THE ROBOT ARM CAN GRAB OR RELEASE SATELLITES

THE SPACE SHUTTLE IS CONTROLLED BY A PILOT SITTING ON THE FLIGHT DECK

THE MAIN FUEL TANK IS NOT RE-USED

BOOSTER ROCKETS SEPARATE AND FALL INTO THE OCEAN

SMALL ROCKETS ENABLE THE SHUTTLE TO MOVE WITHIN ITS ORBIT

Shuttle flight profile
The Space Shuttle blasts off from Cape Canaveral in Florida, USA. At an altitude (height) of about 50 kilometres, the solid rocket boosters separate and drift back down to Earth. At an altitude of about 120 kilometres, the Shuttle ejects the main fuel tank, which is now empty. The Shuttle then moves fast enough to reach orbit.

AT LAUNCH, THE EXTERNAL FUEL TANK SUPPORTS THE BODY OF THE SHUTTLE

SOLID ROCKET BOOSTERS ARE RE-USED FOR OTHER SHUTTLE FLIGHTS

THE LOWER DECK IS WHERE THE ASTRONAUTS LIVE AND WORK DURING THE FLIGHT

AT THE CORRECT TIME, THE SPACE SHUTTLE RELEASES ITS SATELLITE INTO SPACE

Satellites
Many satellites work in much higher Earth orbits than the Space Shuttle can take them. Some are even sent to other planets. So satellites must fire smaller rockets to send them on their way after the Space Shuttle has put them into space.

THE SHUTTLE TRAVELS AT 27,000 KILOMETRES PER HOUR

FIRING THE MANOEUVRING ROCKETS MAKES THE SPACE SHUTTLE RE-ENTER EARTH'S ATMOSPHERE

SATELLITES AND SCIENTIFIC EQUIPMENT ARE STORED IN THE MAIN CARGO BAY

FUEL TANKS SUPPLY THE MANOEUVRING AND ALTITUDE JETS

RE-ENTERING THE ATMOSPHERE SLOWS THE SHUTTLE DOWN TO 348 KILOMETRES PER HOUR

THE MAIN ENGINES ONLY FIRE AT TAKE-OFF

AFTER RE-ENTERING THE ATMOSPHERE, THE SHUTTLE GLIDES TO ITS LANDING SITE

SMALL ATTITUDE (DIRECTIONAL) JETS CONTROL THE DIRECTION IN WHICH THE SHUTTLE POINTS

WING FLAPS ARE USED FOR GLIDING IN THE ATMOSPHERE

SUPPORT STRUTS KEEP THE WINGS STRONG

THE UNDERCARRIAGE IS USED FOR LANDING THE SPACE SHUTTLE ON A RUNWAY

Shuttle landings
Early American spacecraft used to splash down in the ocean. The Space Shuttle lands like an aeroplane, making it much easier to re-use.

THE HEAT PROTECTION TILES MUST FIT PRECISELY TO PROTECT THE SHUTTLE

Heat protection tiles
As the Shuttle re-enters the atmosphere, friction raises its surface temperature enormously. The Shuttle is covered in protective tiles to prevent damage. The strong black tiles can withstand temperatures of 1100°C and the other tiles 500°C.

LANDINGS TAKE PLACE AT EDWARDS AIR FORCE BASE

Space Walking

IN SPACE, there are no gases for humans to breathe. Whenever work needs to be done outside a spacecraft, an astronaut has to put on a spacesuit. The spacesuit supplies the astronauts with oxygen to breathe and water to drink. On Earth the weight of the atmosphere prevents the fluids in our bodies from turning into gases. In space, there is no atmosphere and so a spacesuit must also squeeze the astronaut's body to keep the body fluids liquid.

On Earth and in spacecraft only one fifth of the gas breathed is oxygen but in a spacesuit all of the gas is oxygen. Before astronauts can go outside, they must spend several hours breathing nothing but oxygen through a mask in order to get used to it.

Attitude jets

The attitude jets push the space walker along by blowing out nitrogen gas. The astronaut decides which way to move and pulls or twists the control levers. A computer calculates which jet should be fired. For example, to make an astronaut turn, more than one jet is fired at the same time.

THE VIDEO CAMERA ALLOWS THE ASTRONAUT TO TAKE IMAGES

NITROGEN IS KEPT IN A TANK AND SUPPLIED TO THE ATTITUDE JETS WHEN NEEDED

THE BACKPACK IS KNOWN AS THE MANNED MANEUVERING UNIT (MMU)

ELECTRICAL POWER TO THE MMU IS SUPPLIED BY A BATTERY

NITROGEN GAS IS BLOWN OUT OF THE ATTITUDE JETS

Moving in space

To move around in space the astronaut has to wear a backpack fitted with small jets which are controlled by hand-held levers. The left control lever is used to make the space walker go forwards or backwards. The right hand lever controls the direction the astronaut is facing. It can make the space walker turn left or right, up or down or twist around clockwise or anticlockwise.

PUSH UP TO MOVE FORWARD

PUSH UP TO ROLL OVER

ATTITUDE JETS POINT OUT OF THE BACKPACK IN ALL DIRECTIONS

THE SPACESUIT WILL BE HEATED BY THE SUN TO OVER 100°C

TWISTING THE CONTROL LEVER MAKES THE ASTRONAUT ROLL LEFT OR RIGHT

PULLING THE LEVER LEFT OR RIGHT MAKES THE ASTRONAUT TURN

THE BOOTS ARE ATTACHED TO THE SPACESUIT TO PREVENT OXYGEN ESCAPING

THE LIFE SUPPORT SYSTEM IS WORN ON THE ASTRONAUT'S BACK BETWEEN THE SPACESUIT AND THE MMU

THE OUTER HELMET PROTECTS THE ASTRONAUT FROM THE SUN'S RADIATION

LIGHTS ENABLE ASTRONAUTS TO WORK WHEN THEY ARE NOT IN SUNLIGHT

THE CAP CONTAINS HEADPHONES AND A MICROPHONE FOR TWO-WAY COMMUNICATION

THE UPPER PART OF THE SPACESUIT IS MADE OF HARD FIBREGLASS TO PROTECT THE ASTRONAUT FROM MICROMETEORITES (TINY DUST PARTICLES IN SPACE)

ASTRONAUTS TIE THEMSELVES TO THEIR SPACECRAFT FOR SAFETY

GLOVES MUST FIT WELL SO ASTRONAUTS CAN PICK THINGS UP

ARM LENGTH ADJUSTMENT

THE OUTER LAYER OF THE SPACESUIT IS FIREPROOF

THE FLEXIBLE METAL LAYER HAS CONCERTINA JOINTS AT THE KNEES AND ANKLES

THE RESTRAINT LAYER PREVENTS THE PRESSURE SUIT FROM INFLATING TOO MUCH

THE PRESSURE SUIT FILLS WITH GAS TO SIMULATE THE WEIGHT OF THE EARTH'S ATMOSPHERE

THE UNDERGARMENT CONTAINS WATER TUBES THAT COVER THE BODY TO KEEP THE ASTRONAUT AT A COMFORTABLE TEMPERATURE

Spacesuit control box
The controls for the spacesuit are located on the front of the spacesuit. Every aspect of the spacesuit can be changed using switches on this box. If astronauts want to talk over the radio they select a channel (1), adjust the volume (2), and press the switch to talk (3). If they are hot or cold they can adjust the temperature of their spacesuit (4). More or less oxygen can be supplied by altering (5) and their water supply can be altered using (6).

Space Stations

IN 1971 Russia launched the first space station, called Salyut 1. The early space stations only stayed in orbit for a few months before they fell back to Earth. But gradually better systems were developed. In 1986 Russia launched Mir space station, which is still in orbit today.

The Americans launched the Skylab space station in 1973. Astronauts worked there for 172 days before going back to Earth. But in 1979, before it was re-visited, Skylab burned up in the Earth's atmosphere.

The International Space Station (*right*) is being built by a group of countries, including the USA, Russia, Canada, and Japan. It will be the biggest ever, and will take several years to build. There will have to be over 30 flights to take all the pieces into space, and nearly 40 other missions will be needed to assemble the space station.

STRONG LATTICE FRAMEWORKS WILL SUPPORT THE SPACE STATION

SOLAR PANELS WILL BE USED TO GENERATE POWER

NEW MODULES CAN BE FITTED TO THE STATION AT SPECIAL CONNECTION POINTS

RUSSIA'S SOYUZ SPACECRAFT WILL REMAIN PERMANENTLY ATTACHED TO THE INTERNATIONAL SPACE STATION

SOYUZ CAN SERVE AS A 'LIFEBOAT' IN AN EMERGENCY

AN ADDITIONAL SOYUZ SPACECRAFT – USED FOR TRANSFERRING ASTRONAUTS

Space station construction
The International Space Station will be constructed over several years. The first stage will be the delivery of the central connecting structure (1). During the second stage three astronauts will board the station (2). In the third stage many of the scientific modules will be added (3). Finally, the station will become permanently staffed by more astronauts (4).

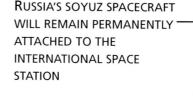

① ② ③ ④

Habitation module
The habitation module is one of the most important parts of the space station because it is where the astronauts will live and sleep. Astronauts have to sleep with fans close to their faces in order to blow away the carbon dioxide they breathe out.

A SPACE STATION IS A HABITABLE BUILDING IN SPACE – IT CAN STAY IN ORBIT FOR MONTHS OR EVEN YEARS

A ROBOTIC MANIPULATOR ARM WILL MOVE HEAVY ITEMS AROUND OUTSIDE THE STATION

THE CREW WILL BE CHANGED EVERY FEW MONTHS

DIFFERENT FORCES OF GRAVITY WILL BE CREATED IN THIS MODULE FOR EXPERIMENTS

IN WEIGHTLESS CONDITIONS SHOWERS MUST BE TAKEN IN A SPECIAL SEALED UNIT

THE US SPACE SHUTTLE WILL BRING SUPPLIES AND TRANSPORT CREW MEMBERS

Science modules
One of the reasons for building the International Space Station is to perform scientific experiments in the weightless conditions of space. There will be several science modules on the space station.

A DOCKING AND STORAGE MODULE

SIX ASTRONAUTS WILL LIVE IN THE HABITATION MODULE

ASTRONAUTS FLOAT IN WEIGHTLESSNESS

SOME ASTRONAUTS WILL WORK IN THIS AMERICAN SCIENCE MODULE

Viking Lander

THE VIKING missions were the first to have landers touch down on the surface of Mars and work properly. The project was begun in 1968. Because there was a high risk of the Viking spacecraft breaking down, two were built. That way, if one went wrong the other could carry on with the work. In fact, both space probes worked very well. They landed in the summer of 1976 and worked for many years.

Along with the landers, each of the Viking space probes had a section that stayed in orbit. Together, the two Viking orbiters surveyed and mapped nearly all of the planet's surface.

Many scientists think that Mars was once very like the Earth. There is evidence that parts of its surface were once covered in water. This means that life may have started on Mars too. The Viking landers had special equipment on board to test the soil in case it contained tiny living organisms called microbes. But the tests did not find evidence of any form of life.

The Viking landings
The site of Viking I's touchdown was *Chryse Planitia*, quite close to the Martian equator. Viking II landed further north in *Utopia Planitia*. Both are flat and desert-like. Heavily cratered areas were avoided in case they damaged the landing spacecraft.

THIS ANTENNA SENT INFORMATION TO EARTH AND RECEIVED COMMANDS

THE CAMERAS OBSERVED A TEST PATTERN TO GET THEIR COLOUR BALANCE RIGHT

MAGNETS ON THE TEST CHART WERE SENSITIVE TO MAGNETIC ACTIVITY ON MARS

A MACHINE FOR MEASURING EARTHQUAKES DETECTED NOTHING OF THAT SORT ON MARS

VIKING USED TWO CAMERAS TO TAKE PICTURES OF THE MARTIAN SURFACE

POWER GENERATORS

FUEL TANK UNDER WINDSHIELD

Flight path
It took the Viking space probes less than a year to reach Mars. Once in the planet's orbit, images of its surface were transmitted to Earth so that scientists could help select landing sites. When a site was chosen the lander was cast off from the orbiter, with a parachute attached to slow it down and help it land gently.

MARTIAN SOIL IS RED IN COLOUR BECAUSE IT IS COVERED IN RUST

THE BIOLOGY PROCESSOR
CHECKED THE RESULTS OF
EXPERIMENTS IN SEARCH OF
MARTIAN LIFE

THIS DEVICE HEATED
MARTIAN SOIL TO TEST FOR
MICROBES

THE METEOROLOGY
ARM CHECKED THE
WEATHER IN THE REGION
VIKING HAD LANDED

Pictures of Mars

Viking I began transmitting pictures to Earth just 25 seconds after it touched down on Mars. Because of the long distance from Mars to Earth the pictures took 19 minutes to arrive on a radio wave. One picture (*above*) showed a large rock. NASA scientists called it 'Big Joe'. There were fewer big rocks in the region where Viking II touched down.

SHOCK ABSORBERS ON THE
LANDING LEGS PREVENTED
VIKING BEING DAMAGED
DURING TOUCHDOWN

THE ROBOTIC ARM ON
VIKING I WOULD NOT WORK
PROPERLY IN THE COLD
MARTIAN MORNING

MARS IS COVERED IN SOIL
AND ROCKS

The robotic arm

Viking was designed to test the surface of Mars for signs of life. It did this by scooping soil from the surface and dropping it into the biology processor and heating device. The robotic arm was sent commands from Earth and then carried them out automatically.

THE DESCENT ENGINE FOR
LANDING

299

Mars Pathfinder

THE MARS Pathfinder mission landed on Mars on 4 July 1997. It was the first spacecraft to land on the planet since Viking 1 and 2. There are rock features on Mars that could have been produced only by flowing water. Yet, today, there seems to be hardly any water on the planet. It is hoped that missions like the Mars Pathfinder will help us to find out what happened to it.

The Pathfinder was very successful and returned data for weeks, even though conditions on Mars were harsh and there were fears that instruments might fail. It finally stopped working on 27 September. Pathfinder was the first in an ambitious programme of space probes that will visit Mars. Another, called the Mars Global Surveyor was sent shortly afterwards to map the planet. Many others will follow and lots of them will have tiny rover space probes which will crawl over the surface of Mars looking for evidence of water.

Mars landscape
The Mars Pathfinder was designed to land in an ancient flood plain. It is estimated that the flood took place several billion years ago. The surface has remained virtually unchanged since then. Pathfinder came to rest in a small dip.

A LARGE ANTENNA FOR COMMUNICATING WITH EARTH

THE APXS INSTRUMENT FIRED TINY PARTICLES AT THE ROCKS AND MEASURED HOW THE PARTICLES REBOUNDED

A SOLAR PANEL ON TOP OF THE SOJOURNER COLLECTED ENERGY

SOLAR PANELS COLLECTED ENERGY

THE ROVER ANALYSED 15 ROCKS IN DETAIL

Mars rover
The rover on the Mars Pathfinder was called the Sojourner. It drove across the surface of the planet and went up close to many of the rocks near the Pathfinder. Once close to a rock, it analysed its composition.

THE APXS INSTRUMENT MEASURED THE COMPOSITION OF THE ROCKS

THE WHEELS ON THE SOJOURNER WERE SPIKED SO THAT THEY COULD GRIP THE SOIL

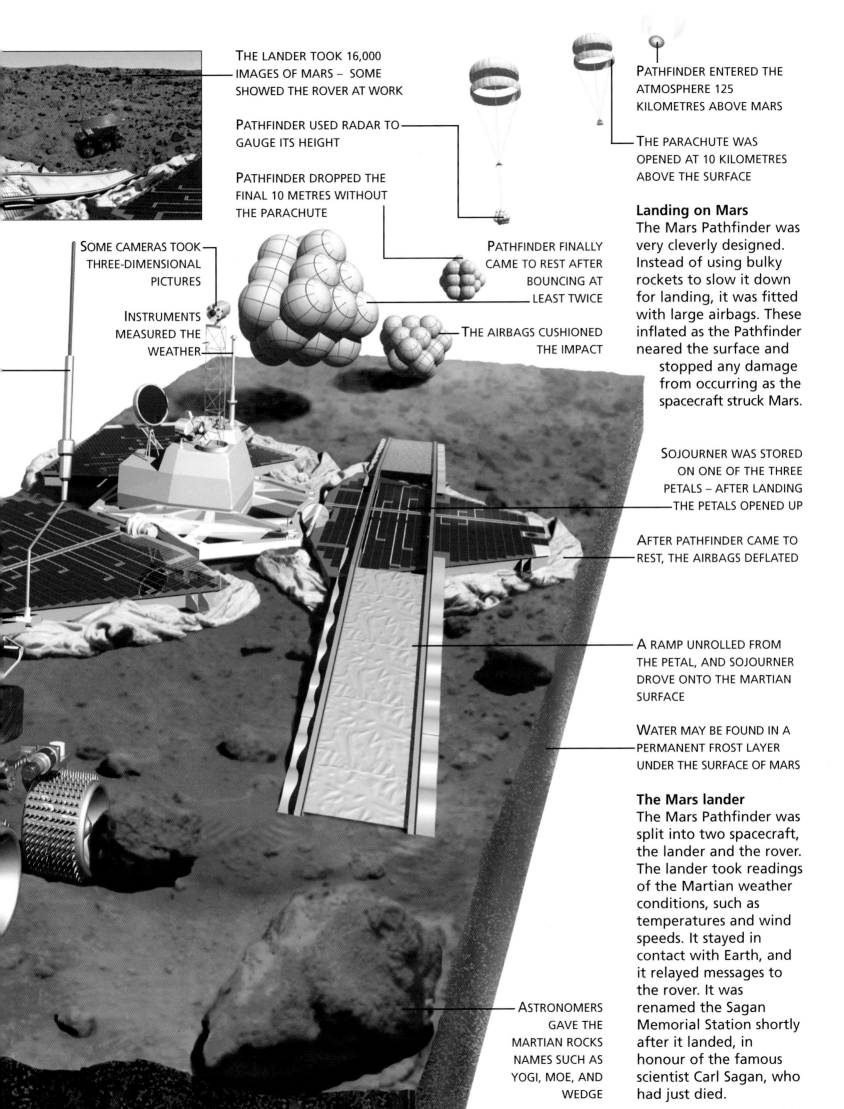

THE LANDER TOOK 16,000 IMAGES OF MARS – SOME SHOWED THE ROVER AT WORK

PATHFINDER USED RADAR TO GAUGE ITS HEIGHT

PATHFINDER DROPPED THE FINAL 10 METRES WITHOUT THE PARACHUTE

PATHFINDER ENTERED THE ATMOSPHERE 125 KILOMETRES ABOVE MARS

THE PARACHUTE WAS OPENED AT 10 KILOMETRES ABOVE THE SURFACE

SOME CAMERAS TOOK THREE-DIMENSIONAL PICTURES

INSTRUMENTS MEASURED THE WEATHER

PATHFINDER FINALLY CAME TO REST AFTER BOUNCING AT LEAST TWICE

THE AIRBAGS CUSHIONED THE IMPACT

Landing on Mars
The Mars Pathfinder was very cleverly designed. Instead of using bulky rockets to slow it down for landing, it was fitted with large airbags. These inflated as the Pathfinder neared the surface and stopped any damage from occurring as the spacecraft struck Mars.

SOJOURNER WAS STORED ON ONE OF THE THREE PETALS – AFTER LANDING THE PETALS OPENED UP

AFTER PATHFINDER CAME TO REST, THE AIRBAGS DEFLATED

A RAMP UNROLLED FROM THE PETAL, AND SOJOURNER DROVE ONTO THE MARTIAN SURFACE

WATER MAY BE FOUND IN A PERMANENT FROST LAYER UNDER THE SURFACE OF MARS

The Mars lander
The Mars Pathfinder was split into two spacecraft, the lander and the rover. The lander took readings of the Martian weather conditions, such as temperatures and wind speeds. It stayed in contact with Earth, and it relayed messages to the rover. It was renamed the Sagan Memorial Station shortly after it landed, in honour of the famous scientist Carl Sagan, who had just died.

ASTRONOMERS GAVE THE MARTIAN ROCKS NAMES SUCH AS YOGI, MOE, AND WEDGE

301

Voyager

TWO OF the most successful space missions ever were those of the space probes Voyagers I and II. Voyager II was launched on 20 August 1977 and Voyager I was launched a few weeks later, on 5 September 1977. Voyager I followed a faster route to Jupiter and overtook Voyager II on the way.

In March 1979, Voyager I flew by Jupiter and transmitted scientific information and images of the planet to Earth. It continued on, flying by Saturn and its largest moon, Titan, in November 1980. Voyager II reached Jupiter in July and Saturn in 1981. Unlike Voyager I, it did not fly close to Titan. Instead it continued to Uranus. In January 1986 it transmitted pictures of that pale blue planet before beginning its journey to Neptune.

In August 1989 Voyager II reached Neptune, the final planet on its mission. Only the distant planet Pluto remains to be visited by a space probe.

The grand tour
The Voyager space probes followed orbits known as gravity-assisted orbits. These orbits were first worked out in 1965 by Gary Flandro, who realized that the four giant planets only line up once every 175 years. This meant that a space probe could visit each giant planet in turn and use the gravity of one to throw it onwards to the next. He calculated that they would next line up in the 1980s, and so the idea for the Voyager missions was born.

THE VOYAGER DISK CONTAINS SOUNDS FROM EARTH, SUCH AS THE WORD 'HELLO' SPOKEN IN 60 LANGUAGES

Voyager I
On 17 February 1998, Voyager I became the most distant object made by humans, as it cruised out of the Solar System. It is now over 10.4 billion kilometres from the Earth.

THE MAGNETOMETER BOOM CONTAINED DETECTORS THAT MEASURED MAGNETIC FIELDS IN SPACE

THE SUN IS TOO FAINT TO BE AN ENERGY SOURCE IN THE OUTER SOLAR SYSTEM, SO RADIOISOTOPE THERMOELECTRIC GENERATORS PROVIDE VOYAGER WITH ENERGY

THIS FUEL TANK WAS USED WHEN VOYAGER TURNED IN SPACE

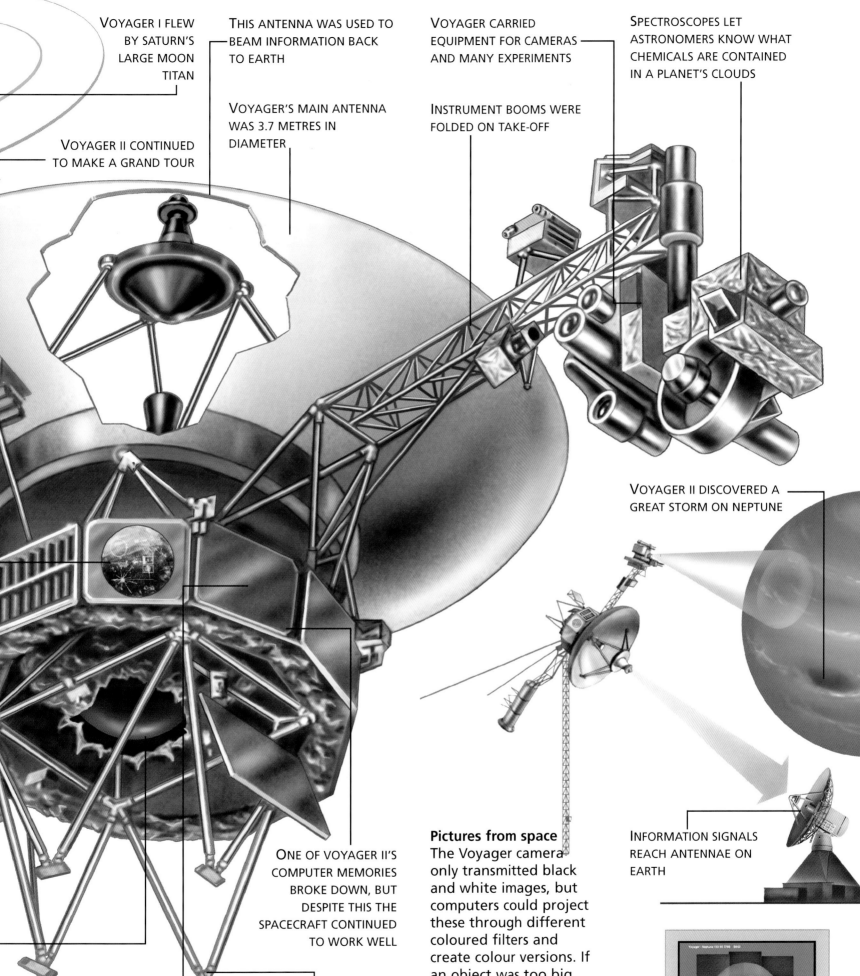

VOYAGER I FLEW BY SATURN'S LARGE MOON TITAN

THIS ANTENNA WAS USED TO BEAM INFORMATION BACK TO EARTH

VOYAGER CARRIED EQUIPMENT FOR CAMERAS AND MANY EXPERIMENTS

SPECTROSCOPES LET ASTRONOMERS KNOW WHAT CHEMICALS ARE CONTAINED IN A PLANET'S CLOUDS

VOYAGER'S MAIN ANTENNA WAS 3.7 METRES IN DIAMETER

INSTRUMENT BOOMS WERE FOLDED ON TAKE-OFF

VOYAGER II CONTINUED TO MAKE A GRAND TOUR

VOYAGER II DISCOVERED A GREAT STORM ON NEPTUNE

ONE OF VOYAGER II'S COMPUTER MEMORIES BROKE DOWN, BUT DESPITE THIS THE SPACECRAFT CONTINUED TO WORK WELL

INFORMATION SIGNALS REACH ANTENNAE ON EARTH

ON-BOARD COMPUTERS WERE REPROGRAMMED DURING THE MISSION

THESE STRUTS WERE USED TO FIX VOYAGER TO ITS LAUNCH ROCKET

Pictures from space
The Voyager camera only transmitted black and white images, but computers could project these through different coloured filters and create colour versions. If an object was too big for the camera, many photographs were taken and then pieced together, again by computer.

Studying Stars

ASTRONOMERS use very large telescopes to study the stars. These telescopes have two mirrors that focus light and are kept in observatories (*right*). Like any piece of machinery a telescope sometimes needs to be repaired, so everything that is necessary to keep it working is found in an observatory.

Using computer-controlled motors the telescope operator, sitting in the control room, can move the telescope. Another astronomer working alongside collects data. A range of cameras and other instruments, known as detectors, can be found at an observatory. Astronomers use them to record their observations by attaching them to the base of the telescope inside a metal cage. Data is fed into the control room and images are then displayed on a computer screen. The images are stored onto computer discs and taken away for detailed analysis at universities around the world.

Taking images

Pictures of the night sky are taken with electronic cameras and displayed on computers. Each picture is made up of tiny dots known as picture elements, or pixels. The image below shows solar systems forming in a cloud of gas known as the Orion nebula. They appear so small on the image that when the picture is enlarged the square pixels can be seen.

THIS OPENING ALLOWS THE TELESCOPE TO SEE OUT

THE FRONT END OF THIS REFLECTING TELESCOPE CONTAINS THE SECONDARY MIRROR

ROTATING THE DOME EXPOSES A DIFFERENT PART OF THE SKY TO THE TELESCOPE

A METAL CAGE HOUSES DETECTORS ATTACHED TO THE TELESCOPE

THE TELESCOPE OPERATOR IN THE CONTROL ROOM MOVES THE TELESCOPE. THE ASTRONOMERS ALSO SIT HERE

THE VENTILATION SYSTEM KEEPS THE TEMPERATURE INSIDE THE OBSERVATORY AT A COMFORTABLE LEVEL

INSTRUMENTS ARE BUILT AND REPAIRED IN THE ELECTRONICS LABORATORY

VISITORS TAKE A LIFT TO THE TELESCOPE

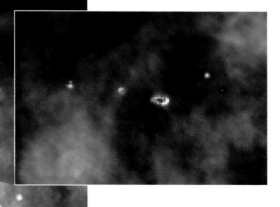

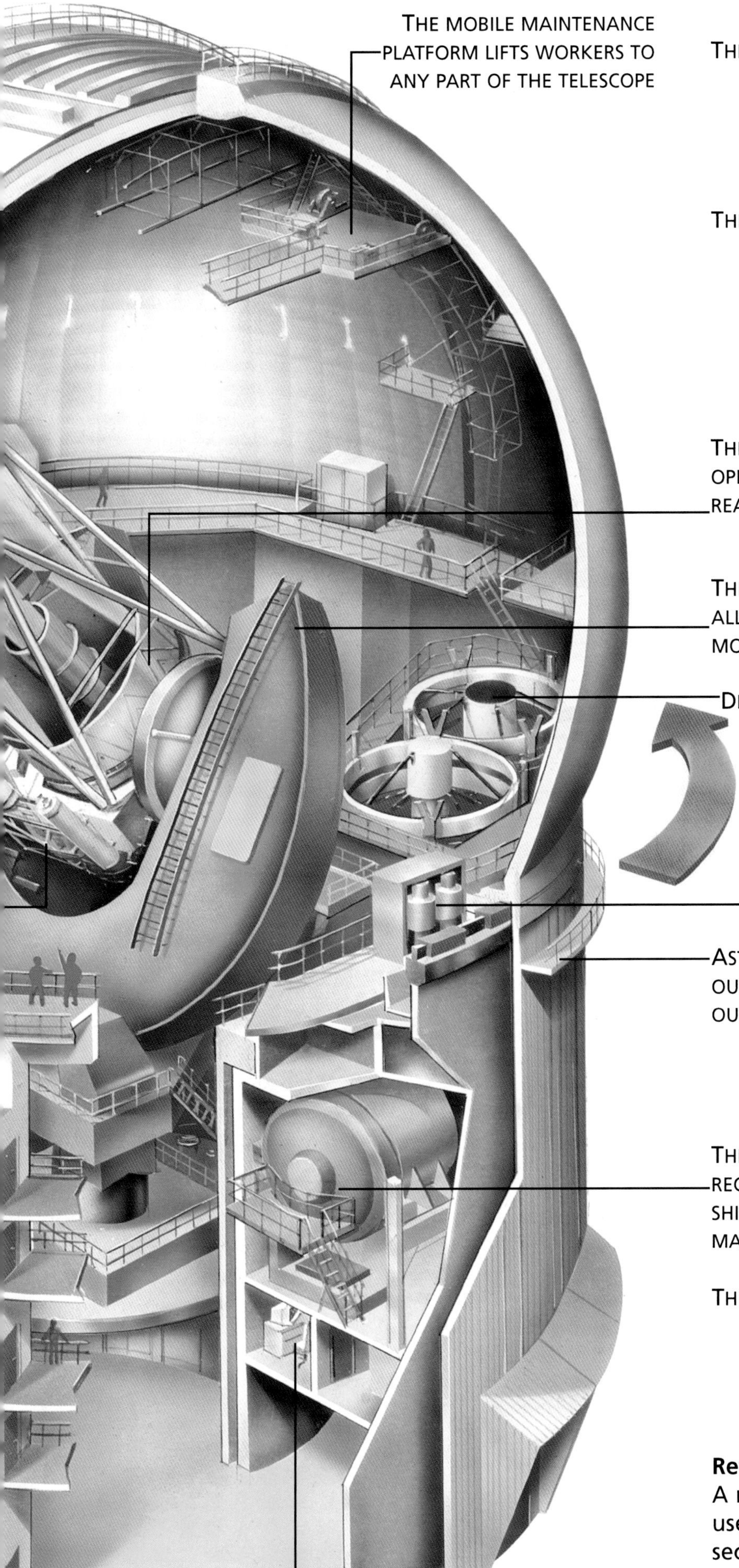

THE MOBILE MAINTENANCE
PLATFORM LIFTS WORKERS TO
ANY PART OF THE TELESCOPE

INCOMING STARLIGHT

THIS LENS FOCUSES LIGHT

THE EYEPIECE

THIS LENS MAGNIFIES
THE IMAGE

THE PROTECTIVE PETALS
OPEN TO ALLOW LIGHT TO
REACH THE PRIMARY MIRROR

THE HORSESHOE BEARING
ALLOWS THE TELESCOPE TO
MOVE

DIFFERENT FRONT ENDS HAVE
DIFFERENT SECONDARY
MIRRORS TO GIVE
DIFFERENT VIEWS

THE DOME DRIVE UNIT
ROTATES THE DOME
WHEN NEEDED

ASTRONOMERS USE THE
OUTSIDE CATWALK TO LOOK
OUT FOR CLEAR SKIES

THE ALUMINIZING PLANT
RECOATS THE MIRROR IN
SHINY ALUMINIUM
MAKING IT AS GOOD AS NEW

THE OFFICES AND LIBRARY
ARE WHERE ASTRONOMERS
WORK DURING THE DAY

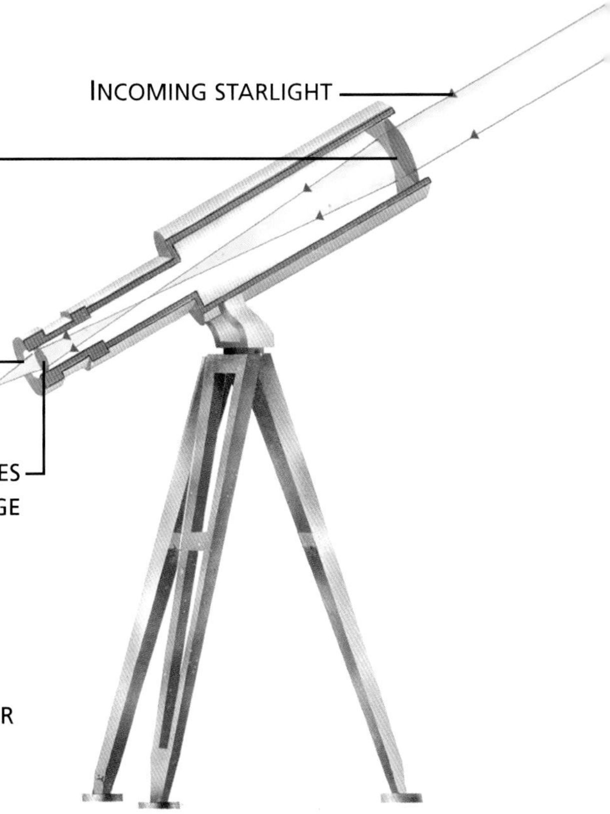

Refracting telescopes
A refracting telescope
brings light to a focus by
using two lenses. The
first is known as the
objective lens and
focuses the light just
before the eyepiece. The
eyepiece lens then
magnifies the image so
the observer can see it
comfortably.

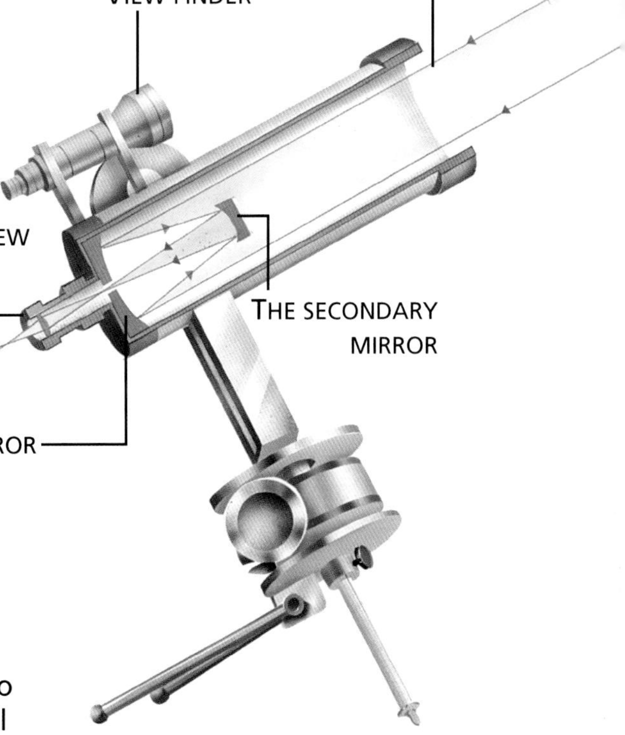

INCOMING STARLIGHT

VIEW FINDER

THE EYEPIECE

THE SECONDARY
MIRROR

THE PRIMARY MIRROR

Reflecting telescope
A reflecting telescope
uses the primary and
secondary mirrors to
focus starlight. The
eyepiece lens is used to
magnify the image. All
the large telescopes are
reflecting telescopes.

Stars

STARS ARE enormous energy generators. They are born in collapsing clouds of hydrogen gas. The gas is squeezed so tightly that its temperature rises. When the temperature in the centre of the star reaches 10 million °C, the hydrogen atoms' nuclei collide with such force that they fuse (stick together) and form new nuclei. This nuclear fusion leads to the formation of helium nuclei and the release of energy which makes the star shine.

Stars come in many sizes. The Sun is a little bigger than most other stars, but some stars have a hundred times the mass of the Sun. Stars that contain the most mass do not live as long as stars with little mass. A very high mass star will only live a few million years, while a low mass star, such as the Sun, could last nine billion years or more.

The life of a star
At the first stage of a star's life, the star is the centre of a collapsing gas cloud (1). When the core of a protostar is hot enough, hydrogen begins to fuse and the protostar becomes a star (2). For most of its

THE CORE OF THE SUN CONTAINS ABOUT ONE TENTH OF THE SUN'S MASS

ENERGY LEAVES THE SUN'S CORE IN LIGHT ENERGY PARTICLES, CALLED PHOTONS

The corona
The outermost gas around the Sun is called the corona. It spreads out very thinly through space and usually cannot be seen because the photosphere of the Sun is so bright. During a solar eclipse, the Moon blocks out the light from the photosphere and the dimmer corona can be seen around the edge.

ERUPTIVE PROMINENCES THROW SUPERHEATED GAS INTO SPACE

THE SUN GIVES OFF TINY PARTICLES WHICH STREAM THROUGH SPACE – THEY MAKE UP THE SOLAR WIND

life a star will generate energy and change very little (3). As a star grows older it begins to increase its size and the amount of energy it generates (4). Late in a star's life it begins to pulsate (expand and contract) (5). Nuclear fusion takes place in bursts rather than continuously. The unstable nuclear fusion in the star lifts its outer layers and throws them off into space. The result is known as a planetary nebula (6) because such an object looked like a planet to astronomers in the 1700s.

THE SUN IS A STAR; IT IS 4.6 BILLION YEARS OLD

THE RADIATIVE ZONE IS PACKED WITH ATOMS AND PHOTONS WHICH ARE CONSTANTLY COLLIDING

WHEN HYDROGEN STOPS FUSING IN A STAR'S CORE THE STAR BECOMES A RED GIANT

THE CONVECTIVE ZONE CONSTANTLY CHURNS LIKE BOILING MILK

A WHITE DWARF IS THE EXPOSED CORE OF AN OLD STAR

VERY LARGE CONVECTIVE CELLS CARRY GAS AND PHOTONS TO THE SOLAR SURFACE

A WHITE DWARF EVENTUALLY BECOMES A COLD, BLACK DWARF

SPICULES ARE STRAIGHT COLUMNS OF GAS THAT RISE AND FALL IN A FEW MINUTES

A PHOTON TAKES A MILLION YEARS TO TRAVEL THROUGH THE RADIATIVE ZONE

SUNSPOTS ARE COOLER AREAS OF THE SOLAR SURFACE; THEY APPEAR DARK BECAUSE THE REST OF THE SUN IS SO HOT

THE PHOTOSPHERE IS THE SURFACE FROM WHICH THE MAJORITY OF THE SUN'S LIGHT IS RELEASED

THE CHROMOSPHERE IS A LAYER OF GAS ABOVE THE PHOTOSPHERE, A FEW THOUSAND KILOMETRES THICK

SOME PROMINENCES ARE NOT ERUPTIVE AND CAN LAST FOR A FEW MONTHS

Black Holes

A BLACK HOLE is one of the most remarkable objects in the Universe. It is an incredibly dense object which possesses so much gravity that nothing can escape from it. Light is the fastest thing in the Universe and yet not even light can travel away from a black hole.

In order to escape the gravitational pull of the Earth, a rocket must reach a speed of 11.2 kilometres per second. This is known as the escape velocity. If the Earth were squeezed into a smaller volume, making it more dense, its gravitational pull would be greater and the escape velocity would increase. If the Earth were squeezed to the size of a marble, the escape velocity would go up so much that it would be equal to the speed of light (300,000 kilometres a second). At this point nothing would escape its gravitational pull and the Earth would become a black hole.

THE PATCHES OF RADIO WAVES AT THE ENDS OF RADIO JETS ARE KNOWN AS RADIO LOBES

Active galaxies

Some galaxies contain supermassive black holes. These are called active galaxies. Sometimes jets shoot out from the core, far into space. The particles collide with each other and produce radio waves which can be picked up by radio telescopes. In the picture above the radio waves have been colour coded by a computer. Only some active galaxies produce radio waves – it is not yet known why.

THE TORUS IS OFTEN SURROUNDED BY CLOUDS OF GAS THAT ARE TURNING INTO STARS

THE TORUS IS A LARGE DISC OF DUST AND GAS SURROUNDING A SUPERMASSIVE BLACK HOLE

Stellar black holes

A stellar black hole is created when a massive star explodes. For example, the black hole Cygnus X-1 (1) was created when a massive star, in a binary (double) star system, exploded. The second star (2) is now being pulled to pieces and swallowed by the black hole. As they orbit, gas streams from the star onto a disc around the black hole before being consumed. The gas becomes so hot that it gives off X-rays – these can be detected by X-ray telescopes.

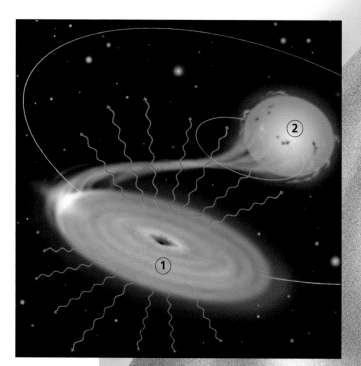

00   000.0000

A SPACECRAFT WOULD NOT BEGIN TO STRETCH UNTIL IT WAS CLOSE TO THE BLACK HOLE

AN OBSERVER'S CLOCK WOULD SHOW THAT TIME WAS SLOWING DOWN FOR THE SPACECRAFT

A CLOCK ON THE SPACECRAFT WOULD APPEAR TO SHOW TIME PASSING NORMALLY

AS THE SPACECRAFT APPROACHES A BLACK HOLE, AN OBSERVER'S CLOCK (*LEFT*) AND THE SPACECRAFT'S CLOCK (*RIGHT*) WOULD SHOW DIFFERENT TIMES

100.0001   100.0000

103.0000   101.0000

AS IT GETS CLOSER TO THE BLACK HOLE, THE DUST EVAPORATES INTO GAS

999.0000   101.1000

THE SUPERMASSIVE BLACK HOLE SITS IN THE CENTRE OF THE GALAXY

ASTRONOMERS IMAGINE SPACE TO BE LIKE A RUBBER SHEET

THE JETS ARE GENERATED SOMEWHERE VERY CLOSE TO THE BLACK HOLE AND THE ACCRETION DISC

THE ACCRETION DISC FEEDS THE GAS FROM THE TORUS INTO THE BLACK HOLE

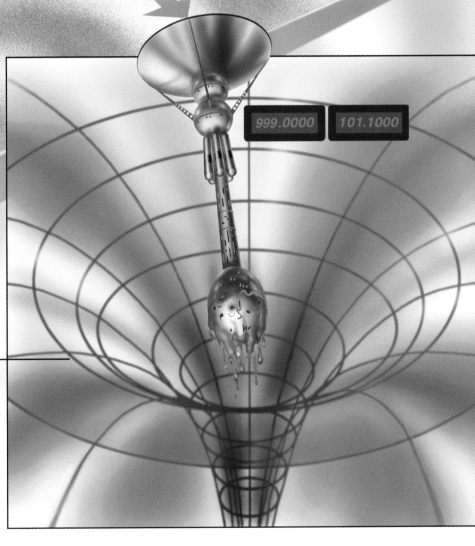

Supermassive black holes

The supermassive black hole is at the centre of an active galaxy (*above*). This is millions of times more massive than a stellar black hole. It is produced when matter falls together to form the galaxy.

JETS ARE MADE UP OF TINY PARTICLES SMALLER THAN ATOMS

Falling into a black hole

If a spacecraft were to fall into a black hole, it would be destroyed. As the spacecraft got closer, the gravitational force would strengthen. The end closest to the black hole would be pulled more, stretching the craft until it was pulled to bits. Time passes more slowly near an object with gravity, such as a black hole, so a distant observer would see time slowing down for the craft as it got closer to the black hole. On the spacecraft, time would appear to pass normally.

Radio Telescopes

FOR CENTURIES telescopes have collected light and focused it into images. However, light is not the only type of radiation released by objects in space. Many also give out radio waves. In order to collect radio waves a special telescope, called a radio telescope, is needed.

Radio telescopes are very large dishes which collect radio waves and focus them onto a small detector in the centre of the dish. The study of radio waves from space has given astronomers new ideas about galaxies. In particular, they have learnt that some active galaxies are powerful emitters of radio waves (*see page 308*).

Some astronomers also use radio telescopes to search for messages from space. They are trying to find other life in the Universe, which may communicate using radio waves. No messages have been received so far.

Radio images from space
Radio waves picked up by the radio telescope's detectors are combined into a single image. Different radio intensities are colour coded. To obtain higher quality images, several radio telescopes can be used together. Two or more radio telescopes observe the same object at the same time. The signals received by each telescope can then be compared and used to form detailed pictures.

The Effelsberg Radio Telescope
The Effelsberg radio telescope has a collecting dish with an area of 8000 square metres. It collects radio waves with this dish and focuses them onto three detectors. The three detectors collect radio waves from three slightly different parts of the sky and this speeds up the process of building an image.

THE RADIO DISH IS SUPPORTED BY A STRONG FRAMEWORK

THE WAVEGUIDES CHANNEL THE RADIO WAVES ONTO PROBES

PROBES CONVERT THE RADIO WAVES INTO ELECTRICAL SIGNALS

THE MAIN DISH IS LIKE THE PRIMARY MIRROR IN A REFLECTING TELESCOPE

A COMPUTER DISPLAYS RADIO IMAGES OF AN EXPLODED STAR

DETECTORS CONVERT THE SIGNALS SO THAT THEY CAN BE READ BY A COMPUTER

RECEIVERS AMPLIFY THE SIGNALS FROM THE PROBES AND PASS THEM TO THE DETECTORS

THE SECONDARY REFLECTOR
ACTS LIKE THE SECONDARY
MIRROR IN AN OPTICAL
TELESCOPE (*SEE PAGE 305*)

SUPER-HEATED GAS ON
THE SUN'S SURFACE
SHOWS UP IN X-RAYS

GAMMA RAYS

X-RAYS

WAVEGUIDES ALLOW THE
RADIO TELESCOPE TO DETECT
RADIO WAVES OF DIFFERENT
FREQUENCIES

ULTRAVIOLET
LIGHT

VISIBLE
LIGHT

INFRARED

RADIO WAVES FROM SPACE
ARE OFTEN VERY WEAK AND
SO VERY LARGE RADIO
TELESCOPES ARE NEEDED

WE SEE THE SUN AT VISIBLE
LIGHT WAVELENGTHS

THE TELESCOPE CAN BE
POINTED AT DIFFERENT
ALTITUDES

MICRO-
WAVES

**Electromagnetic
spectrum**
Visible light is a small part
of the electromagnetic
spectrum (*right*). All
electromagnetic rays are
waves of electric and
magnetic energy. The
wavelength of each ray
decides where it fits into
the spectrum. Radio
waves have long
wavelengths, gamma
rays have very short
wavelengths. Visible
light falls between the
two extremes.

THE RADIO TELESCOPE CAN
BE ROTATED RIGHT AROUND

RADIO
WAVES

STRONG SUPPORTS KEEP THE
TELESCOPE STABLE AND FREE
FROM VIBRATION

Magnetic Fields

A MAGNETIC field is generated every time an electrically charged object moves. Most of the planets in the Solar System are known to generate magnetic fields. The Earth's magnetic field is generated in its fluid, outer core. This is because the heat of the inner core drives the fluid in the outer core up and around in a process called convection. Because this outer core is made of metal, which can be electrically charged, the convection causes a magnetic field to be generated.

The planets Mercury, Venus, and Mars generate their magnetic fields in similar ways, but compared to the Earth's, their fields are weak. In the centre of Jupiter and Saturn, hydrogen gas is compressed to behave like a metal and this generates magnetic fields. In Uranus and Neptune, the generating material is thought to be ice.

Auroral display
Tiny particles carrying electrical charges are always streaming away from the Sun. Sometimes these get caught in the Earth's magnetic field and are drawn into the atmosphere near the North and South Poles. When these charged particles hit molecules in the atmosphere they cause them to glow with light. This is known as an auroral display.

THE MAGNETOSPHERE PROTECTS THE EARTH FROM THE HARMFUL CHARGED PARTICLES OF THE SOLAR WIND

MOST PARTICLES FROM THE SUN STREAM PAST THE EARTH

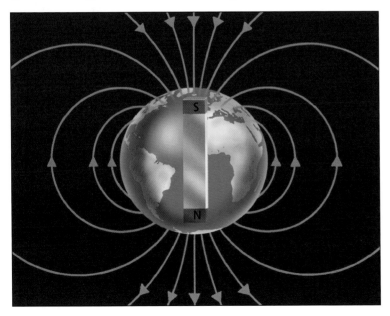

Magnetic poles
All of the magnetic fields behave as if a gigantic bar magnet were buried in the centre of the planet. Invisible field lines of magnetic force come out through the magnetic north pole of the planet and back in through the magnetic south pole. (The magnetic poles are at opposite ends to the geographic poles.)

THE EARTH'S MAGNETIC FIELD STRETCHES AWAY FROM THE SUN FOR MILLIONS OF KILOMETRES

SOME PARTICLES ARE CAUGHT AND TRAPPED IN THE PLASMA SHEET

SOME PARTICLES ARE
FUNNELLED IN TOWARDS THE
POLES

CHARGED PARTICLES FLOW
AROUND THE EARTH'S
MAGNETIC FIELD

THE MAGNETIC
ENVIRONMENT OF A PLANET
IS KNOWN AS THE
MAGNETOSPHERE

THE VAN ALLEN BELTS ARE
PARTICLES TRAPPED BY THE
EARTH'S MAGNETIC FIELD

THE AREA CONTAINING
THE EARTH'S MAGNETIC
FIELD IS CALLED THE
MAGNETOPAUSE

INCOMING SOLAR
WIND PARTICLES

CHARGED PARTICLES HIT THE
ATMOSPHERE NEAR THE
NORTH AND SOUTH POLES

The solar wind
The Sun is constantly
throwing off tiny particles
which carry an electrical
charge. These particles
are bits of atoms that are
flung outwards from
close to the Sun's
surface. As the Sun spins
it flings them off in a
spiral pattern. The wind
of particles blows round
the Earth's magneto-
sphere, pulling it out in
a tail on the far side.

THE OUTER LAYER, CALLED
THE MAGNETOSHEATH, IS
FULL OF TURBULENT
PARTICLES

THE WORLD OF
INSECT LIFE

Gerald Legg and Steve Weston

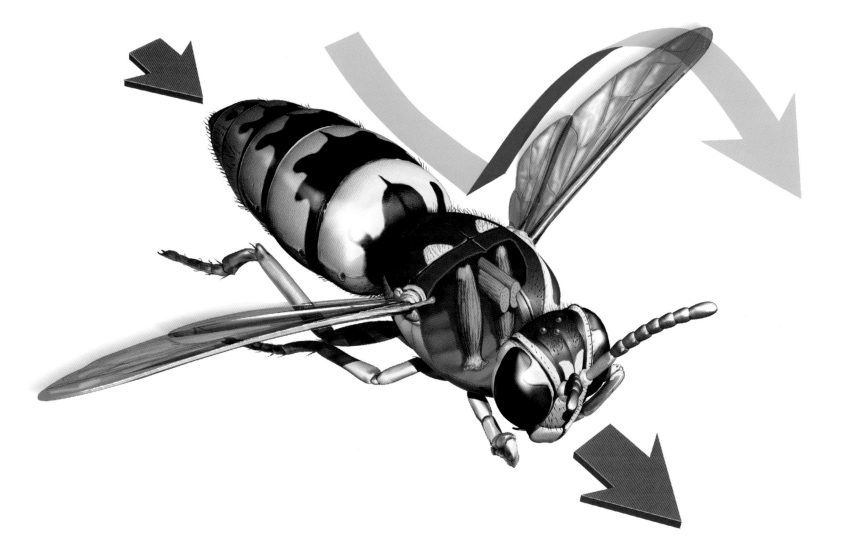

THE WORLD OF
INSECT LIFE
CONTENTS

What is an Insect?

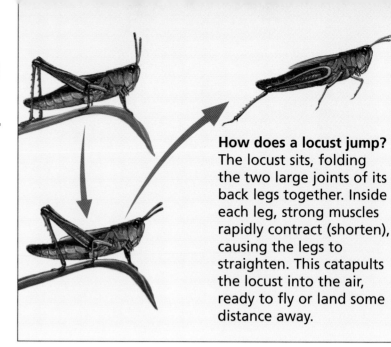

How does a locust jump?
The locust sits, folding the two large joints of its back legs together. Inside each leg, strong muscles rapidly contract (shorten), causing the legs to straighten. This catapults the locust into the air, ready to fly or land some distance away.

THERE are more insects on Earth than any other type of creature. Insects are strong and small, with three pairs of legs but no backbone. Like knights in armour, they have a tough outer covering. This outer skeleton (exoskeleton) supports and protects the insect's body parts and soft insides.

The protected head of an insect holds the brain and carries the antennae, eyes, mouth, and special jaws. Different insects have different shaped jaws, allowing them to eat all kinds of things. The abdomen contains the main organs, including those for digesting food. Throughout the body, special breathing tubes called trachea carry gases to and from the body's tissues. A long thin heart circulates blood. A nerve cord that controls various body processes runs from the brain to the tip of the abdomen.

FOOD PASSES INTO THE GIZZARD WHERE IT IS GROUND UP AND FILTERED

THE CROP RECEIVES AND STORES THE FOOD TO BE DIGESTED

BLOOD IS PUMPED AROUND THE BODY BY THE HEART

THE LOCUST'S THIN, FLEXIBLE ANTENNAE ARE SENSITIVE TO SMELLS

EACH COMPOUND EYE IS MADE UP OF HUNDREDS OF LIGHT-SENSITIVE UNITS

EVERY PART OF THE BODY IS COVERED BY THE EXOSKELETON, WHICH IS MADE OF A HARD MATERIAL CALLED CUTICLE

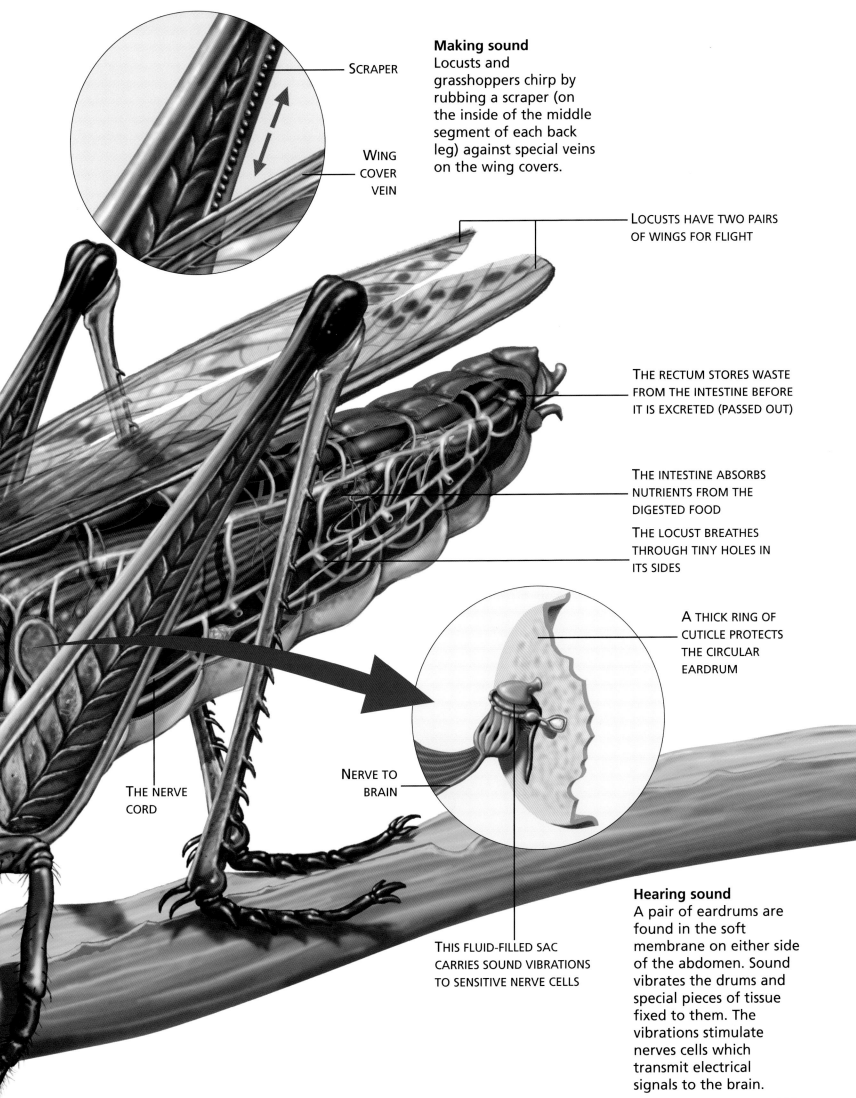

SCRAPER

WING COVER VEIN

Making sound
Locusts and grasshoppers chirp by rubbing a scraper (on the inside of the middle segment of each back leg) against special veins on the wing covers.

LOCUSTS HAVE TWO PAIRS OF WINGS FOR FLIGHT

THE RECTUM STORES WASTE FROM THE INTESTINE BEFORE IT IS EXCRETED (PASSED OUT)

THE INTESTINE ABSORBS NUTRIENTS FROM THE DIGESTED FOOD

THE LOCUST BREATHES THROUGH TINY HOLES IN ITS SIDES

A THICK RING OF CUTICLE PROTECTS THE CIRCULAR EARDRUM

NERVE TO BRAIN

THE NERVE CORD

THIS FLUID-FILLED SAC CARRIES SOUND VIBRATIONS TO SENSITIVE NERVE CELLS

Hearing sound
A pair of eardrums are found in the soft membrane on either side of the abdomen. Sound vibrates the drums and special pieces of tissue fixed to them. The vibrations stimulate nerves cells which transmit electrical signals to the brain.

Armour Plating

INSECTS WEAR their skeleton on the outside, like armour. Out of all the types of animals in the world, insects have been more able to survive because of this amazing exoskeleton. It is made of a tough, skin-like substance, called cuticle, which protects the organs and supports the muscles. Insects' jaws are covered in very hard cuticle, whereas at the joints it is soft and flexible. Thin tubes of cuticle make strong jointed legs. Both the head and thorax are like boxes made of thick cuticle. The head protects the brain and carries the sense organs and mouth parts. The strong thorax supports the wing and leg muscles. In contrast, the abdomen which holds most of the body organs is flexible and made of several rings of cuticle, called segments.

Beetle
There are over 330,000 species of beetle ranging in size from 0.5 mm to over 155 mm. They are found everywhere. Hard, tough forewings protect their delicate flying wings. Shown here, is a scarab beetle.

THE THORAX IS PACKED WITH MUSCLES TO DRIVE THE WINGS AND LEGS

EACH MULTI-JOINTED, FLEXIBLE ANTENNA IS COVERED IN SENSE CELLS TO DETECT SMELLS IN THE AIR

COMPOUND EYE

THE NECK FORMS A FLEXIBLE PART BETWEEN THE HEAD AND THORAX

MUSCLES OF THE UPPER LEG JOINT ARE FIXED TO THE THORAX

THE TOP LIP IS HINGED TO THE FRONT OF THE FACE SO THAT IT CAN MOVE

Insect head
The head carries the main sense organs – this beetle has a pair of compound eyes, simple eyes, and antennae. At the front of the mouth there are three sets of mouthparts: the mandibles (jaws), maxillae, and bottom lip. A top lip covers the mandibles. The head is attached to the thorax by a narrow, flexible neck.

ANTENNA

SENSORY ORGANS STICK OUT BELOW EACH HALF OF THE BOTTOM LIP

INSECTS HAVE THREE PAIRS OF LEGS

MANDIBLE: A SHARP JAW FOR CUTTING FOOD AND FIGHTING

MAXILLA: A SMALL JAW WITH SENSORY ORGANS THAT HELPS CUT UP FOOD

THE THIN HIND WINGS ARE FOLDED BENEATH AND PROTECTED BY THE FOREWINGS

THE SEGMENTED, FLEXIBLE ABDOMEN IS FULL OF SOFT DELICATE ORGANS

THE WAXY TOP LAYER OF THE CUTICLE IS WATERPROOF

Exoskeleton

The exoskeleton consists of the cuticle and epidermis. The cuticle is mainly secreted from the epidermis. It consists of layers of strands of long, sugar-like molecules embedded in a hardened substance, like steel rods in concrete. Some cells in the epidermis secrete the waxy top layer which waterproofs the insect. Sensory cells and bristles also form part of the exoskeleton.

CUTICLE FORMS THE STRONG EXOSKELETON

THE EPIDERMIS SECRETES (OOZES) CUTICLE AND SUBSTANCES THAT MAKE UP THE TOP WATERPROOF LAYER

THE FOREWINGS ARE TOUGH AND HARD

AN UNFOLDED HINDWING – ITS THIN BUT STRONG MEMBRANE IS FURTHER STRENGTHENED BY VEINS

HOLLOW BUT STRONG LEG JOINTS ARE FILLED WITH MUSCLES, TENDONS, AND NERVES

A WING HINGE-JOINT ALLOWS THE WING TO BEAT UP AND DOWN, AND ROTATE

THE END SEGMENTS OF THE LEG MAKE UP THE TARSUS, OR FOOT

SHARP CURVED CLAWS GIVE THIS BEETLE A STRONG GRIP

Joints and hinges

In order to move about easily insects need joints in their armour-like skeleton. Each leg, wing, mouthpart and antenna is jointed. Each of these is joined to the body with a hinge or ball-and-socket joint. Between the joints the cuticle is soft and flexible, allowing for movement. So that an insect can move along uneven surfaces successfully, each leg joint is hinged at a slightly different angle to its neighbour. The wings have complicated hinges where they join the thorax. In beetles, even the wings themselves have hinges. These lie between the veins and allow the wings to be safely folded away.

321

Insect Eyes

INSECTS HAVE two types of eyes. The largest are the compound eyes, which are covered with a honeycomb pattern of hexagons. Each hexagon is the transparent cuticle of an individual organ of sight. Insects can have as many as 30,000 hexagonal shapes in each compound eye or as few as one. Each of these sight organs (called ommatidia) sees only a tiny part of the surroundings. But by joining these parts together in the brain, the insect is able to see a full image.

The second type of eyes, called ocelli, are usually much smaller. They are similar to human eyes, but cannot see an image. Instead they are very sensitive to light. Nocturnal insects, which are active at night, have very large ocelli.

MALE ST MARKS FLIES HAVE DIVIDED EYES

WHIRLIGIG BEETLES HAVE SPLIT EYES – THE LOWER EYES ALLOW THEM TO SEE UNDERWATER

Ommatidia

Light from the outside world enters each ommatidium and is focused by a hexagonal lens. It then passes through the crystal-like cone which also helps to focus it. Next, it reaches the nerve cells which have a light-sensitive inner part (called the rhabdom). From here the light is carried by nerve fibres to the brain. Pigment cells surround the nerve cells and stop light leaking into the rest of the eye, as this would spoil the image.

THE OMMATIDIUM HAS A LIGHT-SENSITIVE INNER PART

NERVE FIBRES CARRY VISUAL INFORMATION TO THE BRAIN

TRANSPARENT CUTICLE COVERS THE LENS

NERVE CELL

PIGMENT CELLS KEEP LIGHT INSIDE THE OMMATIDIUM

THE CRYSTAL-LIKE CONE IS SURROUNDED BY PIGMENT CELLS

A HEXAGONAL LENS FOCUSES LIGHT DOWN INTO THE OMMATIDIUM

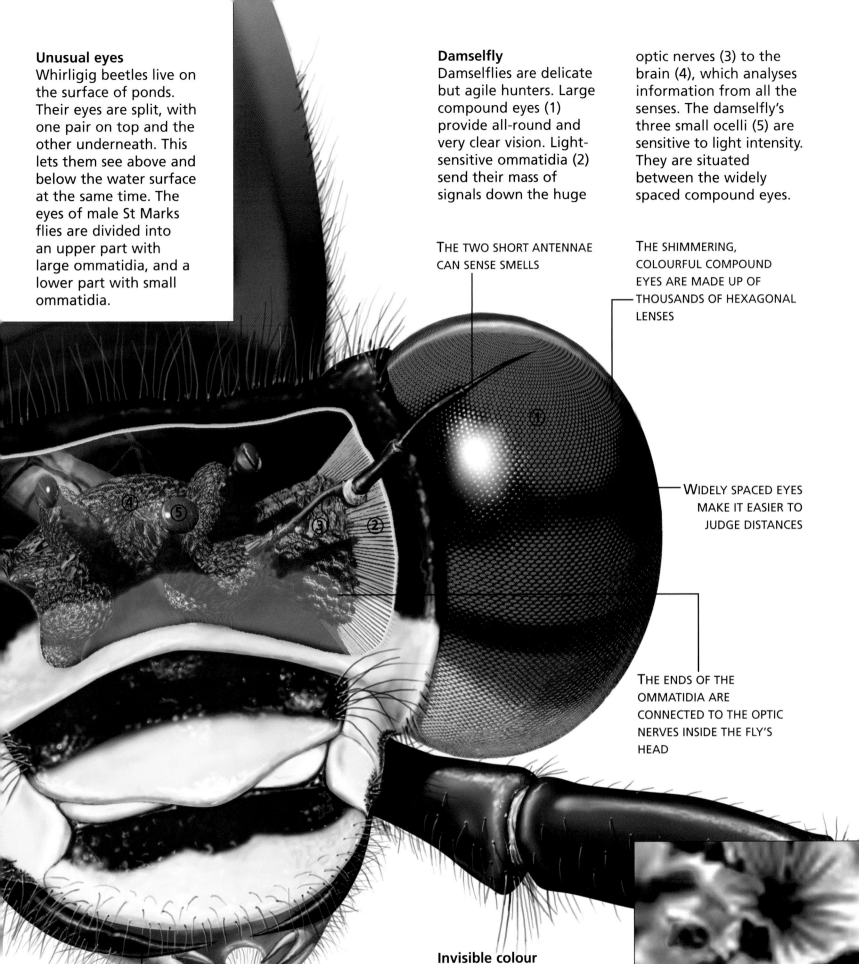

Unusual eyes
Whirligig beetles live on the surface of ponds. Their eyes are split, with one pair on top and the other underneath. This lets them see above and below the water surface at the same time. The eyes of male St Marks flies are divided into an upper part with large ommatidia, and a lower part with small ommatidia.

Damselfly
Damselflies are delicate but agile hunters. Large compound eyes (1) provide all-round and very clear vision. Light-sensitive ommatidia (2) send their mass of signals down the huge optic nerves (3) to the brain (4), which analyses information from all the senses. The damselfly's three small ocelli (5) are sensitive to light intensity. They are situated between the widely spaced compound eyes.

THE TWO SHORT ANTENNAE CAN SENSE SMELLS

THE SHIMMERING, COLOURFUL COMPOUND EYES ARE MADE UP OF THOUSANDS OF HEXAGONAL LENSES

WIDELY SPACED EYES MAKE IT EASIER TO JUDGE DISTANCES

THE ENDS OF THE OMMATIDIA ARE CONNECTED TO THE OPTIC NERVES INSIDE THE FLY'S HEAD

MOUTH PARTS FOR EATING PREY

Invisible colour
Many insects can see ultraviolet, a colour invisible to us. Some flowers reflect this colour so that insects can see special markings that will guide them to the flower's nectaries.

Feelers

INSECT FEELERS are remarkable instruments. The two feelers (antennae) are covered in many thousands of sensory cells, which can detect tiny amounts of chemicals, even a single molecule. This means, for example, that a male moth can detect the scent of a female moth that is over a kilometre away. Insects can even 'see' using their feelers, mapping out the shape of their surroundings from the smells in it. Insects use sensory cells to find their way about and to find many other things – a mate, the right plant on which to lay their eggs, tasty prey or a good host to live on. Although insects have other chemical-sensitive organs, such as taste organs, these are not as sensitive and need direct contact with a substance.

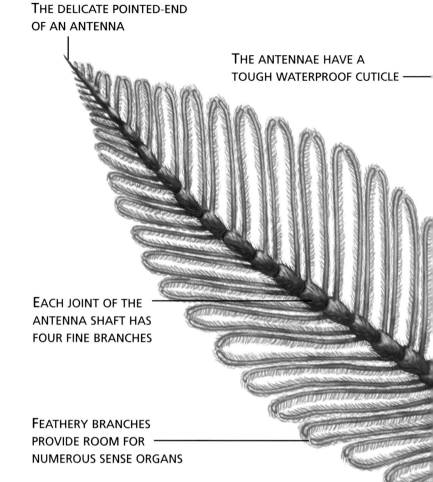

THE DELICATE POINTED-END OF AN ANTENNA

THE ANTENNAE HAVE A TOUGH WATERPROOF CUTICLE

EACH JOINT OF THE ANTENNA SHAFT HAS FOUR FINE BRANCHES

FEATHERY BRANCHES PROVIDE ROOM FOR NUMEROUS SENSE ORGANS

THE LEGS AND BODY ARE COVERED IN A THICK MASS OF 'HAIRS' WHICH MAKES FOR SILENT FLIGHT

LARGE EYES FOR SEEING IN MOON LIGHT

EMPEROR MOTHS INCLUDE THE LARGEST MOTHS – SOME HAVE A WINGSPAN OF UP TO 30 CENTIMETRES

CURVED FURRY FRONT EDGE OF FORE-WING

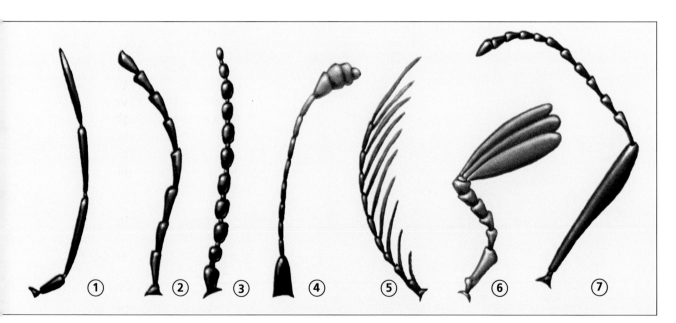

Types of feelers
Feelers come in a great variety of shapes and sizes, especially in the beetle world. Springtails and dragonflies have thread-like feelers (1). Some ground beetles have a saw-edge variety (2). Termites and earwigs have bead-like ones (3) and those of burying beetles are clubbed (4). Sawflies and cardinal beetles have feather-like feelers (5) and the cockchafer beetle and june bug have feather-tipped ones (6). Weevils and parastic wasps have flexible 'elbowed' feelers (7).

A PORE

SENSITIVE NERVE FIBRES IN THE PORES RECEIVE SCENT MOLECULES

A SENSORY PEG SITS IN A PROTECTIVE CUP

Sensory peg
Thousands of sensory pegs on each antenna detect scent molecules in the air. The molecules enter through pores and touch the sensitive parts of a sensory cell, which recognizes them. The information is then sent down to the antenna's main nerve, then to the brain.

EACH SENSORY CELL SENDS ELECTRICAL SIGNALS DOWN NERVES WHEN A SCENT IS DETECTED

Tasting with feet
Using special hairs on their feet, insects can taste what they are walking on. These hairs are short and stout and project from the cuticle. At their tip they have a tiny opening through which chemicals enter. When the chemicals touch the sensory cell the insect 'tastes' it.

THE BRAIN

A MASS OF NERVES GOES FROM THE EYES TO THE BRAIN

A SUBSTANCE IS 'TASTED' WHEN IT COMES INTO CONTACT WITH NERVE FIBRES

A FINE OPENING AT TIP OF EACH SENSORY HAIR HOUSES NERVE FIBRES

TOUGH CUTICLE FORMS RIGID SENSORY HAIRS ON THE MOTH'S FOOT

Flying

INSECTS CAN do just about any flying manoeuvre. They can fly forward, backward, sideways, or upside down; they can loop, hover, swoop, and even do vertical take-offs. An insect's thorax is an extremely complicated, tough but flexible, powerhouse – packed with muscles that control the movement of the wings. Each wing is hinged to the thorax by ball-and-socket joints that pivot near the inner end of the wing. When the wing moves it rocks on these joints like a seesaw that can swivel round in all directions. To move their wings some insects, including dragonflies, use muscles fixed directly to the end of the wings. Most other insects use muscles that are fixed to the top and bottom and the front and back of the thorax.

Wing types

The dragonfly (1) has two pairs of wings that move alternately. They are driven by muscles fixed directly to the wings. A butterfly (2) has slow-beating wings that overlap – the front wing pulls the back one down. Flies (3) use one pair of wings for flying, and a second pair form special organs for controlling flight. Beetles (4) have tough front wings that protect the delicate hind-wings when they are folded away.

AS THE WASP MOVES FORWARDS AND LIFTS INTO THE AIR, ITS WINGS ROTATE UP AND DOWN

EACH PAIR OF WINGS IS LINKED TOGETHER, GIVING EXTRA LIFT

THE WING TILTS WITH THE LEADING EDGE FACING DOWNWARDS

VEINS GIVE THE WING STRENGTH AND SHAPE FOR EFFICIENT FLIGHT

Linked pairs

Wings that are linked together make for efficient flight. Butterflies link their wings by overlapping them, and wasps have hooks on their hind-wing that catch into a fold on the fore-wing.

Wing down

Many insects, like this wasp, move their wings down by contracting (shortening) the thorax muscles that run front-to-back and relaxing (lengthening) those that run top-to-bottom. This makes the thorax bulge. The thorax cuticle (outer covering) is like tough elastic, so when it bulges, the wings, which pivot like a seesaw, are flicked down.

ON THE UP STROKE, THE WING TILTS UPWARDS

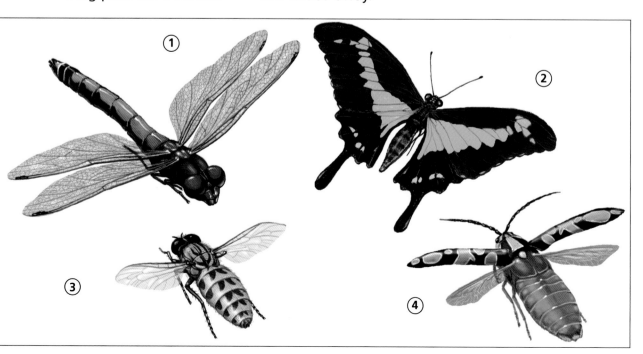

THE HIND-
WING'S ROW OF
HOOKS CATCH
INTO A FOLD
ON FORE-WING

THE STREAMLINED SHAPE OF
THE WING HELPS IT SLIP
THROUGH THE AIR AND
PROVIDES LIFT

LEADING EDGE OF WING
TILTS DOWNWARDS

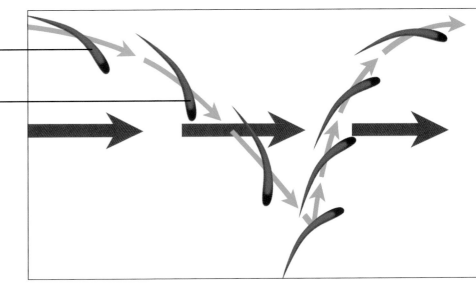

AIR FLOWS EASILY OVER THE
RIDGED WING SURFACE

THE WING
FOLLOWS THIS
PATH ON THE
DOWN STROKE

Wing paths

Insects get their lift (power to keep them up in the air) from their up-and-down wing strokes. As the wing goes down it tilts more and more. At the bottom of the stroke, it flicks round, its front edge facing forward. On the up stroke, this leading edge tilts forward again. By slightly tilting the wing in other directions the insect can carry out various manoeuvres.

THE ABDOMEN IS
KEPT AS LEVEL AS
POSSIBLE

THE LEGS TRAIL
BEHIND AND STAY
CLOSE TO THE BODY,
TO KEEP ITS STREAM-
LINED SHAPE AND
REDUCE AIR RESISTANCE

THE WING FOLLOWS THIS
PATH ON THE UP STROKE

THE LEADING EDGE OF THE
WING FACES FORWARD

THE FRONT-TO-BACK
THORAX MUSCLES RELAX AS
THE OTHERS CONTRACT

THE WASP'S LARGE
EYES GIVE IT GOOD
VISION

Wing up

Each wing pivots on either side of the thorax, like a seesaw. When the top-to-bottom thorax muscles contract (shorten) and the front-to-back ones relax (lengthen) the thorax is squeezed thinner. This is like a heavy weight suddenly being put on one end of a seesaw, so the other end – the wing itself – swings up.

THE TOP-TO-BOTTOM
THORAX MUSCLES CONTRACT,
FLICKING THE WING UP

Hunting

PREDATORS need quick reactions and speed to catch more wary and fast-moving prey. They are armed with powerful jaws, designed to capture, kill, and cut up their meal. Praying mantids (*right*) use their special front legs to catch their victims, before biting the prey to pieces with their jaws. Many insects are active hunters, prowling around looking for suitable prey. Others, such as mantids, employ a wait-and-see method. They patiently keep still until their victim comes within range, and then pounce on it. Such ambush hunters are well-camouflaged to avoid being spotted by their victims until it is too late.

Wait and see
A praying mantis keeps perfectly still, close to somewhere that its prey is likely to land. Its legs are bent, ready to pounce.

THE MANTIS'S EYES ARE FIXED ON ITS PREY

BALANCED ON ITS HIND LEGS, THE MANTIS IS READY TO POUNCE

THE LEAF PERCH HELPS AS CAMOUFLAGE

THE MIDDLE AND REAR LEGS ARE CLOSE TOGETHER AND USED IN WALKING

THE MANTIS'S LONG THIN BODY AND WINGS RESEMBLE A PLANT

In for the kill
The patience of the praying mantis is rewarded. With its keen vision the praying mantis spots a bee landing on a flower. Using its claws, the mantis firmly grips its perch. Then, in the blink of an eye, its powerful back legs catapult its body forwards. At the same time, it shoots out its front legs and grabs the helpless victim, which has no time to avoid the unexpected, deadly lunge.

LONG THIN BACK AND MIDDLE LEGS ARE TYPICAL OF AN INSECT

THE MANTIS USES THE ANGLE OF ITS LEGS AND HEAD FOR A PRECISE AIM

THE STRONG CLAWS KEEP A FIRM GRIP

THE PREY, UNAWARE OF DANGER, HAS JUST LANDED ON A FLOWER

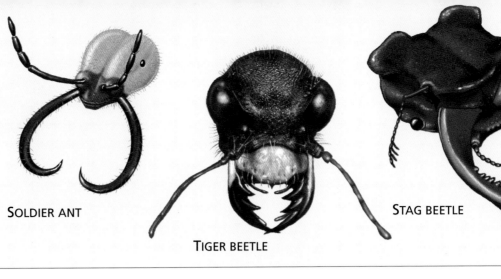

SOLDIER ANT

TIGER BEETLE

STAG BEETLE

THE LONG, THREAD-LIKE ANTENNAE HELP THE MANTIS TO SENSE ITS PREY

THE TRIANGULAR HEAD HAS FLEXIBLE MOVEMENT AS THE NECK ALLOWS IT TO SWIVEL

Powerful jaws
Insect jaws have many uses. Soldier ants use them to catch food and to defend their colony.

Tiger beetles use their jaws to catch their prey. The stag beetle's huge jaws are used in fighting and display.

LARGE, FAR-APART EYES GIVE EXCELLENT BINOCULAR VISION

ITS LEGS HAVE SHARP SPINES THAT FORM A TRAP TO CATCH AND GRIP THE PREY

THE THORAX IS LONG AND THIN

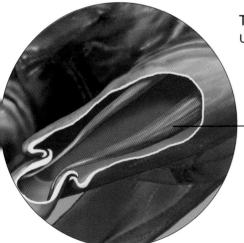

THE LEG MUSCLES LIE INSIDE THE LEG

THE FRONT LEGS ARE NOT USED FOR WALKING

A LARGE CLAW FORMS PART OF THE TRAP

Face-to-face
Large eyes high on a triangular head give the mantis excellent binocular (two-eyed) vision, so it can accurately judge distances. The mantis's neck enables it to swivel its head to almost any angle. Sense organs on its neck and legs also enable it to determine exactly where to strike. Gripped in the mantis's spiny legs, the victim is quickly passed to its mouth and sliced up by the mandibles.

Leg muscles
Strong leg muscles enable the mantis to keep perfectly still until it needs to move forward to catch its meal. Then the leg muscles rapidly

straighten. The mantis's long body allows it to reach prey that is some distance away without having to walk or run up to it, which could give the prey time to escape.

Self-defence

MANY ANIMALS look at insects as a tasty meal, so insects have to defend themselves. Some try to avoid their enemies, by using camouflage, hiding, or running or flying away. Some face their predators. They may have amour that protects them – a thick cuticle, a coat of spines, or poisonous hairs. Or they may be more active in their defence, with strong jaws to bite and stab, a painful (even deadly) sting, or the ability to produce a strong smell or loud noise that will drive an opponent away. Some even secrete poisonous fluids or, like the bombardier beetle (*right*), spray hot irritating chemicals. Most of these masters of chemical warfare are brightly coloured so predators know to leave them alone.

Bombardier beetle
Being a predator, the bombardier beetle is built for speed. When it is not hunting it lives under stones at the edges of fields. If disturbed or threatened in any way, it is well able to defend itself.

WITH ITS LONG ANTENNAE THE BOMBARDIER CAN SEARCH OUT PREY

THE BEETLE'S LARGE EYES ARE TYPICAL OF AN ACTIVE PREDATOR

BRIGHTLY COLOURED MARKINGS WARN PREDATORS THAT THE BEETLE CAN FIGHT BACK

LONG LEGS ENABLE THE BEETLE TO RUN FAST

Methods of defence
Female bees (1) are armed with a sting. Glands in the bees produce a cocktail of irritating chemicals which can be pumped into a victim through a sharp needle-like lance. Many moth caterpillars (2) are covered in spines or fine hairs, which serve as protection. The hairs are sharp and break off easily, causing intense irritation in the mouth of any predator. Some termite soldiers (3) squirt glue at predators to defend their colony. Instead of biting, they spray a sticky substance from their glands, which entangles their enemy's legs and antennae. This leaf beetle (4) exudes an unpleasant drop of blood from its mouth when it is alarmed, which frightens birds, its main predator. When pursued by a bat (5) some moths emit squeaks and clicks. A bat uses sound (echo-location) to find its prey in the dark, and the moth's noises confuse its hearing, which gives the moth a chance to escape.

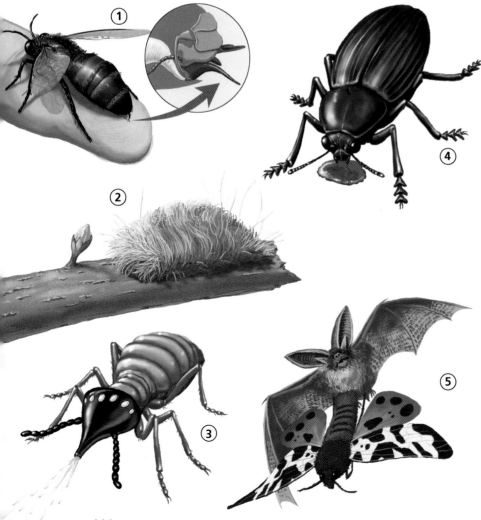

Chemical warfare
Chemicals secreted by glands are stored in chambers. These storage chambers are separated from the explosion chambers by valves. When needed, the valves open and the chemicals are forced into the explosion chambers, detonated, and fired.

CHEMICALS ARE PRODUCED BY THESE GLANDS

EXPLOSIVE MIXTURE IN CHAMBER, READY FOR USE

VALVES SEPARATE THE STORAGE AND EXPLOSION CHAMBERS

Explosive chemicals
The glands produce several chemicals. The main ones are like chemicals used in some rocket engines. When mixed with enzymes they react together producing a hot caustic spray.

MUSCLES FORCE THE STORED CHEMICALS THROUGH TO THE EXPLOSION CHAMBERS

THESE GLANDS SECRETE ENZYMES TO DETONATE AN EXPLOSION OF CAUSTIC SPRAY

THE RECTUM STORES WASTE BEFORE IT IS EXCRETED (PASSED OUT)

THE INTESTINE

PAIRS OF CHEMICAL WEAPONS ORGANS LIE ON EITHER SIDE OF THE RECTUM

EACH STORAGE CHAMBER CONTAINS ENOUGH CHEMICALS FOR 50 BLASTS

THE DUCT FROM THE EXPLOSION CHAMBER IS LINED WITH PROTECTIVE CUTICLE

HOT CAUSTIC SPRAY IS FIRED OUT

Colour and Shape

INSECTS ARE designed for survival. They come in an infinite variety of colours and shapes which help them avoid their predators. The folded wings of many butterflies are beautifully camouflaged, blending in with surrounding leaves, lichens, or tree bark. When open, the wings may use colour in a different way. Vivid eye-spot markings can startle a predatory bird. Bright yellows and reds on black can signal to predators that the butterfly tastes nasty, warning them to leave it alone. So, an insect's cuticle (outer covering) can be used for disguise or, like a flag, as a signal to other animals. The colours and patterns can be produced with pigments (colouring in the wing tissue) and by the cuticle itself. White, blues, and greens are made by the shape of the surface of the cuticle. The varying combinations of pigment and cuticle give insects their distinctive shields of colour.

Morpho butterfly
Morpho butterflies flash blue as they fly through the sun-dappled South American rainforests, alternately exposing their colourful upper and camouflaged lower wing surfaces. The flashing attracts other morphos and confuses predators. When they are still, with their wings folded, eye spots on the wings' undersides can startle predators.

THE WINGS' UNDERSIDES ARE CAMOUFLAGED TO RESEMBLE DEAD LEAVES

EYE-SPOTS STARTLE PREDATORS

WHITE LIGHT SHINES ONTO THE SURFACE OF THE SCALES

DIFFERENT COLOURED LIGHT IS REFLECTED FROM THE RIDGES ACCORDING TO THEIR DEPTH

THIS BEETLE HAS GOLD CAMOUFLAGE BECAUSE IT LIVES ON YELLOW FLOWERS

Glistening like gold
Many beetles, like this gold beetle, look as though they are made of metal. They owe their metallic colouring to light reflecting back off the different layers of their semi-transparent outer cuticle (1). Below this is a softer cuticle (2), beneath which is a layer of cells, glands, and nerves (3).

1
2
3

THE WING OF A BUTTERFLY IS COVERED WITH TINY OVERLAPPING SCALES

AROUND 7000 OF THESE TINY SCALES WOULD COVER THE HEAD OF A PIN

Colourful scales
A butterfly's wings are covered in thin dust-like scales arranged in over-lapping rows, like tiles on a roof. The scales are designed to colour the surface of the wing and produce intricate patterns.

THESE SCALES ARE FROM THE BLUE UPPER WING OF THE MORPHO BUTTERFLY

THE POSITIONS OF THE RIDGES MAKE BLUE THE DOMINANT COLOUR

THE PARALLEL RIDGES ARE FINE AND EVENLY SPACED

A SCALE CAN ALSO CONTAIN PIGMENT WHICH CAN CREATE ADDITIONAL COLOURS

A 'Y'-SHAPED SUPPORT

THE BASE OF A SCALE ON THE BUTTERFLY'S WING

UNDER A MICROSCOPE, THE RIDGES ON A SINGLE SCALE ARE VISIBLE

Stick insects
Stick insects are aptly named. Keeping very still on a branch they are difficult to see. Their body, legs, and antennae are long and thin, resembling small sticks. When they move, they do so very slowly.

Insect twig
Many moth caterpillars, including 'inch worms', are very thin and coloured like plants. Holding on to a twig with their rear sucker-like legs, they often extend out stiffly, pretending to be a short shoot.

Butterfly scales
Each butterfly scale is made up of parallel ridges, held up by supports. The ridges reflect each colour – metallic blues, greens, and purples in a different direction.

Not what it seems
Some caterpillars and pupae have a strange way of disguising themselves. They pretend to be bird droppings – enough to put any predator off.

333

Feeding

INSECTS CAN eat almost anything! Their versatile mouth parts can cut, lick, and suck. Food is taken in through the mouth and enters the long alimentary canal or gut, which is divided into three parts: the fore-gut, mid-gut, and hind-gut. Both the fore-gut and the hind-gut are lined with a thin layer of cuticle. The fore-gut begins with the oesophagus. This leads to the thorax, where it widens to form the crop. Food is stored in the crop before being passed on to the gizzard where it is ground up. The gizzard is lined with thick cuticle and spines or ridges. The mid-gut is not lined with cuticle, and digested food can be absorbed here. The hind-gut is a coiled tube divided into three parts: the ileum, colon, and rectum.

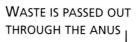

FAECAL MATTER (WASTE) IS FORMED IN THE COLON

WASTE IS PASSED OUT THROUGH THE ANUS

THE RECTUM ABSORBS WATER AND IMPORTANT SALTS

THESE FINE TUBULES FILTER AND CLEAN THE BLOOD OF WASTE WHICH IS PASSED INTO THE COLON

THE ILEUM ABSORBS THE DIGESTED FOOD INTO THE BLOOD

THE AMERICAN COCKROACH CAN SURVIVE FOR THREE MONTHS WITHOUT FOOD BY LIVING OFF STORES IN ITS BODY

① ② ③ ④ ⑤

Mouth parts
A housefly (1) moistens its food with saliva before licking it. The food and saliva are then sucked up. A mosquito's mouth (2) consists of a tube which contains a set of cutting tools. Females pierce the skin of their prey so blood can be sucked up. Males feed on plant juices.

Butterflies (3) have an elongated, coiled mouth part called a proboscis, which sucks up nectar. Bees (4) have licking and biting mouth parts. The mandibles can bite while the tongue can lap-up nectar. Bush crickets (5) are scavengers and hunters. They have powerful mouth parts for biting and cutting.

CAECAE (TUBES THAT EXTEND FROM THE GUT) HELP TO DIGEST AND ABSORB FOOD

THE MUSCULAR GIZZARD GRINDS UP FOOD TO HELP DIGESTION

Digestion

Cockroaches are omnivorous, eating scraps of food and other organic material. The salivary glands open near the mouth and pour saliva on to the food. As the food is chewed and mixed with saliva the digestion of starch begins. In the crop more enzymes (digestive juices), from the mid-gut, are added. These digest proteins, fats, and sugars. In the gizzard the food is ground up and digested further. Fine food particles enter the mid-gut, circulate and are finally digested and absorbed. In the hind-gut, water and important salts are absorbed before the indigestible waste leaves the body through the anus.

BLOOD IN THE BODY CAVITY PICKS UP THE FOOD AND TRANSPORTS IT THROUGHOUT THE BODY

THE CROP EXPANDS AS IT STORES FOOD

FINE SPINES PREVENT ALL BUT THE FINEST PARTICLES FROM ENTERING THE MID-GUT

SALIVA AND FOOD ARE MIXED AND TAKEN IN THROUGH THE MOUTH

THE SALIVARY GLAND POURS SALIVA ONTO FOOD

Taste hairs

Taste hairs on the maxillary palps (feelers) sense chemicals in the air and on the food. They tell the cockroach what it is eating.

THE MAXILLARY FEELERS ARE COVERED IN TASTE ORGANS

LONG ANTENNAE ARE CONSTANTLY ON THE MOVE TO DETECT TASTY FOOD

A COCKROACH KEEPS ITS BODY CLEAN BUT CAN CARRY DISEASES ON ITS FEET

TASTE HAIRS COVER THE MAXILLARY FEELERS

Parasites

BLOOD FROM a living animal can make a tasty meal for some insects. Blood-sucking insects are called parasites and their food source is a live host. Living on another animal can be difficult. The host does not want them and will try to remove them. For example, to survive any attempts by the host to be pulled or shaken off, a flea (*right*), has stout bristles, hairs, and hooks to help it grip the host's hair. Strong claws also grip the host's skin. A flea's exoskeleton is very thick, tough, and slippery, making it hard for the host to squash or grip it. Using its powerful legs, it can jump away from danger and jump back onto its host. The flea's thin body enables it to squeeze between the host's hairs. Its special mouth parts are designed to penetrate the host's skin to reach the blood beneath and draw it up into the flea's large, expandable gut.

Digestion
Ground-up blood from the crop is squirted into the mid-gut and mixed with enzymes. It then moves back up to the mid-gut wall where it is absorbed into the blood stream.

SOME CELLS IN THE MID-GUT SECRETE DIGESTIVE ENZYMES; OTHERS ABSORB DIGESTED FOOD

PARTLY DIGESTED, GROUND-UP BLOOD

UNDIGESTED FOOD AND WASTE LEAVES THROUGH THE ANUS

THE RECTUM ABSORBS WATER AND IMPORTANT SALTS

THE VAGINA RECEIVES THE MALE SEX ORGAN WHEN MATING

SPERM FROM THE MALE IS STORED HERE UNTIL NEEDED FOR FERTILIZATION

AFTER MATING, THE FEMALE'S EGGS ARE FERTILIZED AND SEALED IN EGG SHELLS IN THE OVIDUCT

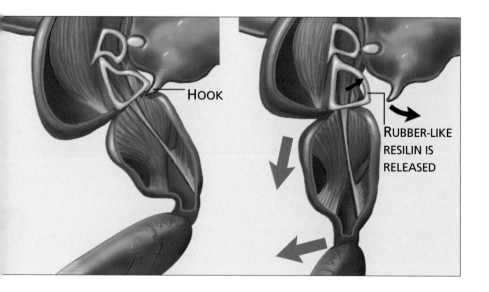

HOOK

RUBBER-LIKE RESILIN IS RELEASED

Jumping legs
Powerful muscles pull the leg up against a hook on the flea's body distorting a piece of rubber-like cuticle called resilin. A sideways movement of the top of the leg pulls the hook off the catch, straightens the pad, releasing all the energy stored in the pad (like twanging a stretched elastic band). The leg is catapulted down, projecting the flea up to 40 centimetres into the air!

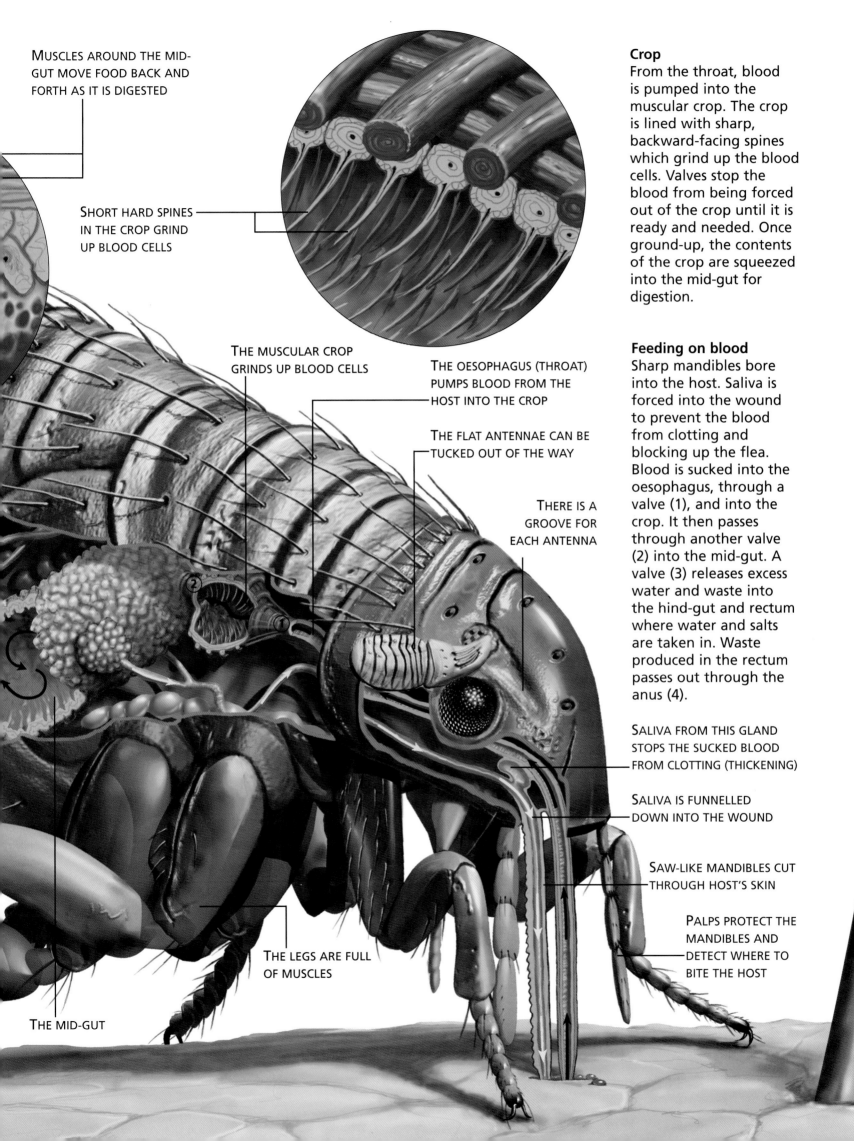

MUSCLES AROUND THE MID-GUT MOVE FOOD BACK AND FORTH AS IT IS DIGESTED

SHORT HARD SPINES IN THE CROP GRIND UP BLOOD CELLS

Crop

From the throat, blood is pumped into the muscular crop. The crop is lined with sharp, backward-facing spines which grind up the blood cells. Valves stop the blood from being forced out of the crop until it is ready and needed. Once ground-up, the contents of the crop are squeezed into the mid-gut for digestion.

THE MUSCULAR CROP GRINDS UP BLOOD CELLS

THE OESOPHAGUS (THROAT) PUMPS BLOOD FROM THE HOST INTO THE CROP

THE FLAT ANTENNAE CAN BE TUCKED OUT OF THE WAY

THERE IS A GROOVE FOR EACH ANTENNA

Feeding on blood

Sharp mandibles bore into the host. Saliva is forced into the wound to prevent the blood from clotting and blocking up the flea. Blood is sucked into the oesophagus, through a valve (1), and into the crop. It then passes through another valve (2) into the mid-gut. A valve (3) releases excess water and waste into the hind-gut and rectum where water and salts are taken in. Waste produced in the rectum passes out through the anus (4).

SALIVA FROM THIS GLAND STOPS THE SUCKED BLOOD FROM CLOTTING (THICKENING)

SALIVA IS FUNNELLED DOWN INTO THE WOUND

SAW-LIKE MANDIBLES CUT THROUGH HOST'S SKIN

PALPS PROTECT THE MANDIBLES AND DETECT WHERE TO BITE THE HOST

THE LEGS ARE FULL OF MUSCLES

THE MID-GUT

Mating

AN INSECT'S main purpose in life is to reproduce. Some insects do not even feed, they just mate, lay eggs, and die. Like most other female animals, a female insect produces eggs from a pair of ovaries. The eggs travel down to her uterus where they are fertilized by sperm produced by the male. The sperm are made in a pair of organs, called the testes, inside the male. As with most insects, when longhorn beetles mate (*right*), the transfer of sperm from the male to the female is direct – they are injected into the female. This makes sure that the sperm are safe. Some male insects leave packets of sperm on the ground for the female to pick up. Shown right is a male longhorn beetle on the back of a female. He has climbed onto her and inserted his sex organ into her. Sperm pumps through this organ into the female. The sperm may be used straight away or stored until needed.

Fighting for territory
Rhinoceros beetles are so-named because the males are armed with 'horns'. They fight each other over the possession of a place where females they can mate with are likely to be. They try to turn each other over. The winner takes possession of the area and the looser leaves.

THE FEMALE LONGHORN BEETLE KEEPS A SHARP LOOK OUT FOR PREDATORS

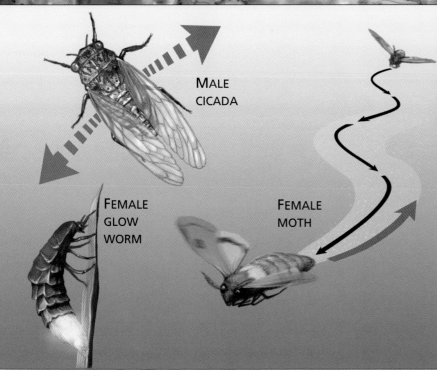

MALE CICADA

FEMALE GLOW WORM

FEMALE MOTH

Ways of finding a mate
Male cicadas use sound. They 'sing', bringing the males together and attracting females to them. Finding a mate through sight is important, too. Glow worms take this to the extreme. The females emit light at dusk to attract males. Many insects use smell. The female moth releases tiny amounts of chemicals called pheromones, which can be smelt by a male many miles away. He follows the scent to find her.

THE MALE'S ANTENNAE CARESS THE FEMALE AS THEY MATE

THE FEMALE USES HER ANTENNAE TO SENSE THE MALE

THE MALE FIRMLY GRIPS THE BACK OF HIS MATE

Sperm
Each sperm consists of a head which contains chromosomes. These contribute half the instructions to make a new beetle once they have joined with another set in a female's egg. A small middle section drives a vibrating tail, which pushes the sperm along.

GLANDS PRODUCE SECRETIONS WHICH CAN STOP THE FEMALE MATING WITH OTHER MALES, OR STIMULATE HER TO LAY EGGS.

EACH TESTIS IS DIVIDED INTO LOBES (SECTIONS)

Male and female organs
In the male beetle, sperm made in the testes (1) travel down tubes, and are stored in sacs (2). During mating, sperm are forced down a tube (3) into the male's sex organ (4), then into the female's uterus (5) and sperm sac (6). The sperm are stored here until needed for fertilization. Eggs from the female's ovaries (7) travel down to where they are fertilized by the sperm before being laid.

TUBES CARRY SPERM FROM THE TESTES INTO A SAC

THE MUSCULAR TUBE DOWN WHICH SPERM ARE FORCED

MATURE EGGS ARE FERTILIZED BY THE SPERM IN THE FEMALE'S UTERUS

THE FEMALE HOLDS THE TWIG TIGHTLY WITH HER CLAWS

New Life

ADULT insects are mainly concerned with producing their young and making sure they are safe and have plenty of food to eat. After being fertilized by a male the female butterfly finds a place to lay her eggs – a suitable plant that will provide her offspring with food and as much protection from predators as possible. She then lays an egg or several eggs. Each egg is an amazing structure. It is not only filled with a rich yolk for the developing embryo to eat, but it is also tough and waterproof, to seal in moisture while the egg is exposed to the dry air. After being laid it may take from several days to several weeks, depending on the surrounding temperature, for the embryo in the egg to develop and hatch.

Laying eggs

Each egg consists of a cell that will join with the sperm and grow, and a ball of cells that surround the yolk. The yolk is the developing insect's source of food. Cells in the ovary produce the surrounding egg shell. Before the egg is laid, sperm that has been stored in a pouch enters the egg through a special pore in the egg shell. The female also produces a gluey substance to stick the egg down.

EACH OVARY PRODUCES OOCYTES RICH IN YOLK

THE OOCYTES GROW AND DEVELOP INTO A BALL OF CELLS

THE EGGS ARE FERTILIZED BY STORED SPERM FROM THE MALE

SPECIAL GLANDS HELP THE EGG-LAYING PROCESS

THE BREATHING AREA OF THE EGG IS PROTECTED BY A HOLLOW

THE LAID EGGS ARE STUCK FIRMLY TO A PLANT

WHEN THE EGGS HATCH THE PLANT WILL BE A FOOD SOURCE FOR THE YOUNG CATERPILLARS

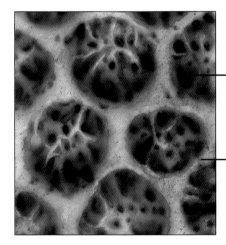

A NETWORK OF FINE PORES LETS THE EGG BREATHE AND KEEPS WATER IN

RIGID SUPPORTS ARE CONNECTED TO COLUMNS BENEATH

Egg shell structure

Through a microscope we can see complicated patterns of pores on the surface of the egg shell. These lead into cavities beneath which let the egg breathe without losing precious water. Many insect eggs allow the developing embryo to breathe in both wet and dry conditions, in case the egg is covered by a rain drop.

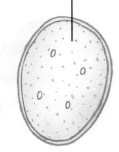

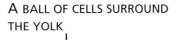

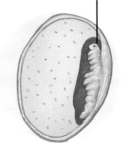

All sorts of eggs

Lacewing eggs (1) are suspended on the ends of fine threads away from predators. Butterflies glue their tiny flask-shaped eggs (2) to plants. Cockroaches lay eight eggs in tough packets called oothecae (3). Stick insects' eggs (4) have a lid which pops open to release the young, and water scorpions' eggs (5) have breathing horns that poke above the water surface. For safety some sawflies lay their eggs (6) inside leaves close to the veins.

BEFORE FERTILIZATION THE EGG IS CALLED AN OOCYTE

A BALL OF CELLS SURROUND THE YOLK

ONCE FERTILIZED, THE EGG IS CALLED A ZYGOTE

THE DEVELOPING EMBRYO SHOWS AN INSECT SHAPE

Embryo development
Before fertilization the egg cell divides to form a sphere of cells called an oocyte, with some scattered cells drifting in

the yolk. The cells continue to divide. The egg shell is produced by the outer cells. One cell is fertilized by the sperm from the male and the

egg is laid. The fertilized cell, called a zygote, divides and forms the embryo, which will develop into the young insect. At this stage the

beginnings of the mouth parts, antennae, and legs can just be seen. Once developed the egg hatches and a pupae will crawl out.

Changing Shape

MANY INSECTS hatch from eggs as nymphs, which moult (shed their outer skin) and gradually change into a different, adult form. But others, such as butterflies, are 'born' twice – once from their egg and a second time from their pupa. A butterfly emerges first in caterpillar form. Its soft cuticle (outer skin) allows its body to expand as it eats and grows. When the cuticle becomes too tight it is shed and the caterpillar continues to get larger. After a few weeks, the caterpillar changes into a chrysalis, or pupa. It spends this final stage in a pupa or case. About a month later the adult butterfly hatches, ready to find a mate and produce more butterflies.

7) New butterfly
Immediately after breaking out, the new butterfly has to stretch and expand its wings by pumping blood down the wing veins. The expanded wings then dry out, and the butterfly uses them to carry it off into the air.

6) Emergence
About a month after the chrysalis was formed, and the process of change is complete, the adult butterfly emerges from its chrysalis. Puffing itself up with air causes the case to split open, allowing the butterfly to crawl free.

POWERFUL WINGS HELP THE BUTTERFLY TO FIND FOOD AND A MATE, AND TO ESCAPE FROM PREDATORS

AN ADULT BUTTERFLY EMERGES FROM ITS CHRYSALIS ABOUT TWO MONTHS AFTER AN EGG WAS LAID

AIR CAN PASS THROUGH SPECIAL HOLES AT THE TOP

1) Eggs
The female butterfly lays clusters of eggs on a plant, which will provide food for the caterpillars after they hatch. The eggs keep the developing caterpillars safe from drying out and enable them to breathe.

2) Hatching
All the eggs hatch at the same time. The young caterpillar bites its way out at the top. It crawls out and eats the egg shell before it starts eating the plant.

A CATERPILLAR SHEDS ITS SKIN (MOULTS) SEVERAL TIMES AS IT GROWS BIGGER

A LARGER, SOFT NEW SKIN ENABLES FURTHER GROWTH

THE EGGS HATCH EIGHT DAYS AFTER BEING LAID

IT SHEDS ITS OLD SKIN

THE ADULT FORMS WITHIN
THE CHRYSALIS SKIN

A SILKEN PAD
HOLDS THE BACK END
OF THE CHRYSALIS TO
THE LEAF

5) Chrysalis

The caterpillar climbs
to a safe place. Here it
spins a silk pad to grip
the leaf and a loop
of silk to hold itself
steady. Already partly
transformed, the
chrysalis appears,
ready for the final
transformation to
be completed.

THE CATERPILLAR'S
COLOURING WARNS
PREDATORS TO KEEP AWAY

4) Fully grown

At about 16 days old, the
caterpillar is as big as it
will ever get. During this
stage its body starts to
change inside. It then
seeks out somewhere
to pupate (change into
a chrysalis) for the final
transformation to
take place.

3) Shedding skin

As it grows, the
caterpillar's skin
becomes too tight. It has
to shed it for a larger
one. A new skin is
produced beneath the
old one. By sucking in air
the caterpillar expands,
splits the old skin, and
releases the 'new'
caterpillar.

THE FULLY
GROWN
CATERPILLAR,
READY TO
PUPATE

THIS CATERPILLAR CAN
EXTEND SMELLY COLOURFUL
'HORNS' TO FRIGHTEN
PREDATORS AWAY

343

Ants' Nest

ANTS LIVE together in complex societies. There are over 5,000 different kinds of ant community. Each nest is headed by a queen who is cared for by her daughters, the female workers. Some ants have different types of workers, called castes, which do different tasks. Ants build their nests in all kinds of places. Here, the nest is on the ground and extends under it. Workers burrow in the soil and pile up the material from below on the surface above. This has been made into a mound full of tunnels and chambers. In the maze of tunnels and chambers the queen ant lives, the eggs and larvae are cared for, and food is stored. At certain times, winged queens and males are produced. These leave the nest to mate.

Egg-laying queen
The queen is much larger than her workers. She is the only ant in the nest that lays eggs. As the eggs are laid they are looked after by attendant workers. On hatching, the young larvae are moved to other chambers where they become pupae (chrysalises). Ants will emerge from the pupae.

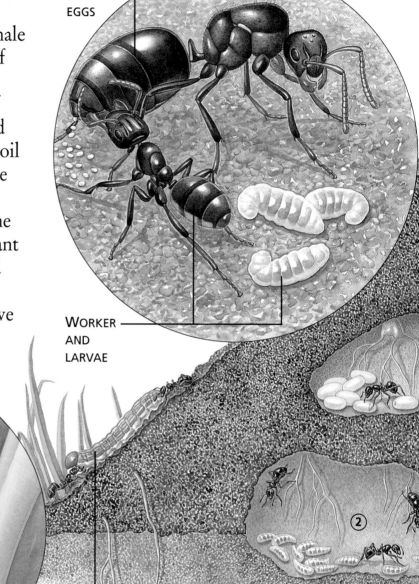

QUEEN, LAYING EGGS

WORKER AND LARVAE

A WORKER ANT HERDING APHIDS FOR THEIR HONEYDEW

A CATERPILLAR IS DRAGGED BACK TO THE NEST FOR FOOD

SECRETIONS FROM THE WORKERS STOP THE EGGS AND LARVAE GOING MOULDY

②

①

QUEEN CHAMBER WITH THE EGG-LAYING QUEEN AND WORKERS TENDING THE EGGS AND LARVAE

Herding aphids
To feed, tiny insects called aphids suck plant sap. This sap contains a lot of water and sugar, far more than the aphids need, so they secrete the excess from the ends of their bodies. Ants have a very sweet tooth and collect this sugary liquid called honeydew. To make the aphids produce more, the ants stimulate them by stroking their backs, milking them like cows. The ants also look after the aphids, guarding them from predators.

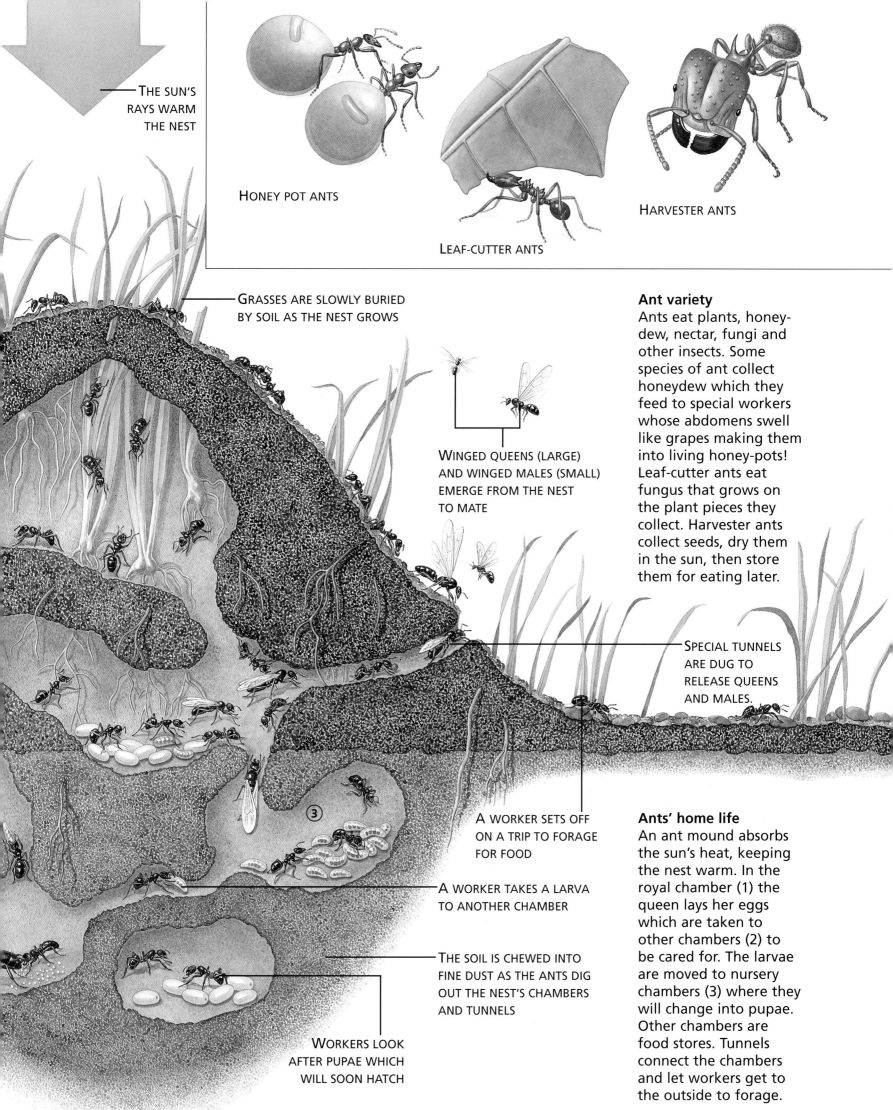

THE SUN'S RAYS WARM THE NEST

HONEY POT ANTS

LEAF-CUTTER ANTS

HARVESTER ANTS

GRASSES ARE SLOWLY BURIED BY SOIL AS THE NEST GROWS

WINGED QUEENS (LARGE) AND WINGED MALES (SMALL) EMERGE FROM THE NEST TO MATE

Ant variety

Ants eat plants, honey-dew, nectar, fungi and other insects. Some species of ant collect honeydew which they feed to special workers whose abdomens swell like grapes making them into living honey-pots! Leaf-cutter ants eat fungus that grows on the plant pieces they collect. Harvester ants collect seeds, dry them in the sun, then store them for eating later.

SPECIAL TUNNELS ARE DUG TO RELEASE QUEENS AND MALES.

③

A WORKER SETS OFF ON A TRIP TO FORAGE FOR FOOD

A WORKER TAKES A LARVA TO ANOTHER CHAMBER

THE SOIL IS CHEWED INTO FINE DUST AS THE ANTS DIG OUT THE NEST'S CHAMBERS AND TUNNELS

WORKERS LOOK AFTER PUPAE WHICH WILL SOON HATCH

Ants' home life

An ant mound absorbs the sun's heat, keeping the nest warm. In the royal chamber (1) the queen lays her eggs which are taken to other chambers (2) to be cared for. The larvae are moved to nursery chambers (3) where they will change into pupae. Other chambers are food stores. Tunnels connect the chambers and let workers get to the outside to forage.

345

Bees' Nest

HONEYBEE nests are busy places. In each nest a bustling community of up to 60,000 insects live together. Nearly all the bees are females, called workers, which hatch from fertilized eggs laid by the queen who is in charge of the colony. A few males that hatch from unfertilized eggs appear during the summer and autumn. They do not work as their only job is to mate with new queens. All the worker bees live together, building and looking after their home, collecting food and water, feeding the young and caring for the queen. They secrete wax to make their nest. Sheets of strong hexagonal cells hang down and hold the eggs, larvae, nectar (which becomes honey) and pollen. Being able to store food allows honeybees to live through times when food is scarce, such as the winter.

A DRONE (MALE BEE) HAS LARGE EYES FOR FINDING YOUNG QUEENS TO MATE WITH

AN INNER CRESCENT OF CELLS IS FILLED WITH POLLEN, A PROTEIN-RICH FOOD

THE OUTER CELLS ARE FILLED WITH NECTAR WHICH IS TURNED INTO HONEY BY THE BEES; THE CELL IS THEN SEALED

A WORKER BEE, CALLED A FORAGER, BRINGS BACK POLLEN TO FEED THE YOUNG

Building cells
A worker bee produces scales of wax from glands under its abdomen. These are spread onto a surface using its jaws. More wax is added and shaped into a hexagonal cell.

Cells are produced together, forming a sheet of honeycomb with cells on both sides, each angled slightly upwards. Combs hang side by side, just close enough to allow two bees to pass each other.

A FORAGER SETS OFF IN SEARCH OF POLLEN, NECTAR, WATER, OR ANY OTHER ITEM THE COLONY MAY NEED

BEES COMMUNICATE WITH EACH OTHER BY PASSING FOOD AND CHEMICALS FROM THE QUEEN

A WORKER BEE MAY TRAVEL 2.5 KILOMETRES TO FIND NECTAR

A LAYER OF WAX ON A TWIG SUPPORTS THE DOWNWARD-HANGING COMB

A HONEY-FILLED CELL PROVIDES A STORE OF FOOD

A CELL THAT HAS BEEN FILLED WIH POLLEN

Queen
A queen can lay over 2000 eggs a day. At certain times some of these are laid in special large cells. Larvae from these eggs get extra food and grow into young queens. When they are about to hatch the old queen leaves the nest with the older workers. This 'swarm' sets up home elsewhere and the new queen takes over the old nest.

A CAP ON A CELL PROTECTS A TEN-DAY-OLD PUPA

A NURSE BEE CLEANS CELLS AND LOOKS AFTER THE BROOD

THE CAP IS OFF THIS CELL – THE FIFTEEN-DAY-OLD PUPA INSIDE WILL SOON HATCH

LARVAE ARE COILED AT THE BASE OF THE CELLS AND FEED ON SPECIAL FOOD

THE QUEEN LAYS EGGS IN EMPTY CLEAN CELLS AS SOON AS THEY BECOME AVAILABLE

A POLLEN LOAD IS PACKED INTO A 'BASKET' ON THE BEE'S BACK LEG

Waggle dance
A bee can tell other bees where it has found a lot of food by dancing. The waggle dance is used when food is a long way away. The angle it dances at tells the other bees which direction to go in to find it. The faster the bee waggles, the more food there is. The number of turns she makes in a given time indicates the distance they must go.

A SPECIAL LARGE CELL ON THE EDGE OF THE COMB CONTAINS A DEVELOPING DAUGHTER QUEEN BEE

Rainforest Life

TROPICAL heat and moisture are ideal for the growth of rainforests. Here, insects are the most numerous and varied form of animal life. Nearly 200 species of butterfly can be found in one hectare of South East Asian rainforest alone. However, we do not know how many rainforest insects there are in total – there may still be millions to discover. Insects can be difficult to see as many fly high in the tree-tops, and many are so well camouflaged that they look just like a flower, thorn or leaf. Others live hidden inside rotting wood, living plants, or leaves. Insects are a very important part of forest life – they pollinate plants and help to recycle waste matter into reusable nutrients.

Mantis
This is not a pretty flower, but a dangerous predator! Disguised to match the flower upon which it sits, this mantis waits patiently for an insect to visit the flower – then it will pounce.

MANTIS

THESE TREE HOPPERS CAN SUCK PLANT SAP IN SAFETY – THEY ARE DISGUISED AS THORNS, HENCE THEIR OTHER NAME: THORNBUGS

POISONOUS SPINES ON CATERPILLARS STOP PREDATORS FROM THINKING THEY ARE AN EASY MEAL

Grasshoppers
Powerful back legs allow grasshoppers to jump out of the way of danger. These green nymphs are well camouflaged and difficult to see in the forest.

GRASSHOPPER NYMPHS (YOUNG)

Leaf-cutter ants
Strong leaf-cutter ants cut pieces of leaves and carry them to their nest. They eat the fungus that begins to grow on the leaf pieces.

A LEAF-CUTTER ANT CARRYING A PIECE OF LEAF BACK TO ITS NEST

NOT A DEAD LEAF BUT A LEAF INSECT

Pond on a tree

The bases of the leaves of bromeliads, which include the pineapple, wrap around the stem and trap water. These form ponds in which many creatures, such as these insect larvae, live.

PITCHER PLANTS ARE CARNIVOROUS – INSECTS THAT SLIP INSIDE ARE DIGESTED

ANT LARVAE INSIDE PLANT

Pitcher plant ants

The hollow coiled base of a pitcher plant stem makes a safe place for these ants to live and rear their young. In return for their home the ants guard the pitcher plant against the attack of insects and other animals.

Weavers

Ants nest everywhere in the rainforest. Even living leaves can be made into a home. Weaver ant larvae secrete sticky silk. These larvae are used as tubes of glue by the ants to bind the leaves together.

LEAVES ARE WOVEN TOGETHER WITH SILK FROM LARVAE

HERDSMAN ANTS TEND A FLOCK OF APHIDS FROM WHICH THEY COLLECT HONEYDEW TO EAT

BRIGHT MARKINGS STARTLE PREDATORS

Termites

Dead leaves and wood collect on the dark forest floor. These are eaten by all kinds of creatures. Termites gather dead leaves and take them back to their nest.

BRIGHTLY COLOURED SHIELD-BUGS WARN PREDATORS THAT THEY ARE BITTER-TASTING AND POISONOUS

A TERMITE SOLDIER WITH POWERFUL JAWS GUARDS THE WORKERS AND NEST

Great Mormon butterfly

Many butterflies have wings that camouflage them when at rest. If disturbed, a move of the wings exposes colourful markings which can frighten a predator.

Insects in Water

MANY TYPES of insect live in freshwater at some time in their lives. Several, including flies such as the dragonfly as well as true flies, only spend the earliest part of their lives there – as nymphs (young which resemble the adult insect) or larvae (a worm-like form that does not resemble the adult until later on). Other freshwater insects, like beetles and bugs, live in water both during their early and adult stages. The adults also live on land, travelling through the air to new habitats. Because water can dissolve large amounts of oxygen, many insects are able to breathe in it. Most nymphs use gills to breathe, but other insects breathe at the water's surface. A few take a packet of air down with them when they dive, returning to the surface to get more when the oxygen runs out. Insects use their legs and even their wings to swim about.

A mayfly's life
Mayfly nymphs feed on dead vegetation and live in tubes in mud or crawl amongst aquatic plants. As adults, they have just a day to live. During that time they do not eat but only mate and lay eggs.

A MAYFLY

MOSQUITO LARVAE AND PUPAE BREATHE THROUGH THE SURFACE FILM OF THE WATER

WHIRLIGIG BEETLES SPIN AROUND ON THE SURFACE LOOKING FOR FOOD

AIR IS TRAPPED UNDER THE GREAT DIVING BEETLE'S WING COVERS

ITS LEGS PUSH AGAINST THE WATER, FORCING IT FORWARD

IT HAS BROAD OAR-LIKE BACK LEGS FOR SWIMMING

Great diving beetle
During adulthood and as larvae, these beetles are fast aggressive predators. Adults are sleek and smooth, and have broad oar-like back legs, fringed with bristles for rapid swimming. Their front legs are designed to grasp their prey. When they are under water, they breathe using air trapped in hairs beneath their wing covers.

THE DIVING BEETLE'S STRONG FRONT LEGS CAN GRASP PREY

350

AN ADULT DRAGONFLY CATCHES ITS PREY USING BASKET-LIKE SPINY FRONT LEGS

④

③

⑤

⑥

②

⑦

①

Life cycle of a dragonfly

The dragonfly lays its eggs under water, in or on water plants. The eggs hatch as predatory nymphs (1). As each nymph grows, it moults and gradually changes. Eventually it crawls out of the water (2) and emerges as an adult dragonfly with tiny wings (3), which it inflates and dries before flying off in search of food or a mate (4).

Life on the surface

The surface film is home to several insect hunters and scavengers. Tiny wingless springtails called Podura (5) scavenge for food. They usually crawl but can also jump if disturbed. Aptly named pond skaters (6) are fast hunters but also take trapped and drowned prey. Water boatmen (7) hang from the surface of the water waiting for prey. With powerful legs it chases its victim, killing it with its stabbing mouth parts.

A DRAGONFLY NYMPH CATCHES A TADPOLE USING ITS 'MASK'

FLY LARVAE FEED ON DEBRIS AT THE BOTTOM OF PONDS

A dragonfly nymph feeding

A hungry dragonfly catches a tadpole using its special 'mask' mouth part. The 'mask' remains folded under the head until the nymph shoots it forward and catches the prey using the strong jaws at its tip.

THE CADDIS LARVA MAKES A HOME OF STONES OR PLANT REMAINS

A MAYFLY NYMPH SCURRIES ALONG THE POND FLOOR LOOKING FOR FOOD

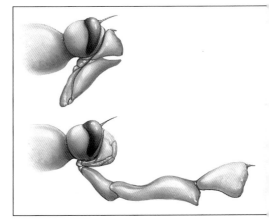

Woodland Life

TREES MAKE perfect homes for many insects, providing plenty of food and places to shelter. One tree in particular, the oak, supports a huge variety of insect life, including over 210 species of moths and butterflies. Insects make use of all the tree – from the leaves, shoots, and flowers in the canopy to the roots underground. They chew the leaves from the outside and inside, burrow under the bark and into the wood, and live inside the tree's fruits, the acorns. As well as eating the tree they also use it as a refuge, hiding in the crevices of the bark. Other insects are parasites that live on other insects that feed on the plant. Still others are predators, searching and hunting for prey. Throughout the year different insects can be found on different parts of every tree in a woodland.

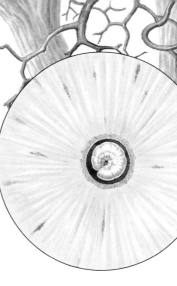

Marble gall
Gall wasps have two types of larvae. Those of one species produce marble galls on one type of oak and bud-galls on another.

Purple hairstreak
This butterfly only lives on oak. Its caterpillars feed at night on young leaves. When full grown they pupate in the soil. If taken into an ants' nest they are better protected from predators.

Oak bark beetle
Just below the bark a female beetle makes a tunnel where she lays her eggs. The grubs that hatch make long vertical tunnels as they feed.

Acorn weevil
Like all nut weevils the acorn weevil has a long thin snout. At its tip are the mandibles, which it uses to pierce a hole and bore into the acorn. Here it lays an egg, and the grub (larva) feeds in its ready-made larder. When the acorn falls, the grub comes out and develops into a pupa in the soil.

Lacewing
Delicate lacewings are active in the evening. Both adults and larvae hunt aphids. The larvae camouflage themselves by sticking pieces of debris to their back, including the dried husks of their prey.

Thorn moth
Adult moths are well camouflaged – their brown jagged wings look like dead leaves. If a thorn moth caterpillar is disturbed or at rest it makes itself look (very convincingly) like a twig.

Oak sawfly
Sawflies are related to bees and wasps. Their larvae are slug-like caterpillars. Oak sawfly caterpillars produce blistering marks as they feed in the upper surface of the leaf.

Lobster moth
When resting the lobster-moth caterpillar has a strange appearance, hence its name. Although it eats oak leaves it will also eat the leaves of other trees.

Seven-spotted ladybird
Most ladybirds are predators. As larvae and adults they eat huge numbers of sap-sucking aphids. Their bright colours warn predators that they taste nasty and so should leave them alone.

Dark crimson under-wing moth
When at rest, with its wings folded, this moth is perfectly camouflaged on the oak tree's bark. Its caterpillars eat oak buds and pupate amongst the lichen on the tree trunk.

Types of gall
To stop unwanted insect larvae from feeding inside them, some plants produce thickened tissue called galls. But instead of getting rid of the larvae, the tissue provides food for them. Different species of attacking gall wasp lead to different types of galls, such as curved leaf galls (1), cotton-wool galls (2), spangle galls (3), and oak apples (4).

Desert Insects

DESERTS ARE mainly hot and dry, having little rainfall, so the environment is a difficult one for animals to survive in. Those that do are specially adapted to the harsh conditions. Many hide away during the extreme heat of the day, either under rocks, or buried in the sand or deep in burrows. Only at night and early morning when it is cool do they emerge to feed. Those insects that do come out during the day move from place to place quickly, keeping in the shade. Their feet are often specially adapted so that they are able to touch the hot sand when necessary, and they have a thick cuticle to reduce the loss of moisture. Some gather moisture to drink in the early morning mist, while others rely on the moisture in their food to sustain them. Even if they do lose water they can withstand a great deal of dehydration (water loss).

Dune cricket
The dune cricket (3) uses its flower-shaped feet to dig in the sand to escape the heat of the sun and predators. When the temperature falls, the cricket emerges to feed on the sparse vegetation.

Tiger beetle
Like a tiger in the jungle, a tiger beetle (4) hunts its prey. These agile and fast predators have powerful jaws to kill even quite large insects.

Head-stander
Water droplets from early morning mist condense on this darkling beetle (5). It stands on tip-toe so the droplets run together and down to its mouth.

Hunting wasp
A hunting wasp lives a solitary life. A female (1) digs a burrow and then hunts for insects. Using her sting she paralyses her prey and takes it back to the burrow. Here she lays an egg on it. The larva that hatches feeds on the living victim.

Harvester ants
Harvester ants (2) nest underground, away from the sun's killing heat. Foragers gather seeds for food which they first dry in the sun before storing them in special chambers inside their nest. They eat the seeds as needed. They also eat insects such as caterpillars.

DEEP UNDER-GROUND, THE NEST CHAMBERS ARE COOL

Ant lion
At the bottom of its pit an ant-lion (6) flicks sand at an ant, making it slip down into the ant-lion's jaws.

354

Eburnea beetle
Most darkling beetles are black so this one is unusual in being white (7). Darkling beetles form a large part of the desert fauna. Their hard thick armour protects them against desiccation (drying up).

Long-legged beetle
Extra long legs allow this species of darkling beetle (8) to move fast and keep its body well clear of the hot desert sand. Moisture gathers on its back in the early morning.

Jewel wasp
Flying insects like this jewel wasp (*above*) need a lot of fuel to work their wings. They get this from nectar produced by desert flowers. In return the plant is pollinated.

Laying eggs
Locusts (9) produce their eggs in batches inside tough water-proof packages called oothecae. Using a special egg-laying tube, a female deposits these beneath the surface of the sand away from predators.

FLYING LOCUSTS CAN TRAVEL THOUSANDS OF KILOMETRES IN SEARCH OF FOOD

Darkling beetle
Most species of darkling beetles are a dull black (12) but their body shape can differ greatly. The majority are scavengers that feed largely on plant remains.

Dung beetle
Dung beetles (11) gather dung into balls, roll it to safety and bury it. Underground, they lay their eggs on the dung so the larvae which hatch have their own private larder.

Desert grasshopper
Is it a stone? No, it's a desert grasshopper (10). These grasshoppers live wherever there is sufficient plant life. To avoid being eaten they are well-camouflaged to resemble the stones of the surrounding desert.

Microscopic Life

HIDDEN AWAY in their secret worlds are thousands of microscopic insects. Insects are the most successful group of living animals on Earth partly because many of them make use of the tiniest of spaces – including the gaps between grains of cereal, the crevices of tree bark, and the fur of mammals. Within almost every group of insects there is a type that is microscopic. Despite their small size they are still made to the same body plan as their larger cousins. Breathing is easier for tiny insects, as the oxygen breathed in and the carbon dioxide breathed out only have to travel very short distances. But being small can be a problem. For example, flying in the air for them would be like swimming in treacle for humans, so their wings are specially designed to make it easier.

Head louse

Head lice are a type of sucking lice that live in human hair. More than a thousand can live on one head, but the normal number is about a dozen. For camouflage they match the colour of the hair in which they live. Anyone can be a host to lice, catching them from other people and clothing. When feeding, the louse grabs a hair and stands on its head, gripping the scalp with a ring of hooks before inserting a long mouth-part into the skin to suck blood. They feed twice a day, causing irritation and sometimes disease.

THIS TYPE OF LOUSE HAS SMALL EYES, BUT MOST HAVE NONE

THE SHORT STUBBY ANTENNAE ARE SENSITIVE TO HEAT AND HUMIDITY

UNLIKE MANY INSECTS, THE LOUSE HAS NO WINGS

ITS FLATTENED AND TOUGH BODY MAKES THE LOUSE HARD TO KILL AND REMOVE

BREATHING TUBES CALLED TRACHEA TAKE OXYGEN TO AND CARBON DIOXIDE AWAY FROM THE TISSUES

THE LOUSE'S HEART PUMPS BLOOD AROUND ITS BODY

THE LOUSE IS DARK WHEN ITS INTESTINES ARE FULL OF DIGESTED BLOOD

THE NERVOUS SYSTEM

SPINES

ITS STOUT, STRONG HOOK-LIKE LEGS GRIP HAIRS

THE STRONG, CURVED CLAWS
CAN BE MOVED TO GRIP THE
HAIR

Climbing feet
To a head louse, hair is a
jungle. Its special feet are
armed with spines and a
curved claw that is
hinged and grips with
the help of its 'peg'.
This gives it a very strong
hold and makes climbing
easy. It also makes it
difficult for the host to
remove the louse.

Fairyfly
Less than a quarter of
millimetre long, fairyflies
are the smallest of all
insects. They are wasps
that lay their eggs in
other insects. Aquatic
species can use their
wings for swimming.

WITH THE
CLAW, A 'PEG'
HELPS THE LOUSE
TO FIRMLY GRIP
THE HAIR

A HUMAN HAIR, VIEWED
THROUGH A MICROSCOPE

THE EGG SHELL IS TOUGH TO
PROTECT THE EMBRYO

THE LOUSE EMBRYO
DEVELOPS SAFELY INSIDE
ITS EGG SHELL

Springtail
Springtails can spring
several centimetres.
Normally the springing
organ is tucked under
the abdomen, secured by
a special hook. When
released it catapults the
insect into the air.

THE DEVELOPING EMBRYO
FEEDS ON
YOLK REMAINS

Eggs
Head lice lay up to about
eight eggs, called nits,
and glue them very
firmly each day to a hair
shaft. The eggs hatch in
6 to 15 days, depending
on the temperature. The
young louse hatches by
lifting off the egg's cap,
like a service-hole cover,
and sucks blood at once.

VERY STICKY GLUE HOLDS
THE EGG TO THE HAIR

THE LOUSE IS
CAMOUFLAGED BY
MATCHING THE
COLOUR OF
THE HAIR SHAFT

THE CAP OF THE EGG
FALLS AWAY AFTER A
YOUNG LOUSE EMERGES

Silverfish
Silverfish are covered
in fine gleaming scales.
They hide away,
appearing only at night
indoors to eat paper,
leather and food scraps.

THE EMPTY EGG CASE
REMAINS FIRMLY GLUED
TO THE HAIR

357

Index